Essentials of
HISTOLOGY

Essentials of

HISTOLOGY FOURTH EDITION

Gerrit Bevelander, Ph.D.
NEW YORK UNIVERSITY
NEW YORK, N. Y.

With 183 Text Illustrations
and 4 Color Plates

ST. LOUIS
The C. V. Mosby Company
1961

FOURTH EDITION

Printed in the United States of America
Library of Congress Catalog Card Number 61-11755
Distributed in Great Britain by Henry Kimpton, London

Preface to fourth edition

In the preface to the first edition of *Essentials of Histology* it was stated that the purpose of the book was to present the essential facts concerning the tissues and organs in a clear and concise manner. In the present edition the objective is the same.

To set forth in detail or even in an abbreviated manner the vast body of accumulated data bearing on the structural-functional relationships and interrelationships which have been shown to exist in cells and organs would require a text of voluminous proportions and extreme complexity. Such a text has not as yet appeared. At present most textbooks of histology deal with the multidisciplinary approach to some degree. In keeping with the original purpose for which this text was first written, the scope of this edition has not been greatly modified. Greater emphasis, however, has been placed upon the functional aspects of histology, with several disciplines drawn upon to illustrate these relationships.

The introductory chapter has been completely rewritten and emphasis directed to the relation between cell structure, chemical composition, and function of some of the cell components. The chapter dealing with epithelia has been revamped, and several new illustrations have been added. Similar revisions and additions have been made in chapters dealing with connective tissue, cartilage, bone, nervous tissue, and the circulatory system. The new illustrations include selected autoradiographs and electron micrographs. The chapter on glands has been extensively revised and enlarged. Since many of the so-called organs are glands or contain glandular structures, this amplification will be helpful in the subsequent study of organology. The discussion on the kidney has been thoroughly revised and includes two color plates which illustrate the detailed circulation of the kidney, a feature which lends itself to an understanding of structural and functional relationships. Other changes, modifications, and new illustrations too numerous to mention in detail are also included throughout the text.

In preparing this revision I wish to express my appreciation for permission to reproduce the several electron micrographs and Dr. Homer Smith's color plates illustrating the circulation of the kidney, individual acknowledgments of which are included in the legends. I wish also to express my thanks to Dr. Gloria K. Rolle for constructive criticism rendered and to Miss Judith Hardy for preparing several new drawings included in this edition. Finally, I wish especially to express my appreciation to Mr. Leo Schatz for his extremely valuable assistance in the execution and revision of the text.

New York, N. Y. Gerrit Bevelander

Preface to first edition

The purpose of this book is to present in simple and systematic form the most important morphological characteristics of the tissues and organs discussed. We have endeavored to make it clear in the text what features are to be seen in ordinary preparations, what points require special techniques for demonstration, and what is to be accepted as a result of investigation outside the scope of an elementary course. Most of the illustrations were drawn from slides in our student loan collections, and they may be taken as a guide to any similar set of preparations. Text and illustrations are intended to serve as a foundation for histological study on which the individual teacher may build such superstructure of detail or theoretical material as the conditions of his own course permit. What we have included are the facts which after some years of teaching we believe a beginner should have readily available before he undertakes the study of each tissue or organ.

Such material as was not obtained from direct observation of the microscopic preparations was drawn from various standard sources. Some of the figures, also, have been taken from other texts, a fact which is duly acknowledged in the accompanying legends.

Margaret M. Hoskins
Gerrit Bevelander

New York, N. Y.

Contents

CHAPTER I

Introduction 17

The cell, 17; Nucleus, 17; Cytoplasm, 19; Cellular activities, 22; Vegetative activities, 22; Growth and reproduction, 22; Special activities, 22; Tissues and organs, 22.

CHAPTER II

Epithelia 24

Epithelial cells, 24; Epithelial tissues, 25; Simple epithelia, 25; Squamous epithelium, 25; Cuboidal epithelium, 27; Columnar epithelium, 28; Pseudostratified epithelium, 29; Stratified epithelia, 30; Stratified columnar epithelium, 30; Stratified cuboidal epithelium, 30; Transitional epithelium, 30; Stratified squamous epithelium, 31.

CHAPTER III

Blood and lymph 33

Blood, 33; Red blood corpuscles (erythrocytes), 33; White blood corpuscles (leukocytes), 34; Granulocytes, 35; Lymphocytes, 35; Monocytes (large mononuclears), 35; Platelets, 36; Lymph, 36.

CHAPTER IV

The connective tissue proper 37

Mucous connective tissue, 39; Reticular tissue, 39; Fibrous tissue, 41; Areolar tissue, 41; Fibroblasts, 42; Mesothelial cells, 43; Macrophages, 43; Plasma cells, 44; Mast cells, 44; Blood cells, 45; Fat cells, 46; Dense fibrous tissue—irregular, 46; Dense fibrous tissue—regular, 47; Elastic tissue, 47; Adipose tissue, 48; Serous membranes, 49; Reticuloendothelial system, 49.

CHAPTER V

Blood-forming organs 50

Bone marrow, 50; Reticular tissue cells, 50; Adipose tissue cells, 50; Hemocytoblasts (stem cells), 50; Promyelocytes, myelocytes, metamyelocytes, 51; Proerythroblasts, erythroblasts, normoblasts, 51; Giant cells or megakaryocytes, 51; Development of blood cells in embryo, 52; Germinal centers of lymph nodes, 52.

CHAPTER VI

Cartilage 53

Fibrocartilage, 54; Hyaline cartilage, 55; Elastic cartilage, 57.

CHAPTER VII

Bone 58

Development, 58; Intramembranous bone, 59; Cartilage replacement bone, 62; Formation of haversian systems, 67; Adult bone, 71; Periosteum, 74; Blood supply and nerves, 74; Marrow, 75; Joints, 76.

CHAPTER VIII

Muscle 77

Smooth muscle, 77; Skeletal muscle, 79; Cardiac muscle, 83; Circulation and innervation of muscle, 85.

CHAPTER IX

Nervous tissue 86

Perikaryon, 86; Nerve fibers, 89; Nerves, 91; Nerve fiber endings, 93; Motor endings, 93; Sensory endings, 94; Free endings, 94; Encapsulated endings, 94; Muscle spindles, 94; Neuron interrelations, 95; Somatic reflex, 95; Sensory neuron, 95; Association neurons, 98; Somatic motor neurons, 98; Visceral reflexes, 99; Autonomic system, 99; Anatomic aspects of the sympathetic division, 100; Anatomic aspects of the parasympathetic division, 100; "Local reflex" of the gut, 100; Visceral sensory neurons, 101; Sympathetic outflow, 101; Summation, 102; Neuroglia (glia), 103; Astroglia, 104; Oligodendria, 104; Microglia, 105; Other types, 105.

CHAPTER X

Circulatory system 106

Blood vessels, 106; Capillaries, 106; Arteries, 107; Aorta, 107; Medium-sized arteries, 108; Small arteries and arterioles, 110; Veins, 111; Small veins and venules, 112; Veins of medium caliber, 112; Large veins, 113; Comparison of veins and arteries, 113; Intima, 113; Media, 114; Adventitia, 114; Size of vessels, 114; Shape of vessels, 114; The heart, 114; Endocardium, 114; Myocardium, 115; Epicardium, 115; Lymphatic system, 115.

CHAPTER XI

Lymphoid organs 117

Lymph node, 117; Cortex, 120; Capsule and trabeculae, 120; Cortical sinuses, 120; Nodules, 120; Blood vessels, 120; Medulla, 120; Medullary cords, 120; Medullary sinuses, 120; Medullary trabeculae, 120; Spleen, 120; Capsule and trabeculae, 123; Red pulp, 123; White pulp, 124; Function of the spleen, 124; Tonsils, 125; Palatine tonsil, 125; Pharyngeal tonsil, 126; Thymus, 126; Summary and comparison of the lymphoid organs, 129; Lymph node, 129; Spleen, 129; Tonsil, 129; Thymus, 129.

CHAPTER XII

Glands 130

Endocrine glands, 131; Clumps, 131; Follicles, 131; Cords, 132; Epithelioid cells, 133; Exocrine glands, 133; Ducts, 133; Secretory ducts, 133; Excretory ducts, 133; Intercalated ducts, 133; Classification, 133; Secretions, 135; Unicellular glands, 135; Multicellular glands, 136.

CHAPTER XIII

Integument 139

Hairless skin, 139; Epidermis, 139; Stratum corneum, 139; Stratum lucidum, 139; Stratum granulosum, 139; Stratum germinativum, 140; Corium, 141; Hairy skin, 142; Glands of the skin, 143; Sweat glands, 143; Sebaceous glands, 144; Nails, 144.

CHAPTER XIV

Oral cavity 146

Lips, 146; Lining of the oral cavity, 146; Lips and cheeks, 147; Gingivae and hard palate, 147; Teeth, 150; Early development, 150; Development of the enamel organ, 151; Enamel formation, 152; Mature enamel, 153; Development of dentin, 154; Mature dentin, 156; Variations, 156; Cementum, 156; Pulp, 157; Gingiva, 157; Peridental membrane, 158; Alveolus, 159; Tongue, 159; Filiform papillae, 159; Fungiform papillae, 159; Foliate papillae, 160; Vallate (circumvallate) papillae, 161; Glands of the oral cavity, 163; Pharynx, 164.

CHAPTER XV

Digestive tract 165

Mucosa, 165; Submucosa, 165; Muscularis, 165; Adventitia or serosa, 165; Esophagus, 167; Mucosa, 167; Submucosa, 167; Muscularis, 168; Stomach, 168; Mucosa, 168; Submucosa, 171; Muscularis, 171; Serosa, 171; Small intestine, 171; Mucosa, 172; Submucosa, 175; Muscularis, 176; Serosa, 176; Large intestine, 176; Mucosa, 176; Submucosa, 177; Muscularis, 178; Serosa, 178; Vermiform appendix, 179; Mucosa, 179; Submucosa, 180; Muscularis, 180; Serosa, 180; Rectum and anus, 180; Blood supply of stomach and intestines, 181; Nerve supply of stomach and intestines, 181.

CHAPTER XVI

Glands associated with the digestive tract 182

Salivary glands, 182; Parotid gland, 182; Submaxillary glands, 184; Sublingual glands, 185; Nerve supply, 185; Pancreas, 185; Blood supply, 187; Nerve supply, 187; Summary, 187; Liver, 187; Liver cells and sinusoids, 189; Portal canal, 190; Circulation, 190; Nerve supply, 193; Gallbladder, 193; Blood supply, 193; Nerve supply, 193.

CHAPTER XVII

Respiratory tract 194

Upper parts of respiratory tract, 196; Nasal passages, 196; Nasopharynx, 197; Larynx, 197; Lower parts of respiratory tract, 198; Trachea, 198; Bronchi, 199;

Bronchioles, 201; Respiratory bronchioles, 201; Alveolar ducts, 202; Blood supply of the lungs, 204; Nerve supply of the lungs, 205.

CHAPTER XVIII

Urogenital system 206

Urinary system, 206; Kidney, 206; Gross structure of the unilobar kidney, 206; Gross structure of the multilobar kidney, 208; Circulation, 210; Finer structure of the kidney, 211; Ureter, 218; Mucosa, 218; Submucosa, 219; Muscularis, 219; Adventitia, 219; Urinary bladder, 219; Urethra, 220; Female urethra, 220; Male urethra, 220; Prostatic portion, 220; Membranous portion, 220; Cavernous portion, 221; Blood and nerve supply of the excretory passages, 221; Male reproductive system, 221; Testis, 221; Epididymis, 224; Ductus deferens, 226; Seminal vesicle, 226; Prostate, 227; Penis, 227; Nerve supply, 228; Female reproductive system, 228; Ovary, 228; Atretic follicles, 233; Fallopian tube (oviduct), 234; Uterus, 235; Endometrium, 235; Proliferative stage, 236; Secretory (progravid) stage, 236; Premenstrual stage, 236; Menstrual stage, 236; Pregnancy, 236; Vagina, 238; Mammary gland, 240; Resting gland, 240; Active gland, 240; Blood vessels, lymphatics, and nerves, 242.

CHAPTER XIX

Endocrine organs 243

Thyroid gland, parathyroid glands, hypophysis, adrenal glands, and islands of Langerhans, 243; Gonads, 244; Thymus and pineal glands, 244; Organs from which hormones isolated, 244; Liver, 244; Thyroid gland, 244; Parathyroid glands, 246; Hypophysis, 248; Anterior lobe, 248; Chromophobe cells, 249; Chromophil cells, 249; Posterior lobe, 249; Pars intermedia, 249; Pars nervosa, 249; Functions, 250; Adrenal gland, 250; Cortex, 251; Medulla, 253.

CHAPTER XX

Brain and special sense organs 254

The brain, 254; Cerebrum, 254; Cerebellum, 257; Meninges, 259; Eye, 261; Coats of the eye, 262; Fibrous coat, 262; Vascular layer, 263; Retina, 264; Contents of the eye, 268; Aqueous humor, 268; Vitreous body or humor, 268; Lens, 268; Optic nerve or stalk, 268; Circulation and innervation of the eye, 268; The ear, 269; External ear, 269; Middle ear, 269; Inner ear, 270; Osseous labyrinth, 270; Membranous labyrinth, 270; Olfactory organ, 274; Sustentacular cells, 275; Olfactory cells, 276; Basal cells, 276.

Color plates

PLATE 1. Cells from smear preparation of normal human blood 34

2. Normal vertebral bone marrow, male adult 50

3. Circulatory plan of kidney 207

4. Details of a renal pyramid and cortex 209

Essentials of
HISTOLOGY

CHAPTER I

BEN W. SANDERS

Introduction

Histology is the science that deals with the detailed structure of animals and plants and in its broader aspects correlates structural features with function. Vital functional units are called cells. Not only do different kinds of cells exhibit variations in form and structural content, but the same cell may vary in these respects with changes in its physiological status. Our knowledge about cells and cell products has been obtained by a study of "fixed" or dead cells and by a variety of ingenious methods developed to study living cells. Each of these methods has advantages and disadvantages, but they are mutually complementary and we may conclude that all normal cells have certain attributes in common.

Cell structures and cell products are made visible by the use of certain dyes. The traditional stains are hematoxylin and eosin (H & E). The basic dyes, like hematoxylin, stain the chromatin of the nucleus (basophilia), whereas the acid dyes, such as eosin, tend to stain the cytoplasm (acidophilia, oxyphilia). Although many other dyes are used, most slides utilized in routine histology and pathology are hematoxylin and eosin preparations. These dyes have the great advantage of relative stability, universal use, and reproducible results.

THE CELL

Most cells (Fig. 1) are composed of a single nucleus embedded in cytoplasm. The term *protoplasm* is used to designate the living substance of both the nucleus and cytoplasm. Protoplasm is a grayish viscous liquid (in colloid chemistry it is called a hydrosol) enclosed at all interfaces by a membrane (cell membrane). The cell membrane selectively regulates the interchange of materials between the cell and surrounding environment and upon death becomes completely permeable, or nonselective.

Nucleus

The nucleus, or *karyon*, usually appears as a spherical or ovoid body bounded by a nuclear membrane. The nucleus contains a fluid (nuclear sap) in which is found a dark-staining eccentrically placed small sphere,

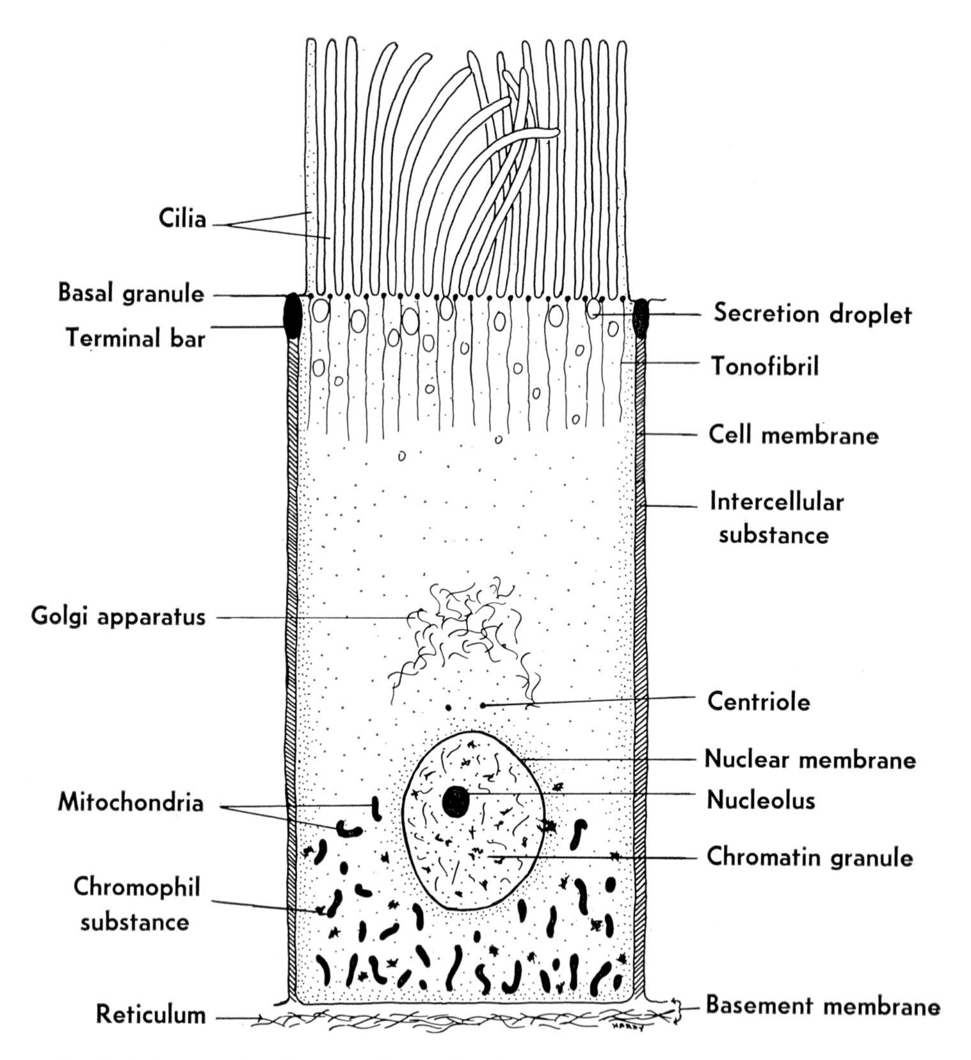

Fig. 1. Schematic drawing of a "typical" columnar epithelial cell and its intracellular inclusion bodies.

the *nucleolus,* and in addition contains a fine lacy network upon which dark-staining *chromatin granules* or flakes appear to be lodged. Whereas the nuclear sap is rarely stained, both the nucleolus and chromatin granules are strongly *basophilic* and stain a deep purple or blue with hematoxylin. The nucleolus contains ribonucleic acid (RNA), whereas chromatin granules contain desoxyribonucleic acid (DNA). With certain dyes the two may be distinguished. Toluidine blue stains chromatin blue (orthochromasia), but the RNA-containing nucleolus stains purplish (metachromasia) with the same dye. Many nuclei exhibit two or three nucleoli. Nuclei are said to be *vesiculate* (bladderlike) when chromatin granules are finely dispersed (or dustlike) and *condensed* when chromatin granules are clumped into one or several dark-staining masses.

In some cells, such as white blood cells and megakaryocytes, the nuclei may be *lobed,* the lobes being connected by fine strands. In others, such as liver cells, osteoclasts, and skeletal muscle fibers, the cell may contain two, three, or more nuclei embedded in the same cytoplasmic mass (a condition sometimes referred to as a *syncitium*). In degenerating megakaryocytes and giant embryonic yolk cells the lobes may become completely separated *(karyorrhexis).* In red blood cells the nucleus is extruded, and these enucleated cells cannot divide.

Cytoplasm

Cytoplasm, when observed in the living state, appears as a relatively transparent viscous *ground substance.* This ground substance is strongly acidophilic and stains with acid dyes like eosin or orange G. It contains numerous granules, filaments, and globules. These fall into two main groups known as *organoids and inclusions.* The organoids are believed to perpetuate themselves by autoduplication and to perform most of the metabolic functions of living systems. During cell division these particles are distributed between sister cells in what appears to be a systematic but semiquantitative manner. Included in this group are mitochondria, the Golgi apparatus, fibrils, centrioles, and the so-called chromophil substance.

Mitochondria occur in all animal cells as rods, filaments, or granules. With the aid of phase microscopy they are usually demonstrable in living cells or may be made visible by exposing living cells to the dye Janus green B in the presence of oxygen. After special fixation they may be demonstrated with iron hematoxylin or acid fuchsin. In routine hematoxylin and eosin preparations they are destroyed. Histochemical and microchemical methods demonstrate that mitochondria are involved in the oxidative metabolic processes of cells and perhaps in all major syntheses in cells.

The *Golgi apparatus* consists of a meshwork of lipid-containing fibrils that are usually supranuclear in position, that is, between the nucleus and the free surface of the cell. By the use of special fixatives, which may contain osmic acid or silver salts, the Golgi bodies appear black. Fat solvents may remove the lipid portions of these structures. Correlated with the secretory activities of certain cells is the occasional appearance of small vacuolated structures within the filaments known as vesicles (bladder). In addition to variations in the appearance of the Golgi bodies from cell to cell, cyclic variations occur in the same cell, as noted previously.

The *central body* (attraction sphere) also lies in the supranuclear position, sometimes producing a small indentation in the nucleus. It consists of a sphere of clear cytoplasm, the *centrosphere,* which contains one or two prominent granules known as *centrioles.* In many instances the centrosphere is surrounded by a group of delicate radial fibers called the *aster*. During cell division the centrioles separate and migrate to opposite sides of the nucleus during division of the nucleus. In addition to being implicated in the process of cell division some investigators believe that they may also perform other physiological functions.

The *chromophil substance* appearing prominently in nerve cells, salivary gland cells, and acinar cells of the pancreas is strongly basophilic and metachromatic, suggesting the presence of RNA. Extraction of stainable material by the enzyme ribonuclease supports this contention. Changes in chromophil substances occur during cellular activity, and recent evidence indicates that RNA is implicated in protein synthesis.

Fibrils occur in many cells. They are especially prominent in nerve (neurofibrils) and muscle cells (myofibrils). In epithelial cells they are known as *tonofibrils* and do not pass from cell to cell, as previously supposed.

The *inclusions* are considered nonliving, transitory constituents of the cell, frequently appearing as the result of metabolic events. Cytoplasmic inclusions often occur as globules or granules and may be lipids, carbohydrates, proteins, or some combination of these. Carbohydrates, such as glycogen, are easily demonstrated in liver, cartilage, muscle, and numerous other cells by the periodic acid-Schiff reaction (PAS) or other appropriate techniques. Secretory granules associated with cellular activity occur in many cells, especially epithelial cells such as those lining the digestive tract. Some of the latter cells produce the precursor of mucus known as mucigen, whereas others, known as zymogen granules, are the precursors of enzymes. Black or brown pigment granules, such as melanin, are the result of amino acid metabolism and are prominent in the skin of amphibi-

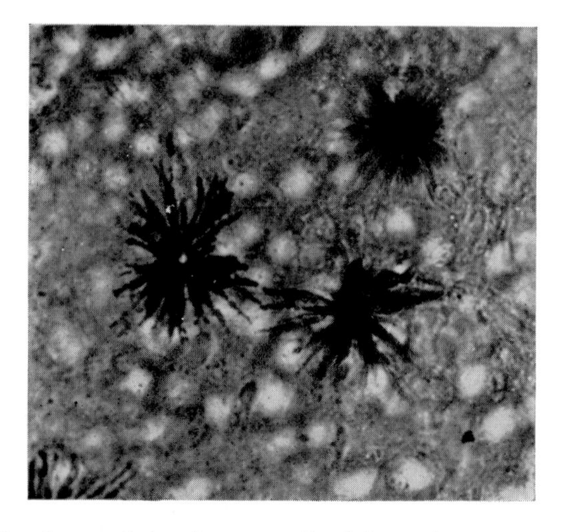

Fig. 2. Contracted and expanded melanocytes, Fundulus scale.

Table 1. Staining characteristics of cell components

	Cell constituent	*Chemical constituent*	*Characteristics*
Nucleus	Chromatin	DNA	Purple, blue, or black with hematoxylin—basophilia Blue with toluidine blue—orthochromasia Blue-green with methyl green—pyronin
	Nucleolus	RNA	Purple, blue, or black with hematoxylin—basophilia Purple with toluidine blue—metachromasia Red with methyl green—pyronin
		Ribose	Red-purple with Feulgen reaction
Cytoplasm:	Ground substance	Protein	Pink-red with eosin—acidophilia, eosinophilia
Organoids	Mitochondria	Complex	Blue with Janus green B supravital black with iron hematoxylin, red with acid fuchsin
	Centrioles	Protein	Rarely seen in hematoxylin and eosin, black with iron hematoxylin
	Chromophil substance	RNA	Same as nucleolus
	Fibrils	Protein	Special methods, argyrophil in nerve cells
Inclusions	Lipids	Fats	Blackened by osmic acid—osmiphilia Negative image in hematoxylin and eosin removed by solvents
	Zymogen	Protein	Red with eosin—acidophilia
	Mucigen glycogen	Carbohydrate	Unstained in routine hematoxylin and eosin negative image; red to purple with PAS

ans and fish (melanocytes) (Fig. 2) but occur to a lesser extent in higher forms.

Table 1 summarizes the staining reactions of cell constituents most frequently mentioned in modern texts.

Cellular activities

Activities of cells may be divided into three categories: vegetative, growth and reproduction, and special activities.

Vegetative activities. Vegetative activities are concerned with minimum activity for maintenance of the cell, such as resorption, assimilation, and excretion of waste products. These cells, capable of further division, are called *intermitotics*.

Growth and reproduction. Growth involves the elaboration of additional structural materials. Reproduction is a complex series of events involving division of the cells into two genetically equal daughter cells in the usual method of cell division (mitosis). Prominent roles are played by the centriole and nucleus in this process.

Special activities. In addition to the usual vegetative activities common to all cells, certain cells in multicellular animals have become differentiated, which means that certain cell activities become more prominent, whereas others become less prominent or may even be lost. Thus muscle cells exhibit the property of contractility; epithelial cells, of secretion and absorption; nerve cells, of hyperirritability, which permits reception, integration, and transmission of impulses. At the same time, however, such highly differentiated cells may lose the properties of mobility and reproduction. Those that lose the ability to reproduce are called *postmitotics*. Macrophages and certain white blood cells retain the property of mobility and also have the ability to phagocytize particulate matter, including bacteria.

The several changes in form and function occurring during the life of the cell are referred to as *cytomorphosis*. Distinct enlargement or growth of cells is called *hypertrophy*. Most of the life span of the cell is spent in the vegetative state, which represents a dynamic equilibrium between the cell and environment. With the passage of time the cells undergo regression or *atrophy*, until finally death (*necrosis*) and cell loss occurs. In the latter phase the nucleus shrinks and the chromatin forms a deeply staining mass, a process known as *pyknosis*.

TISSUES AND ORGANS

It has already been indicated that living cells carry on a number of physiological processes, such as response to stimuli, contraction, metabolism, and reproduction, in connection with their own maintenance and perpetuation. In multicellular organisms, moreover, groups of cells have the ability to perform one or another of these functions beyond their own needs for the benefit of the organism as a whole. Such specialized collections of similar cells are called *fundamental tissues* and are divided into groups as follows: (1) epithelia, (2) connective and supporting tissues, (3) blood and lymph, (4) muscle, and (5) nervous tissue. Some authors include reproductive tissue as a separate group because of certain special characteristics.

The fundamental tissues are not evenly distributed throughout the body but are gathered together to form organs, and the location of these organs are studied in gross dissection. Further analysis of organs is afforded by microscopic study from which we may learn what kind or kinds of tissue are present in each and form an estimate of the activity the organ performs. We shall find in such examination that many organs consist of an arrangement of epithelium, connective tissue, and muscle, with a supply of nerves and blood vessels. Some, however, may lack epithelium, or muscle, or both of these tissues.

It will be our object in the study of organs to analyze each organ into its component parts and relate this analysis to the results of histochemical and physiological studies. Before undertaking the study of organs, however, it will be necessary to acquire a full knowledge of the fundamental tissues. Each of the groups already mentioned has subdivisions, and these subdivisions have morphological and physiological peculiarities which must be recognized and understood in order to make organology intelligible. The first chapters of this book are accordingly devoted to the subject of the fundamental tissues, whereas the remaining chapters present the various combinations of such tissues forming the different organs.

CHAPTER II

Epithelia

Epithelial tissues have two types of arrangement and two functions. First, they are arranged in sheets, one or more layers in thickness, covering the surface or lining the cavities of the body to form a protective sheath or limiting membrane. Second, they are grouped in solid cords, tubules, or follicles, which have developed as outgrowths from an epithelial sheet and are specialized for secretion, absorption, or excretion. The separation of function is not complete however, since cells are present in many lining epithelia which have a secretory function.

EPITHELIAL CELLS

Epithelial tissues are composed of cells of somewhat regular form without extensive protoplasmic processes. These cells are closely applied to each other and there is present only a small amount of *intercellular substance* cementing them together. Near the free surface of certain epithelia the intercellular substance viewed under the optical microscope appears to be thicker and forms the *terminal* bar network. Adjacent cells may occasionally communicate through minute *intercellular bridges.* This, however, is the exception rather than the usual situation. The epithelia which are arranged as coverings and linings rest upon a membrane called the *basement membrane (membrana propria).* This is commonly believed to be a modification of the underlying connective tissue, although there is evidence that in some cases a secretion from the epithelial cells takes part in the formation. The basement membrane may appear hyaline and structureless or composed of a band of tightly or loosely packed (reticular) fibers. The hyaline material stains with the PAS method, whereas the fibers require special silver techniques for visualization. The basement membrane is often so fine as to be imperceptible in routine hematoxylin and eosin preparations, and some epithelia are said to lack it entirely (transitional epithelium). Other types exhibit a well-marked membrane (pseudostratified epithelium of the trachea). Epithelial tissues are avascular, and blood capillaries are found only below basement membranes.

Epithelial cells lining moistened membranes or tubules usually exhibit free surfaces which are smooth, whereas others exhibit protoplasmic projections known as *cilia.* Cilia of the *motile* variety are prominent structures in well-preserved material and usually exhibit a small granule at the base of each one. Motile cilia are associated with the respiratory passages and the female reproductive tract. In living animals motile cilia or flagellae produce currents in the abdominal cavity. *Stereocilia* are a very elongate, nonmotile variety, lacking basal granules, relatively broad at the base, and gradually tapering to an extremely fine wavy filament. Stereocilia are found in portions of the male reproductive tract and are thought to be associated with secretion. *Striated borders* are composed of many extremely thin, short, uniform, and closely packed protoplasmic projections found in locations where absorption and secretion are the primary activities of the cell. In the small intestine the striated border is covered by a thin layer of mucoprotein secretion, and in poorly stained or preserved material one sees an ill-defined region covered by secretion. In the latter condition it appears as a thin membrane. Previously it was referred to as the *cuticle* or cuticular border. Cell surfaces beset with short protoplasmic projections in which the arrangement is irregular and appears somewhat like a brush are known as *brush borders.* When brush borders are not well preserved the edge of the cell presents a ragged appearance. Striated and brush borders as well as smaller suboptical projections of cells are now collectively known as microvilli.

EPITHELIAL TISSUES

The epithelia are divided into two main groups: simple epithelia and stratified epithelia. Simple epithelia consist of a single layer of cells, all of which are in contact with the basement membrane. Stratified epithelia consist of cell layers superimposed one upon the other, and only the basal cell layer is in contact with the basement membrane. The two main groups are further subdivided according to the shapes of the component cells, as shown in the following classification outline.

Simple epithelia	*Stratified epithelia*
Squamous	Stratified columnar
Cuboidal	Stratified cuboidal
Columnar	Transitional
Pseudostratified	Stratified squamous

A more detailed description of each type follows.

Simple epithelia

Squamous epithelium. The cells of simple squamous epithelium are extremely flattened. Viewed from the surface they appear as fairly large cells with clear cytoplasm. The nucleus of each is round or oval and ec-

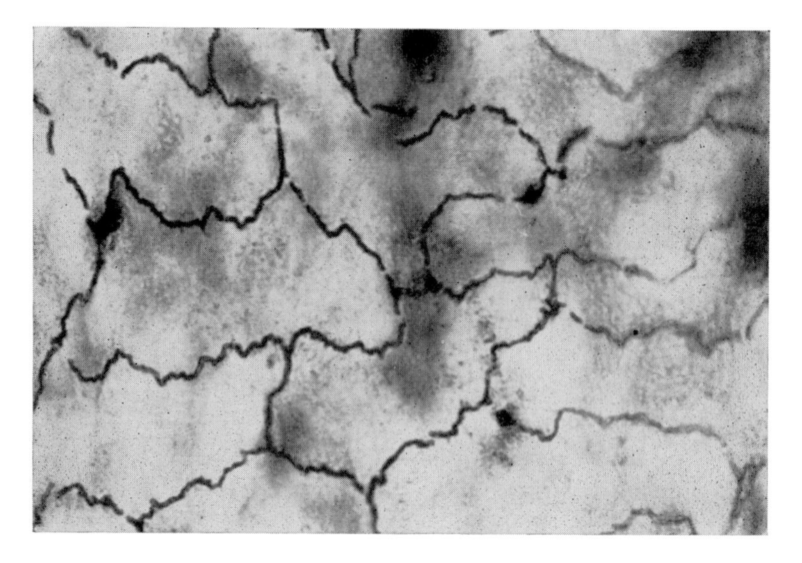

Fig. 3. Surface view of mesothelium. (Silver nitrate preparation.)

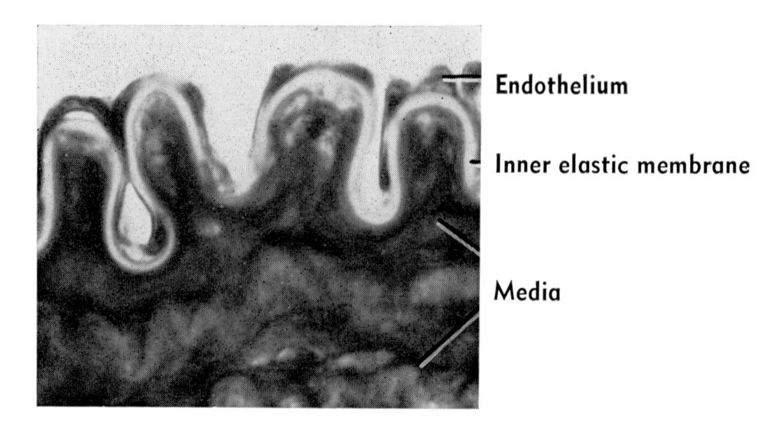

Fig. 4. Endothelium lining lumen of medium-sized artery.

centrically placed. Cell outlines are not ordinarily visible but may be demonstrated by the reaction of silver nitrate on intercellular substance. In such preparations the polygonal cell boundary may be somewhat wavy, serrated, or sometimes smooth (Fig. 3). In section the cytoplasm is barely visible but may be seen in the region of the nucleus where the cytoplasm appears to bulge (Fig. 4). The boundaries between adjacent cells are not visible in routine preparations.

Simple squamous epithelium is not found in exposed regions or in sites where absorption or secretion are the primary activities. In general it forms barriers in regions where diffusion or filtration rather than protection is the basic requirement. This is the case in Bowman's capsule of the kidney and in lung alveoli, which are used as examples of this tissue type. It forms the barriers of the blood-tissue fiuid, tissue fluid-lymph and tissue fluid-gas interfaces. *Endothelium* is the type of simple squamous epithelium found lining blood vessels, heart, lymphatic ducts, and bone marrow. It forms the entire thickness of the walls of blood and lymph capillaries. *Mesothelium* is the same type of tissue found on the so-called serous membranes lining the peritoneal, pleural, and pericardial cavities of the body. The distinction between endothelium and mesothelium is based on the embryological mode of formation. They are not, however, morphologically distinguishable other than by location. The mesothelium-like layer found lining the anterior chamber of the eye, the inner ear, and the cerebrospinal spaces is known as mesenchymal epithelium. The flattened cells lining joint cavities are said to be fibroblasts derived from the dense connective tissue in those regions and are not considered to be epithelial at all.

Cuboidal epithelium. In surface view the cells of cuboidal epithelium are smaller and more regular than simple squamous cells and appear roughly hexagonal in outline (Fig. 5). The cell boundaries are often clearly visible because of the presence of terminal bars. In vertical section (Fig. 6)

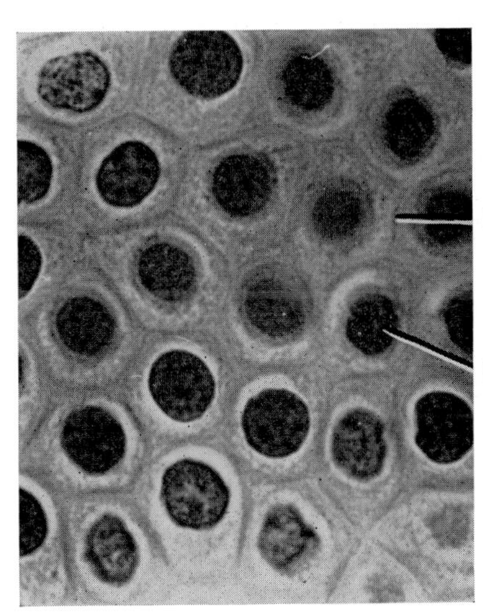

Fig. 5. Transverse section of cuboidal epithelium from kidney.

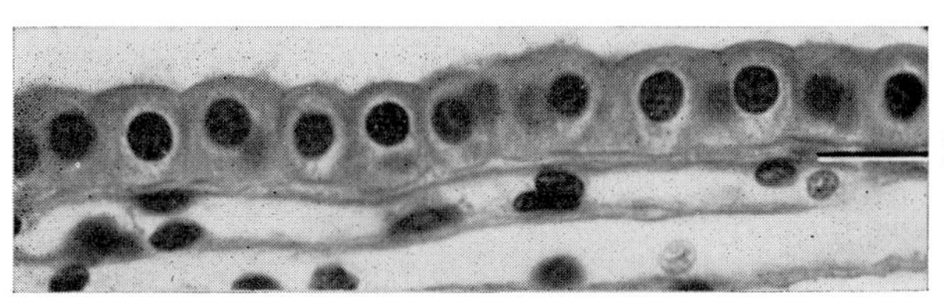

Fig. 6. Vertical section of cuboidal epithelium from kidney.

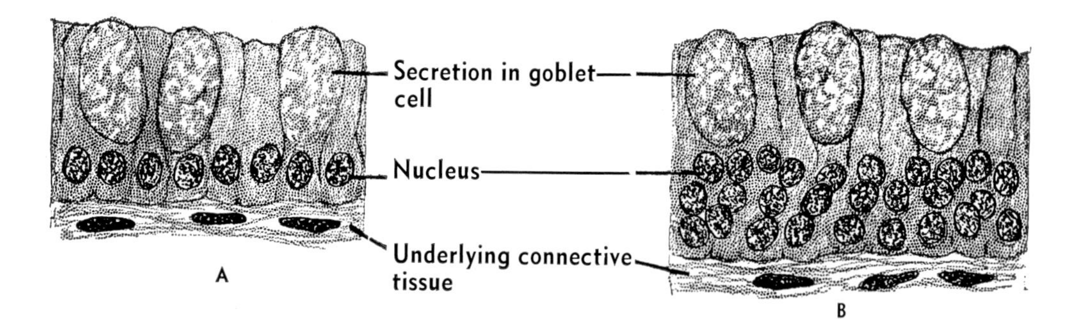

Fig. 7. Tall columnar epithelium from intestine. **A,** Vertical section. **B,** Tangential section.

the cell appears square with a rounded nucleus in the center of each, and in specially stained preparations the terminal bars are visible. The square shape is modified to that of a trapezoid when the cells are grouped around the lumen of a small duct. When they are closely packed around the lumen of some glands the cells resemble a truncated pyramid and are accordingly called pyramidal cells. The cytoplasm of these cells may appear clear or granular, and in the latter case the cell boundaries are often indistinct in sectioned material. Examples of simple cuboidal epithelium may be found in certain kidney tubules (Fig. 6) and in the partly distended cells of the thyroid gland. In the thyroid the cells elaborate secretions, although this function is more commonly associated with columnar cells.

Columnar epithelium. In surface view columnar epithelium fits the description given for cuboidal epithelium, including the terminal bars as well. In sections, however, the cells are seen to be taller than they are broad, that is, they have the form of rectangles with the long axis perpendicular to the free surface. The nucleus is characteristically close to the base of the cell, except when the cells are extremely compressed. The free surface may be composed of a smooth plasma membrane covered by a thin or thick mucous secretion, or it may have microvilli or cilia of the varieties described in the introduction to this chapter. The cytoplasm may be clear or may contain granules, secretion droplets, or a large clump of secretion droplets in a vacuole near the surface of the cell (Fig. 7, *A*). (See discussion on goblet cells.)

The mucus secreting cells (goblet cells) found in columnar epithelium have the purpose of moistening the epithelium as well as the imprisonment of foreign particles. The basement membrane is usually prominent.

The difference between cuboidal and columnar cells is not sharply marked. It depends on the height of the cells as seen in vertical section. An organ may be said by one author to be lined with cuboidal epithelium, whereas another will use the term low columnar in describing the tissue. An example of low columnar epithelium is shown in the illustration of the kidney (Fig. 6). Tall columnar epithelium is illustrated in Fig. 7, *A* and *B*, drawn from a section of the small intestine.

In studying columnar epithelium it is important to select a region in which the section passes through the tissue in a plane perpendicular to its surface. When a slanting, or tangential, section is studied, the appearance is that of two or more layers of cells, and the tissue may be erroneously classified as stratified or pseudostratified epithelium (see Fig. 7, *B*). Columnar cells are found in regions where the epithelial lining of an organ combines the function of secretion with that of a limiting membrane (for example, digestive tract).

Pseudostratified epithelium. Pseudostratified epithelium consists essentially of columnar cells which are crowded very closely together. Because of this, the rectangular form is distorted and not all of the cells reach the free surface of the epithelium. Those which do reach the surface have an upper part like a columnar cell and a much-constricted base. Some have a wide base and an irregular spindle shape, and still others are short and rounded. The nucleus of each cell lies at its widest portion, and this gives the tissue the appearance of a stratified epithelium with nuclei at several levels. Only in the best preparations can it be demonstrated that whereas approximately only one cell in three touches the free surface, all have a portion touching the basement membrane. In all preparations there seems, at the first glance, to be little difference between a vertical section of pseudostratified epithelium and the tangential section of simple columnar epithelium described. The nuclei of the two kinds of tissue offer the best means of distinguishing between the two. In pseudostratified epithelium these are of several sorts, those at the base of the tissue being small and dark, those nearer the surface larger and paler. In the tangential section of columnar epithelium, on the other hand, only one type of nucleus is present. The cytoplasm of the cells of pseudostratified epithelium is sometimes clear, sometimes granular. It may con-

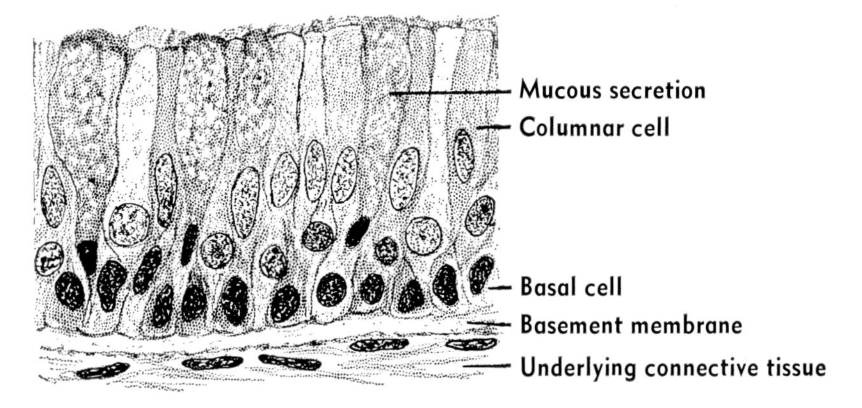

Fig. 8. Pseudostratified epithelium from trachea.

tain drops of secretions, and the surface cells are ciliated. The nuclei are round or oval according to the shape of the cells in which they lie. The usual appearance of this type of epithelium is illustrated in Fig. 8 (trachea). It is functionally adapted to serve as a fairly resistant limiting membrane.

Stratified epithelia

In all stratified epithelia a complete layer of small modified cuboidal or columnar cells lies next to the basement membrane. These cells are called *basal cells.* Above this, except in the case of a two-layered epithelium, there are one or more layers of polygonal cells. At the free surface lies a layer of cells which have a different shape in each subdivision of the group. The shape of the cells at the free surface of a stratified epithelium determines its classification into one of the four subdivisions.

Stratified columnar epithelium. Stratified columnar epithelium differs from the pseudostratified type in having a continuous layer of small rounded cells next to the basement membrane. The columnar cells at the surface of the epithelium are thus entirely cut off from the basement membrane, and the epithelium is truly stratified. This type is of rare occurrence. (Fig. 183).

Stratified cuboidal epithelium. This type is extremely rare, the best example occurs in the ducts of the sweat glands. A definite basement membrane is present, whereas the free surface bears a distinct border. Certain cell layers in the testis and ovary are also included in this group by some authors.

Transitional epithelium. Transitional epithelium is a stratified epithelium whose surface cells do not fall into the truly squamous, cuboidal, or columnar categories. The basal cells are like those of stratified columnar epithelium. Above them are a varying number of polygonal cells of which those immediately below the surface layer tend to have an elongated, pearlike (pyriform) shape. The layer at the surface is composed of large, some-

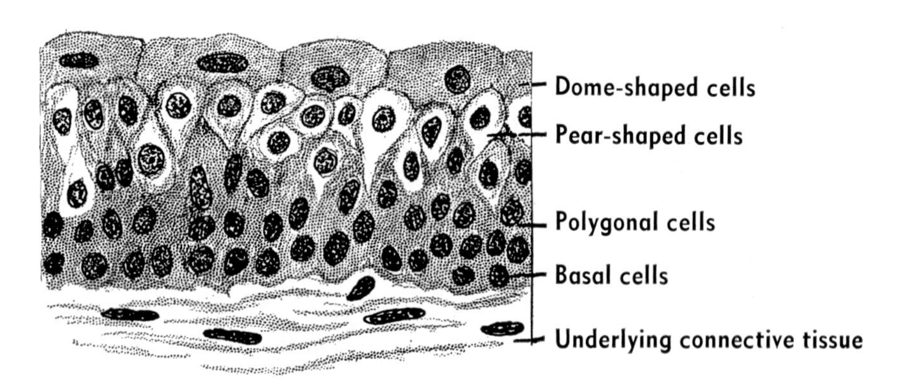

Fig. 9. Transitional epithelium from urinary bladder.

what flattened cells, generally described as dome shaped. One of these cells often covers three underlying pear-shaped cells, with indentations to receive the latter. The dome cells are so large that in sectioned material many of the nuclei are not visible because they are not in the plane of the section, although dome cells are known to have as many as two or three nuclei each. The cytoplasm just under the free surface of the dome cell appears to be more condensed and deeply staining, which is an aid in the identification of this tissue. Basement membrane, terminal bars, and cilia are not found in this nonsecretory tissue (Fig. 9).

The cells of this epithelium possess to an unusual degree the ability to change their position by sliding over each other, so that if the viscus they line is distended the epithelium is reduced to three or four layers. When the viscus is empty the cells heap up, forming several layers between the basal and surface cells. This tissue changes in appearance not only with the state of distention of the lined structure but also from place to place along the urinary tract to which it is confined. It is accordingly advantageous to examine this tissue from different regions of the urinary tract.

Stratified squamous epithelium. In stratified squamous epithelium the thickness and number of cells vary in different parts of the body; the shape

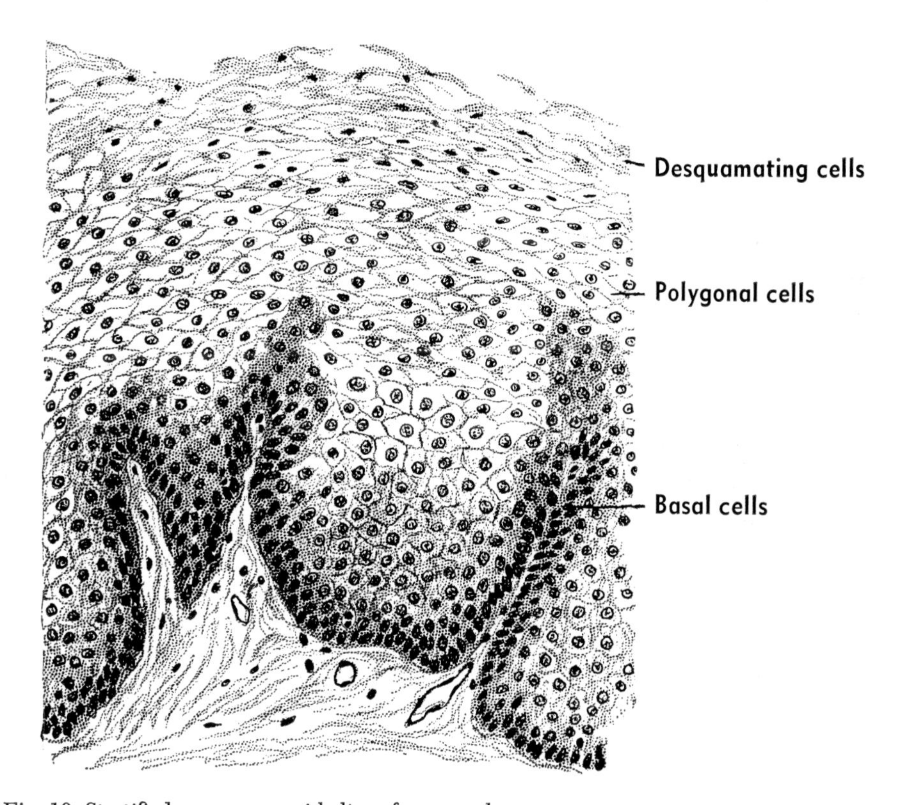

Fig. 10. Stratified squamous epithelium from esophagus.

and arrangement of component cells, however, follow the same general plan. In this epithelium the basal cells are covered by several layers of polygonal cells. Near the base the polygonal cells are quite small, but they gradually increase in size toward the middle of the tissue (hypertrophy); beyond this point they begin to flatten out and become smaller (hypotrophy). As they approach the surface they may become flattened, shriveled, (atrophy) and scalelike with pycnotic nuclei, which is the situation existing in the mucous membranes of the mouth and esophagus (Fig. 10). In more exposed, dry epithelia, such as the skin, the cells may incorporate a tough resilient material (keratin). When this condition exists the epithelium is said to be *cornified* or *keratinized.* This tissue is particularly well adapted to perform its protective function because of (1) its great thickness and keratinization, (2) its ability to slough off surface cells under the impetus of abrasion, and (3) the replacement of these cells from below. Whereas surface cells are typically flattened, as on the surface of the cornea of the eye, or scalelike, as described above, they differ from simple squamous cells in that the flattened nuclei do not generally produce an enlargement of the cell. The addition of hair also increases the protective function of this epithelium.

The cells which make up the basal and polyhedral layers of this tissue, the so-called *stratum germinativum,* are characteristically basophilic, suggesting their great metabolic activity. In addition shrinkage of this region produced during preservation (fixation) reveals prominent intercellular bridges containing tonofibrils, a characteristic which has earned for them the name "prickle cells." Since none of the epithelia described are penetrated by blood vessels, their nutrition apparently depends on transmission through interstitial cellular fluids. This would create a serious nutritional problem for epithelia as thick as stratified squamous epithelia. At any rate, it has been suggested that the death of surface cells and possibly keratinization may be the result of lack of nutrients. The thicker stratified squamous epithelia have fingerlike projections of connective tissue, known as *papillae,* penetrating quite deeply into the stratum germinativum, thereby increasing the surface area available for the diffusion of nutrients. In summary, then, we have surface cells which may be flattened or scalelike, keratinized or nonkeratinized. The epithelia appear papillate or nonpapillate.

CHAPTER III

Blood and lymph

Mesenchyme, an embryonic connective tissue derived from the mesoderm, contains characteristic cells which are stellate in shape and connected one to the other by their cellular processes. These cells undergo many changes which result in the elaboration of blood, lymph, blood vessels, connective tissue proper, cartilage, and bone. In blood and lymph the intercellular substance is fluid; in the connective tissues fibers occur; in cartilage the intercellular substance is semirigid and contains fibers, whereas in bone the fibers present are impregnated with mineral salts.

The various connective tissues in the adult tend to blend together in some respects. For example, the fibers of the connective tissue proper become incorporated into cartilage and bone; similarly, certain chemical substances such as acid polysaccharides are found in the intercellular areas of connective tissue as well as in cartilage and bone. In the case of blood cells the constant exchange between them and the cells of the connective tissue make sharp distinctions between these tissues difficult.

Blood and lymph are the fluid tissues of the body. Their function is to distribute oxygen, nutritive substances, and the products of the endocrine glands to all parts of the body and to remove waste substances and toxins. Both consist of a fluid matrix called the plasma and cells of various types.

The cells or corpuscles of blood are of two types: the red and the white. Together they are about equal in bulk to the plasma. The red cells are more numerous than the white; there are from four to five million of them in a cubic millimeter of normal blood compared to but eight or ten thousand of the white cells.

BLOOD

Red blood corpuscles (erythrocytes)

When a drop of freshly drawn blood is examined under the microscope the red corpuscles are seen as biconcave discs, having a diameter of approximately 8μ. In the fresh state they appear greenish in color rather than red. The depression in the center of each corpuscle makes a light spot which might at first sight be mistaken for a nucleus. The adult red cells are, however, nonnucleated in mammalian blood. Often they stick together in rows, or rouleaux. As a drop of blood dries at its edges the red cells lose fluid and change their shapes. Some are cup shaped, others are very irregular in outline. In sections of organs and tissues stained with hematoxylin and eosin the red blood cells have a bright orange or red color. The disc shape is the most common in such preparations; but, especially in small vessels, the cells are sometimes cup shaped, sometimes compressed into angular forms. The usual method of preparing blood for microscopic study is to spread a drop on a slide so that it forms a thin smear and then stain it with a special stain. Wright's stain is commonly used. The red corpuscles when so treated lose volume without changing shape. Those at the center of the smear, when there have been no changes due to rapid drying, have the form of biconcave discs which average about 7.5μ in diameter. The cells are nongranular, colored pale brown or pink by the stain.

Since the red blood cells are nonnucleated it is sometimes said that they should not be called cells. The name erythroplastid may be used, but erythrocyte is the more common term. The cytoplasm of the red corpuscles contains a substance called hemoglobin, which is readily oxidized and reduced, and it is this substance that enables the erythrocytes to perform their function of carrying oxygen from the lungs to the tissues. Hemoglobin imparts a reddish tint to cells containing it if the latter are stained with Wright's stain. This fact is important in recognition of early stages of development of red blood cells. (See discussion on bone marrow, Chapter V.)

White blood corpuscles (leukocytes)

The white blood corpuscles are so called because of their lack of color in the fresh state. The group of leukocytes is divided into three main subgroups: granulocytes, lymphocytes, and monocytes. They have various shapes and exhibit different degrees of ameboid movement when studied in tissue culture preparations. Ordinarily, however, little information regarding these cells is obtained from a drop of fresh, unstained blood.

In sections stained with hematoxylin and eosin the leukocytes stand out among the erythrocytes because of their darkly stained nuclei. It is sometimes possible to identify lymphocytes, granulocytes, and monocytes in such preparations, but for a critical examination of white blood cells one must use preparations made with special stains.

In a blood smear treated with Wright's stain, the following types of cells are to be distinguished (Plate 1).

Granulocytes
- (1) Neutrophilic—60 to 75 per cent of white cells
- (2) Eosinophilic—2 to 4 per cent of white cells
- (3) Basophilic—0.5 to 3 per cent of white cells

Lymphocytes—20 to 25 per cent of white cells
Monocytes—3 to 8 per cent of white cells

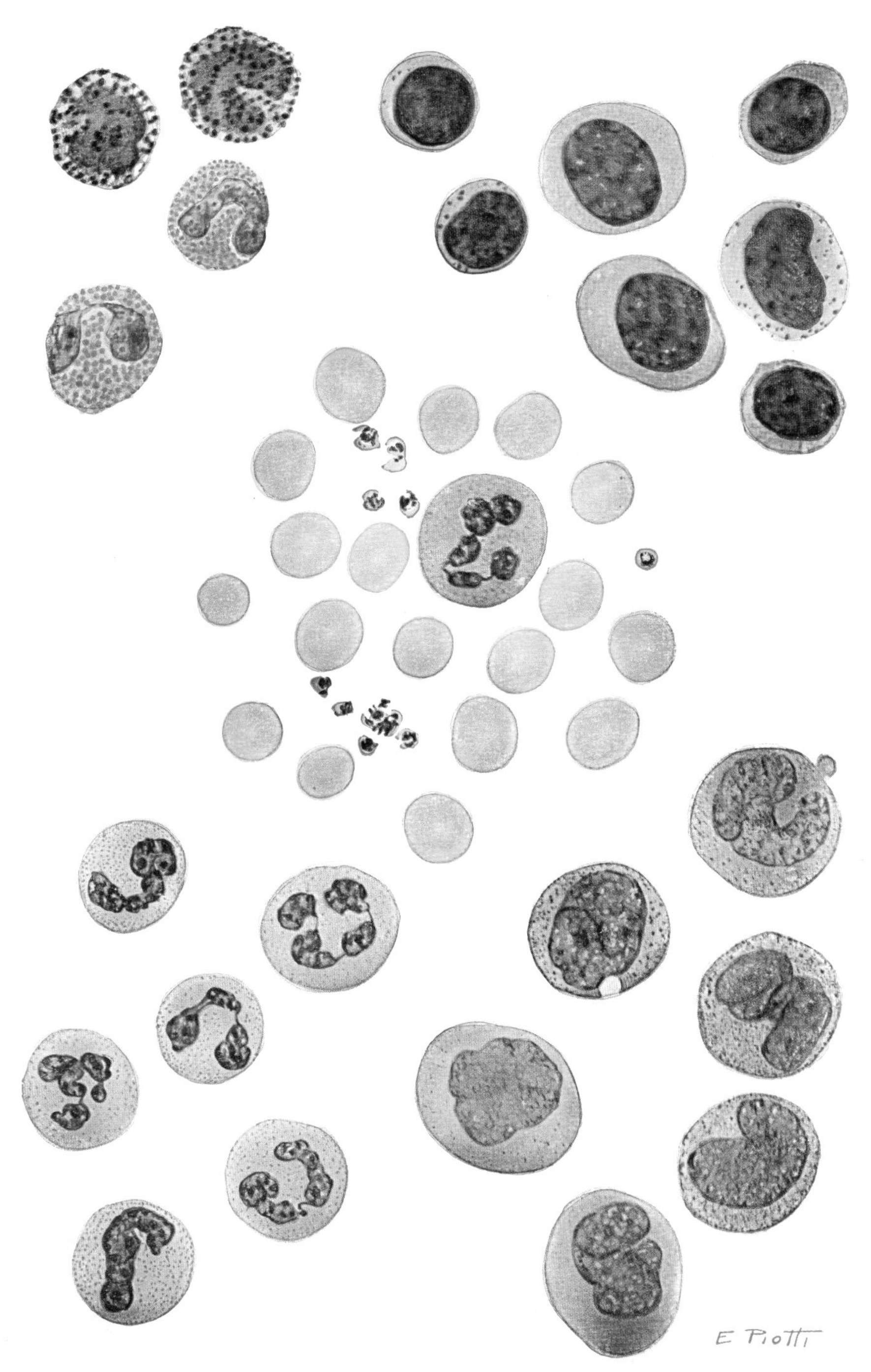

Plate 1

Cells from smear preparation of normal human blood. (Wright's stain.) In center: Adult red blood corpuscles, blood platelets, and a polymorphonuclear neutrophil. At left above: Two polymorphonuclear basophils and two polymorphonuclear eosinophils. At right above: Three large and four small lymphocytes, some with granules in protoplasm. At left below: Polymorphonuclear neutrophils; two of these cells, the uppermost and the lowermost of the group, are young, with merely crooked nuclei, sometimes known as band, stab, or nonfilamentous forms; mature cells have multilobed nuclei. At right below: Six monocytes, some containing more protoplasmic granules than others; in the younger cells nuclei tend to be rounded and in the adult cells they are horseshoe shaped, indented, or lobed. (From Bremer and Weatherford: A Text-Book of Histology, New York, 1948, The Blakiston Co.)

The leukocytes as a group respond differently from the red cells to the treatment involved in making a smear. Erythrocytes lose a slight amount of volume and are, therefore, smaller in the smear than in the fresh state. Leukocytes, on the contrary, are flattened by the treatment and acquire a greater diameter.

Granulocytes. Granulocytes are characterized by two morphological peculiarities: their cytoplasm contains granules and their nuclei are shrunken, presenting a great variety of forms. To the latter characteristic they owe their name, polymorphonuclear leukocytes. The most common of them, in fact of all leukocytes, is the neutrophilic polymorphonuclear leukocyte. This cell is slightly larger than the erythroplastid (from 8 to 12μ); its cytoplasm is not strongly acid or basic in its reaction. The color which it takes in this stain is lavender. The protoplasm is filled with fine granules. The nucleus is densely chromatic and beaded or shrunken to from three to five rounded masses connected by fine strands. Two other kinds of polymorphonuclear leukocytes are present in normal blood. These are eosinophilic and basophilic, respectively. The cytoplasm of each kind is filled with large granules, which in the eosinophilic cell stain a bright scarlet and in the basophilic a deep purplish blue. The granules are sometimes so prominent as to obscure the nucleus and seem actually to project from the cytoplasm. The nucleus of the eosinophil is generally bilobed and deeply stained, while that of the basophil is paler and often has the shape of an irregular letter S. Neither of these nuclear forms is, however, an exclusive or universal characteristic of the cells in question. As will be seen from the percentages given above, eosinophilic and basophilic granulocytes are somewhat rare, and diligent search may be necessary before they are found.

Lymphocytes. The kind of leukocytes next in abundance to the neutrophilic polymorphonuclear is the lymphocyte. Lymphocytes are divided by some authors into two groups, small and large. There are, in fact, intermediate sizes, so that such a division is difficult to make. The smaller lymphocytes are the most numerous. They are about the size of erythrocytes. The nucleus is very dark purple and has a spherical shape. The cytoplasm stains a greenish blue and in the smallest of these cells is reduced to a thin film around the nucleus. In the larger lymphocytes the cytoplasm is more abundant and may contain a few scattered granules. The nucleus is spherical and stains deeply. The size of the large lymphocytes may be as great as 15μ in diameter.

Monocytes (large mononuclears). The monocyte often resembles a large lymphocyte, so that it is difficult to distinguish betwen the two kinds of leukocytes. However, the monocytes range in size from 15 to 20μ in smears, so that the largest of them are recognizable by their size. They also have staining reactions and nuclear forms which, when fully developed, differentiate them from other leukocytes. Wright's stain usually gives the cytoplasm of the monocyte a dull grayish blue or lavender color and shows it to be slightly granular. The nucleus of the monocyte is characteristically indented to a kidney or horseshoe shape. While these features appear in many monocytes, some examples less easily classified will be found in a smear.

Platelets

In addition to the cells just described, blood contains groups of very minute cytoplasmic fragments which are called platelets or thrombocytes and are not generally included under the head of corpuscles. The individual platelet, about 2μ in diameter, is composed of a cytoplasm which stains blue with Wright's stain. It has a dark granular center but no nucleus. These minute structures are believed to assist in the clotting of blood, although it is not known whether their role is active or passive.

LYMPH

Lymph is of less interest to the student of histology than blood. It consists of a fluid plasma which is somewhat different chemically from blood plasma. In it are floating leukocytes, principally lymphocytes and large mononuclear leukocytes. In sections of lymph vessels one sees only a fine granular coagulum with occasional nucleated corpuscles.

CHAPTER IV

The connective tissue proper

In the connecting and supporting tissues the arrangement of cells and intercellular substance is quite different from that seen in the epithelia. The cells, instead of being closely applied to each other in the form of a sheet or a cord, lie more or less scattered, sometimes not in contact, sometimes touching only at the ends of long protoplasmic processes. The intercellular substance is much more prominent than among the epithelia and becomes the most important part of the majority of the tissues in the group.

The type of cell most frequently found in these tissues is of an irregular branching form, sometimes called stellate. Its nucleus is vesicular and its cytoplasm is somewhat granular and prolonged in the form of processes. Cells of this type make up the mesenchyme, the embryonic tissue from which all the members of the group are derived. The original shape of the cell is retained in some of the connecting and supporting tissues after they have been fully differentiated. In others it is modified.

The intercellular components of this group consist of three components: (1) fibers, (2) ground substance, and (3) tissue fluid. The ground substance contains acid polysaccharides. Three kinds of fibers are distinguishable by their appearance and chemical reactions. The three kinds are collagenous, or white, reticular, and elastic fibers. White fibers are the most common. They consist of bundles of extremely delicate striated fibrillae which may vary from 0.5 to 1μ in diameter. The fibrillae are held together in bundles by a cementing substance. The fibrillae themselves do not branch, but the fibers of which they are composed do. They possess little elasticity, are dissolved by weak acids, and yield gelatin when boiled. They stain fairly readily with eosin, giving a pink color to tissues containing many of them. Reticular fibers are similar to white fibers in some respects but stain less readily with eosin and have a special affinity for silver stains. They are therefore a less prominent feature in sections prepared in the ordinary way. On boiling they yield reticulin, which differs slightly from the gelatin obtained from white fibers. Reticular fibers also resist peptic digestion longer than do the white fibers. Some authors consider these differences

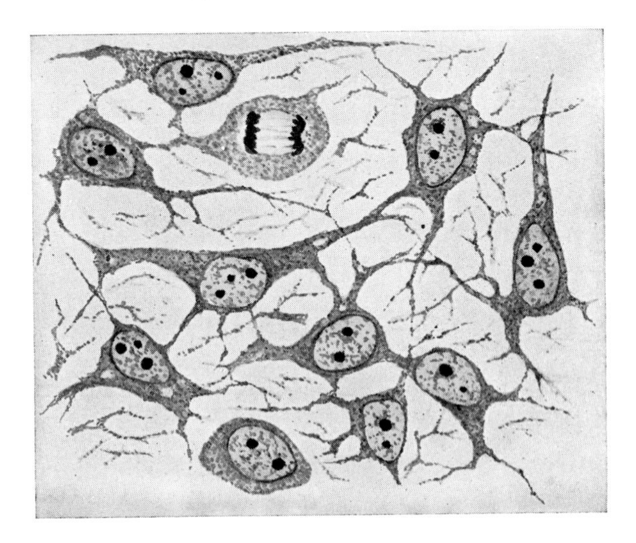

Fig. 11. Mesenchyme in a 60-mm. dog fetus. (Silver stain; ×1,200.) (From Nonidez and Windle: Textbook of Histology, New York, 1953, McGraw-Hill Book Co., Inc.)

unimportant and class reticular and white fibers together. Others consider reticular fibers to be the precursors of collagenous fibers, since in the development of many organs the connective tissue is reticular at first and becomes collagenous later. Elastic fibers occur singly or in the form of sheets. In ordinary preparations they are hardly distinguishable from the white fibers. If the sections are stained with resorcin, however, the elastic fibers will be sharply differentiated, as this dye colors them deeply but leaves the white fibers pale. In such slides the elastic fibers appear as stout, branching structures, heavier than the individual white fibrils or reticular fibers. On boiling they yield elastin, a different substance from the gelatin obtained from white fibers, and they show a greater resistance to acids than do the white fibers. As their name implies, their most important physical characteristic is their elasticity, but this is not apparent in histological preparations. The matrix in which the cells and fibers of the connecting and supporting tissues lie embedded also varies. In some instances (the connective tissues) it is a nonstainable fluid, represented in sections by colorless, apparently empty areas. In the supporting tissues the fluid is replaced by a solid mass which takes stains more or less deeply. In cartilage this matrix is firm but pliable, whereas in bone the presence of mineral salts makes it hard and rigid.

The process by which these intercellular structures are formed is a subject for controversy. Two views are held: (1) that fibers and matrices develop from cells themselves and represent transformed cytoplasm from the peripheral part of the cells; (2) that the cells cause a transformation of the intercellular substance from a fluid to a fibrous or solid condition without contributing any of their own protoplasm. It is not within the scope of this book to enter into a discussion of this controversy.

From the foregoing description of the elements composing the tissues of this group it is evident that they have, in varying degree, the function of binding together the parts of the body and furnishing it with a supporting framework. Less obvious are other functions performed by the connective tissues. The fluid intercellular substance of connective tissue plays a part in the nutrition of the body, and the cells provide new phagocytes. These functions are best described in Chapter II. For the present we shall consider the connective tissues in relation to their connective and supporting qualities. From that point of view one may arrange them in order of their degree of differentiation and their solidity, although it must be pointed out that any classification is difficult and cannot be adhered to rigidly, since the different varieties have transitional forms.

Mucous connective tissue

Mucous connective tissue, which must not be confused with mucus-secreting epithelium, retains much of the appearance of mesenchyme, the primitive tissue from which it is derived. The cells are spindle shaped or branching. The intercellular fluid of mesenchyme is replaced by a mucoid jellylike mass from which the tissue derives its name. Fibers of the white or collagenous variety are present, lying in close proximity to the cells (border fibrils or fibroglia). In microscopic preparations the jelly stains faintly, the fibers more deeply. In the adult body mucous connective tissue is present in the vitreous humor of the eye. It is usually studied in sections of the umbilical cord and is of interest chiefly because it illustrates a relation between fibers and cells which is less evident in the more highly differentiated tissues.

Reticular tissue

In ordinary preparations reticular tissue also has an appearance somewhat similar to that of mesenchyme. The cells composing it are sometimes called primitive reticular cells. They are branching cells, the processes of which are generally in contact with each other. The intercellular substance consists of a nonstainable fluid and fine reticular fibers. The latter take the same color as the cell processes when the preparation is stained with eosin, and this makes it difficult to distinguish them. By careful examination, however, one may see among the slightly granular cytoplasmic processes other fine hyaline strands which are intercellular fibers. With special stains (silver nitrate) the fibers may be more clearly demonstrated. They then appear as short fine fibers, for the most part closely associated with the cells (Fig. 14).

Reticular tissue such as has just been described is illustrated in Figs. 12,

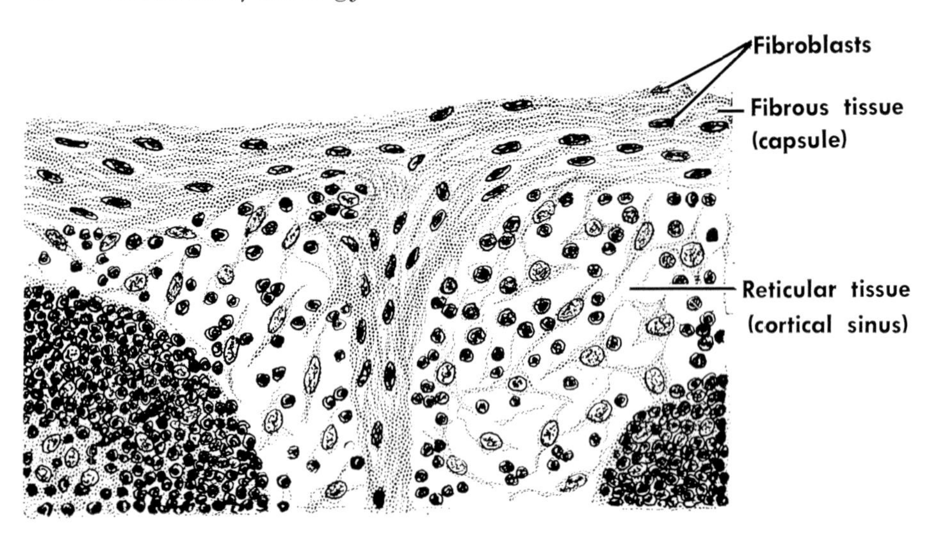

Fig 12. Peripheral portion of a section of lymph node.

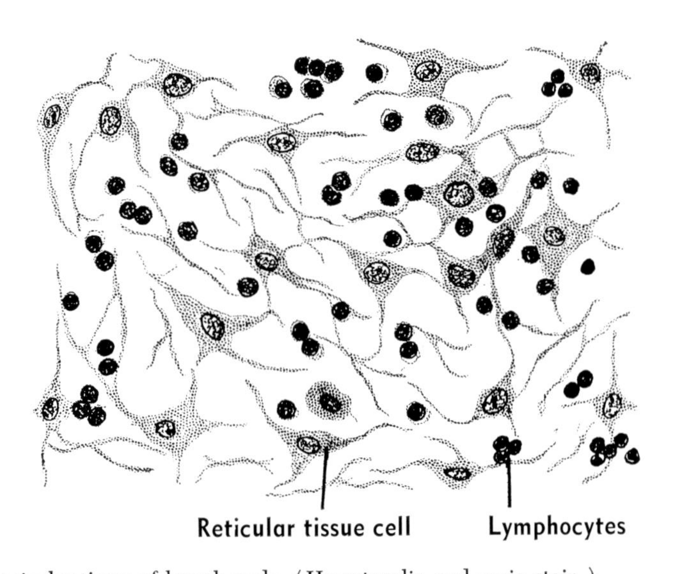

Fig. 13. Reticular tissue of lymph node. (Hematoxylin and eosin stain.)

13, and 14. It forms the basis of the lymphoid organs, such as the lymph nodes, where it is combined with lymphocytes and other blood cells. The latter are present in such numbers as to obscure the reticular network in parts of the preparation, and care must be taken to avoid such regions in finding a place to study the fundamental tissue.

A more attenuated form of reticular tissue is found immediately subjacent to the epithelium of many organs (for example, the digestive tract). Here the cells are more widely separated, and the appearance presented is

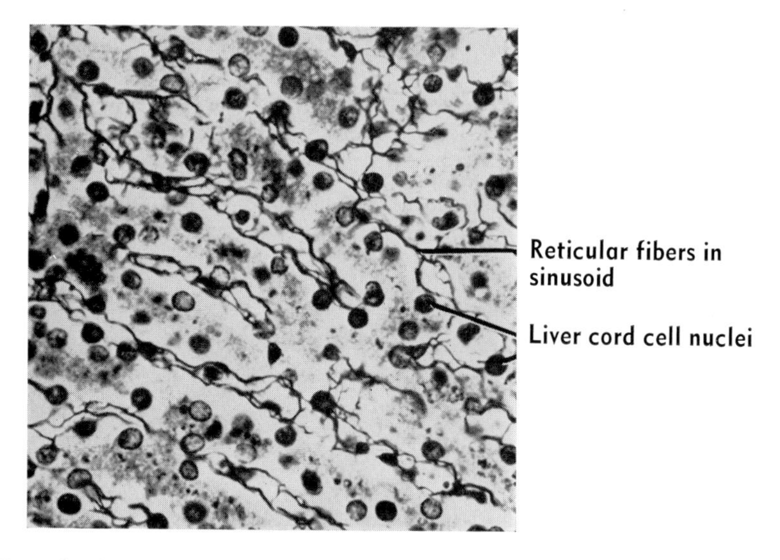

Fig. 14. Reticular fibers of liver. (Silver preparation.)

like that of fine areolar tissue. Stains specified for the reticular fibers must be used in such cases to distinguish between the two kinds of tissue.

Fibrous tissue

All fibrous tissues (areolar, irregular and regular dense fibrous, and elastic) are composed of cells, intercellular fluid, and fibers. In the looser tissues there are relatively few fibers irregularly arranged, a large amount of intercellular fluid, and numerous cells. In denser tissues there is an increase in the number of fibers and a corresponding decrease in intercellular fluid as well as cells.

Areolar tissue

In an earlier discussion it was indicated that reticular tissues appear as a typically loose fibrous type. In this discussion we shall consider areolar tissue, in which white fibers predominate but in which elastic fibers are also present. This type of tissue is found in mesenteries, in omenta of the alimentary canal, in the subcutaneous tissues (under the skin), and immediately below mucosal epithelium of the alimentary canal. The predominating collagenous fibers branch and are of variable thickness. They also intertwine to form a network. In sections they are cut in all possible planes, and since they twist and interlace bundles can be traced for only short distances. Elastic fibers are usually nearer the surface of the tissue and when stretched form a network of straight fibers which give rise to Y-shaped branches, often curling at the free ends. In hematoxylin and eosin-stained sections elastic fibers are not generally distinguishable from the white fibers.

Sectioned materials stained with elastic tissue stain shows elastic fibers as scattered short single pieces cut obliquely. The fibrous elements, produced and maintained by cells called fibroblasts, form the main morphological component of connective tissue proper utilized in binding organs together so as to resist stress, strains, and displacements. The intercellular fluid fills in the spaces between fibers and cells and provides transport for nutrients and metabolic wastes. This fluid does not ordinarily stain and is usually conveyed to and through areolar tissue by small blood vessels and drained by the blood and lymphatic capillaries. Since tissue spreads of mesenteries are the usual source of areolar tissue for study, a description of cells follows in the subsequent paragraphs. The reader is cautioned to distinguish between cells that are properly a part of fibrous connective tissues everywhere and epithelial types which happen to be located around or passing through areolar tissue.

Fibroblasts. Cells called fibroblasts, which form or maintain the fibers, are present in all forms of fibrous tissue. There are, in addition, cells which have no part in carrying out the connective function of the tissue. They are fairly constant elements in the tissue, and their morphology will be de-

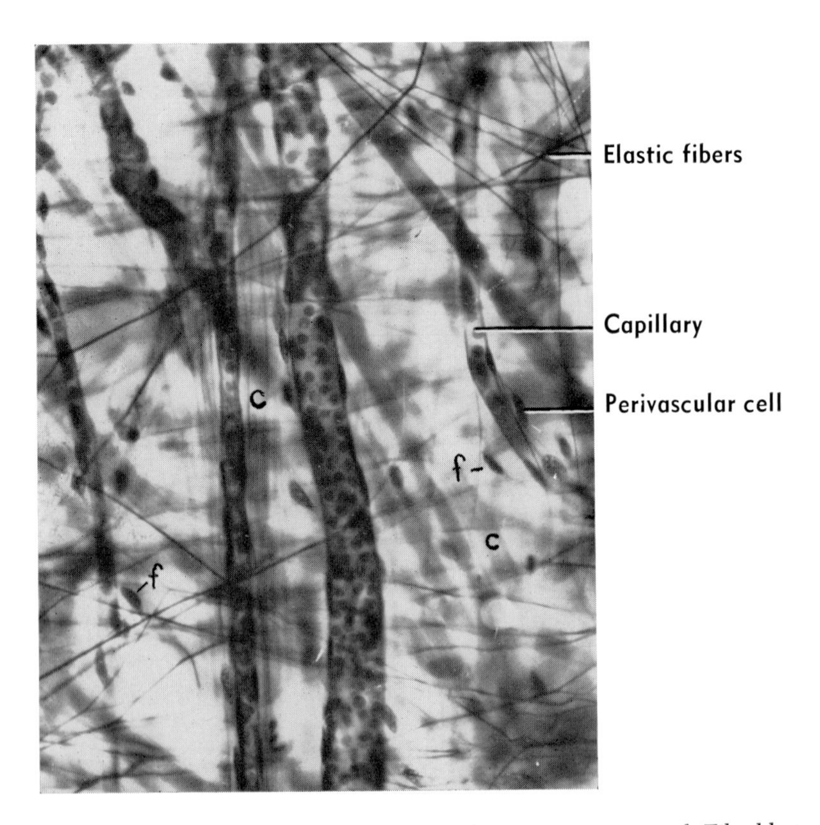

Fig. 15. Stretch preparation of omentum, showing areolar connective tissue. f, Fibroblast; c, collagen fibers.

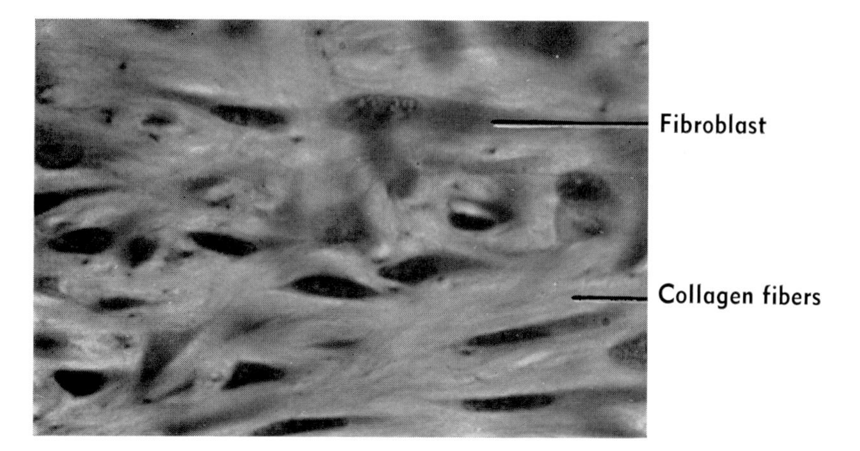

Fig. 16. Connective tissue of periodontal membrane.

scribed in this chapter since they are to be distinguished from the fibroblasts, but their significance, like that of the cells of reticular tissue, will be discussed in a later section.

Fibroblasts are present in all types of fibrillar tissue, from the finest areolar to the tendons and elastic membranes. In loose areolar tissue when seen in surface view they appear as rather large branching cells with pale oval nuclei. The cytoplasm is so lightly stained as to be often barely perceptible, so that one may distinguish the nucleus alone. Often the cells lie in such a position that they are seen from the side. In that case they are fusiform and somewhat easier to see. In fully formed areolar tissue there are no fibroglia or border fibrils connected with the fibroblasts. The cells sometimes lie very close to the fibers, especially in the denser kinds of tissue, but careful examination makes it evident that cells and fibers are actually separate. The fibroblasts are sometimes called the fixed cells of connective tissue in contrast to the remaining ones, which are called wandering cells. They are the most common cells of areolar tissue and usually the only kind to be found in the dense fibrillar tissues. (Figs. 15 and 16.)

Mesothelial cells. The nuclei of mesothelial cells occur in mesenteries and are frequently confused with the nuclei of fibroblasts. Mesothelial nuclei are much larger, somewhat lighter staining, and appear as elongated ovals, never fusiform in tissue spreads (Fig. 17). In addition the mesothelial cytoplasm does not usually stain. These cells are not a regular feature of areolar tissue but belong to the epithelium which forms the boundary of mesenteric and serous membranes.

Macrophages. Macrophages are one of the so-called wandering cells of fibrous tissues. The active phagocytic cells are frequently detected after the ingestion of insoluble stain particles or carbon particles. Whereas the cytoplasm may extend for some distance, these cells are said to be smaller

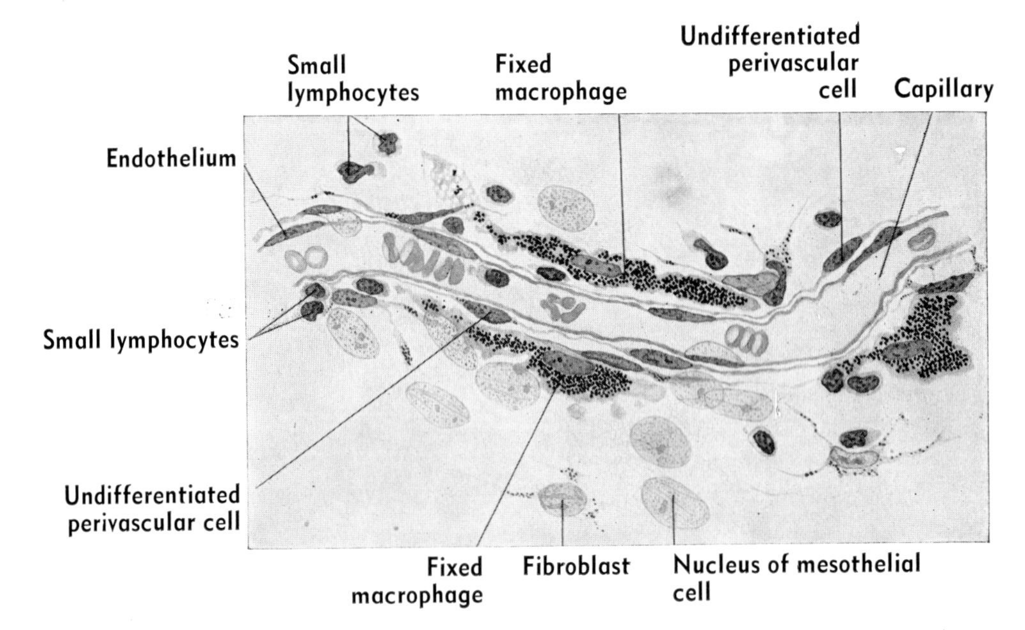

Fig. 17. Stretch preparation of omentum of rabbit vitally stained with lithium carmine. (Hematoxylin stain; ×500.) (A.A.M.) (From Maximow and Bloom: A Textbook of Histology, Philadelphia, 1952, W. B. Saunders Co.)

than fibroblasts. They have darker staining and smaller nuclei, frequently indented on one side. The cytoplasm is irregular in outline, containing numerous vacuoles and granules which require special staining techniques for adequate demonstration. They occur less frequently than fibroblasts. These cells are active in inflammatory conditions and are part of the reticulo-endothelial system. They are also called clasmatocytes, histiocytes, pyrrol or "dust" cells, and resting wandering cells (Fig. 17). The so-called inactive or resting macrophages are oval shaped with an irregular outline. The nuclei of the latter are as described above, but they do not appear to ingest particles unless mobilized and activated.

Plasma cells. Plasma cells are comparatively rare in most connective tissue. They may be found in considerable numbers in the tunica propria of the digestive tract and in the loose connective tissue surrounding the secretive portions of the lactating mammary gland. They are smaller than macrophages and differ from them and from fibroblasts in having a definitely rounded or oval shape without cytoplasmic processes. The cytoplasm is basophilic and nongranular. The nucleus is small and eccentrically placed. The chromatin of the nucleus is gathered in large granules along the nuclear membrane (so-called "cartwheel" nucleus). The cytoplasm near the nucleus stains less intensely and appears as a perinuclear halo (Plate 2).

Mast cells. These cells exhibit basophilic and metachromatic cytoplasmic granules composed partly of polysaccharide. They are large round cells with pale nuclei frequently obscured by the abundant granules. In hematoxylin and eosin preparations these are sometimes referred to as tissue basophils. They are frequently found in the vicinity of blood vessels, and should not be confused with flattened cells known as undifferentiated perivascular cells.

Blood cells. Fully-formed leukocytes and red blood cells are often found in areolar tissue. Of these tissue eosinophils are of frequent occurrence in

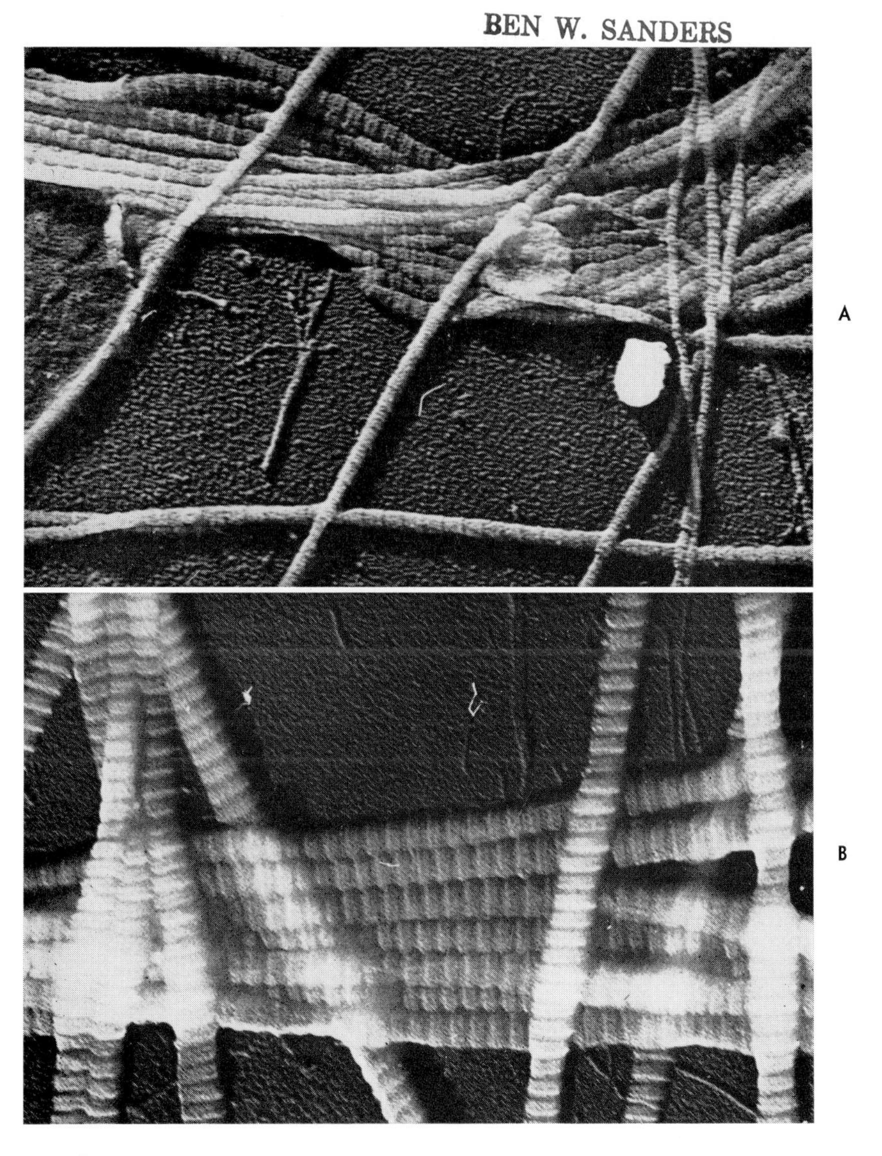

Fig. 18. Electron micrograph of connective tissue of skin. **A,** Reticular fibers (two days). **B,** Collagenous fibers (ninety days). Reticular fibers are smaller in diameter than collagenous fibers but apparently have the same periodicity. (×45,000.) (Courtesy Dr. Jerome Gross.)

some animals but not in others. Lymphocytes are of frequent occurrence in regions of inflammation. To be certain of the various kinds of cells observed one must use special stains. Many authors do not consider these cells part of the connective tissue but rather an invasion from blood and lymphatic capillaries.

Fat cells. Occasional fat cells are seen in areolar and other kinds of connective tissue. Details of fat cells are presented later in this discussion.

Dense fibrous tissue—irregular

The number of white fibers is increased tremendously, whereas there is a definite decrease in intercellular fluid and number of cells. The thick collagenous bundles are arranged in an intertwining network (Fig. 19). In routine hematoxylin and eosin-stained sections the whole mass stains a bright yellowish pink or red; widely scattered fusiform fibroblast nuclei are also a feature of this tissue. This tissue occurs in the form of sheets. Examples of the latter variety occur in the perichondrium, periosteum, in

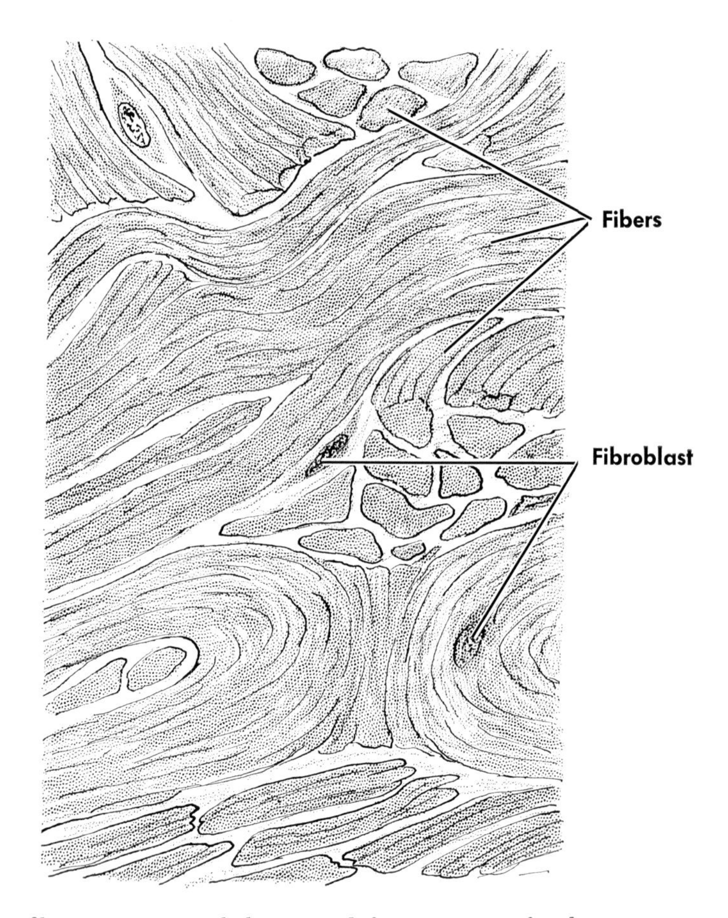

Fig. 19. Dense fibrous tissue, irregularly arranged, from a section of scalp.

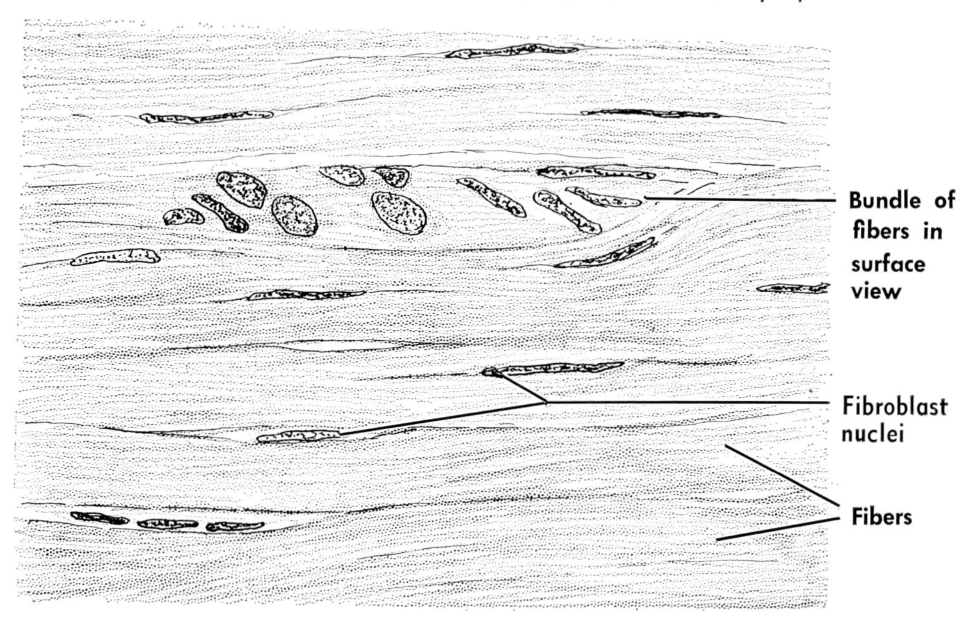

Fig. 20. Tendon cut longitudinally. Bundle of fibers in surface view shows fibroblasts diagonally placed.

the dermis, and in capsules of many organs. In certain encapsulated organs, pillars of dense irregular connective tissue known as trabeculae, penetrate and subdivide the structure. The trabeculae usually bear blood vessels, nerves, and sometimes the ducts of glands. The latter are almost entirely composed of collagenous fibers but in some instances may include elastic fibers, reticular fibers, and even smooth muscle.

Dense fibrous tissue—regular

This tissue occurs in cords or bands and is typified by tendons, ligaments, and aponeuroses. In tendon the fibers are densely arranged in thick, parallel, unbranching bundles. These bundles are so closely crowded that the cells between them are flattened to a platelike form (Fig. 20). The cells lie in rows parallel to the fibers. In profile the nuclei are very long and thin, whereas in surface view the individual nuclei are elongated ovals. In cross section the cells are so compressed that they appear as winglike projections between adjacent bundles. Tendons are composed almost entirely of white fibers.

Elastic tissue

Elastic fibers are of rather general occurrence in connective tissue, but they are not considered elastic tissues. In certain situations the elastic fibers predominate, whereas the collagenous fibers are sparse. In the walls of arteries elastic fibers have developed and fused to such an extent that they form an incomplete (fenestrated) membrane, enclosing cells and a few white fibers (Fig. 4). As such, this arrangement might be termed dense irregular elastic tissue. A form of dense regular elastic tissue is found in the neck ligament of the ox (ligamentum nuchae) and in the smaller ligaments found between the vertebrae (ligamentum flavis). In this type thick, long, branching elastic fibers lie in nearly parallel arrangement in association with very few cells and an extremely small number of fine collagenous fibers. In such a dense arrangement the fibers, especially in older animals, appear yellow in color; hence the term yellow fibers, which is, however, obsolete.

Adipose tissue

Adipose tissue is commonly included in the groups of connective and supporting tissues, although it differs from the other members of the group in several respects. The cells composing it do not form intercellular fibers or matrix but are specialized for the storing of fat. They thus form a reserve of foodstuffs as well as supporting pads of tissue. The cells are mesenchymal in origin, like those of connective tissue. They lose their protoplasmic processes early in the course of their transformation and become round, with abundant cytoplasm and central nuclei. The fat is deposited in the cytoplasm in minute droplets that gradually increase and unite in one large drop which pushes the nucleus to one side of the cell. As still more fat accumulates the nucleus becomes flattened and the cytoplasm is reduced to a mere film enclosing the fat globule. In tissues which have been treated with or-

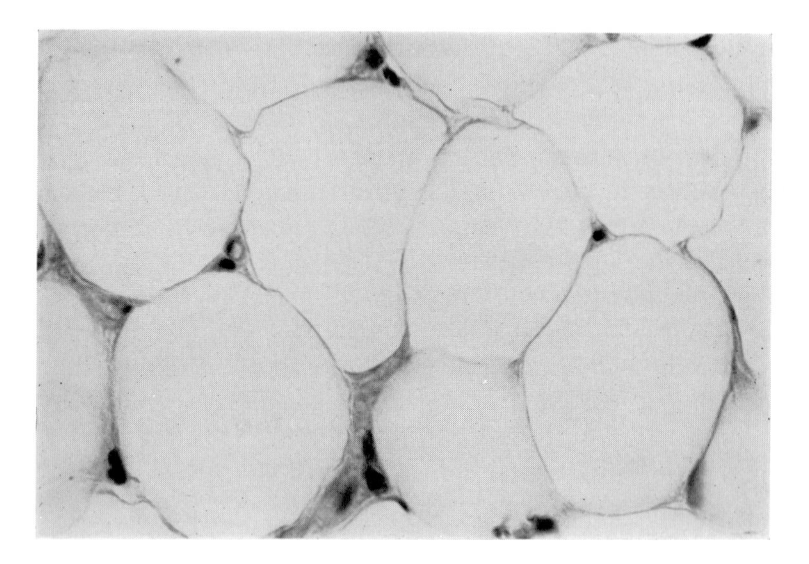

Fig. 21. Adipose tissue, showing fibroblast nuclei between fat cells. (Hemotoxylin and eosin stain.)

dinary fixatives followed by alcohol, the fat is dissolved out, leaving the cytoplasm of the cells in the form of large irregular rings, each having a dark flat nucleus at one side. In preparations made with osmic acid the fat resists the action of the alcohol and appears as a deeply stained mass occupying the center of each cell. There is no intercellular substance elaborated by adipose tissue cells. They lie embedded in reticular or areolar tissue, the fibers among them being the product of reticular cells or fibroblasts. Adipose tissue is illustrated in Fig. 21.

Serous membranes

These membranes, the pleura, peritoneum, and pericardium, consist of a thin layer of loosely arranged connective tissues covered by a layer of relatively flat mesothelial cells. The membrane is made up of loosely arranged collagenous fibers, scattered elastic fibers, fibroblasts, macrophages, mast cells, adipose cells, and a varying number of other cells all suspended in a fluid, the serous exudate. The amount of fluid exudate and the variety and number of cells suspended in it increase greatly in adverse physiological or pathological conditions.

Reticuloendothelial system

The reticuloendothelial system, sometimes referred to as the system of macrophages, has as its most significant function the ingestion and removal of particulate matter. These cells are found in the loose connective tissue, lymphatic and myeloid tissues, in sinusoids of the liver, spleen, adrenal, and hypophysis, and also as "dust" cells in the lung and some perivascular cells.

The cells which occur in the sites mentioned here differ morphologically but react in a similar fashion when subjected to certain adverse conditions. When for example a weak solution of a dye such as trypan blue is injected into an animal, subsequent examination will show an appreciable accumulation of this dye in all the cells in the system to a degree not observed in any other cells. While this experimental confirmation shows the similarity in function of this group of cells, it has been shown that macrophages in specific tissues or organs phagocytize materials of a rather selective nature. The macrophages in the spleen and liver phagocytize degenerating red blood cells, retaining the iron for reutilization. In the lungs dust and other particles of this nature are removed by the cells. Particulate matter of several kinds is removed by macrophages in the lymph nodes. The kinds of matter ingested by the macrophages may be relatively inert or noxious in character. Another function attributed to these cells is the production of antibodies. The function of macrophages is accordingly concerned with the defense mechanism of the body. The cells of this system arise from primitive reticular cells, from pre-existing macrophages, lymphocytes, and monocytes.

CHAPTER V

Blood-forming organs

In the adult body, blood cells are normally formed in two organs which are alike in having a framework of reticular tissue but different in the kinds of corpuscles which they produce. Bone marrow is the normal source of the red blood cells and the granulocytes, and lymph nodules of the lymphocytes.

BONE MARROW

It will be remembered that in the formation of a bone a space is left at the center by the resorption first of the cartilage and later of endosteal bone. This space is invaded by mesenchyme which develops into an organ having no part in the supportive function of the bone itself. This is the red bone marrow, which in the adult is the source of the majority of the blood corpuscles. The primitive mesenchyme of the embryo develops in this location into three main types of cells: (1) a framework of reticular tissue, (2) adipose tissue, and (3) hemopoietic or blood-forming cells. In early life all three kinds of cells are present in the marrow of any bone. Later the hemopoietic cells disappear from the marrow of some of the bones, leaving only reticular tissue and fat cells, which make up the yellow marrow. In other bones the marrow continues to form blood cells throughout life, and their presence makes the tissue red.

Marrow may be studied in smear preparations or in sections. For critical examination a blood stain must be used. In such a preparation one may recognize the cells shown in Plate 2.

Reticular tissue cells. In sections reticular tissue cells are somewhat obscured by the hemopoietic cells, but they may be distinguished in smears or thin sections.

Adipose tissue cells. Adipose tissue cells are generally scattered in red marrow and appear under the low power of the microscope as holes in the marrow.

Hemocytoblasts (stem cells). Hemocytoblasts are from 10 to 12μ in diameter and have a basophilic, usually nongranular, cytoplasm. The form

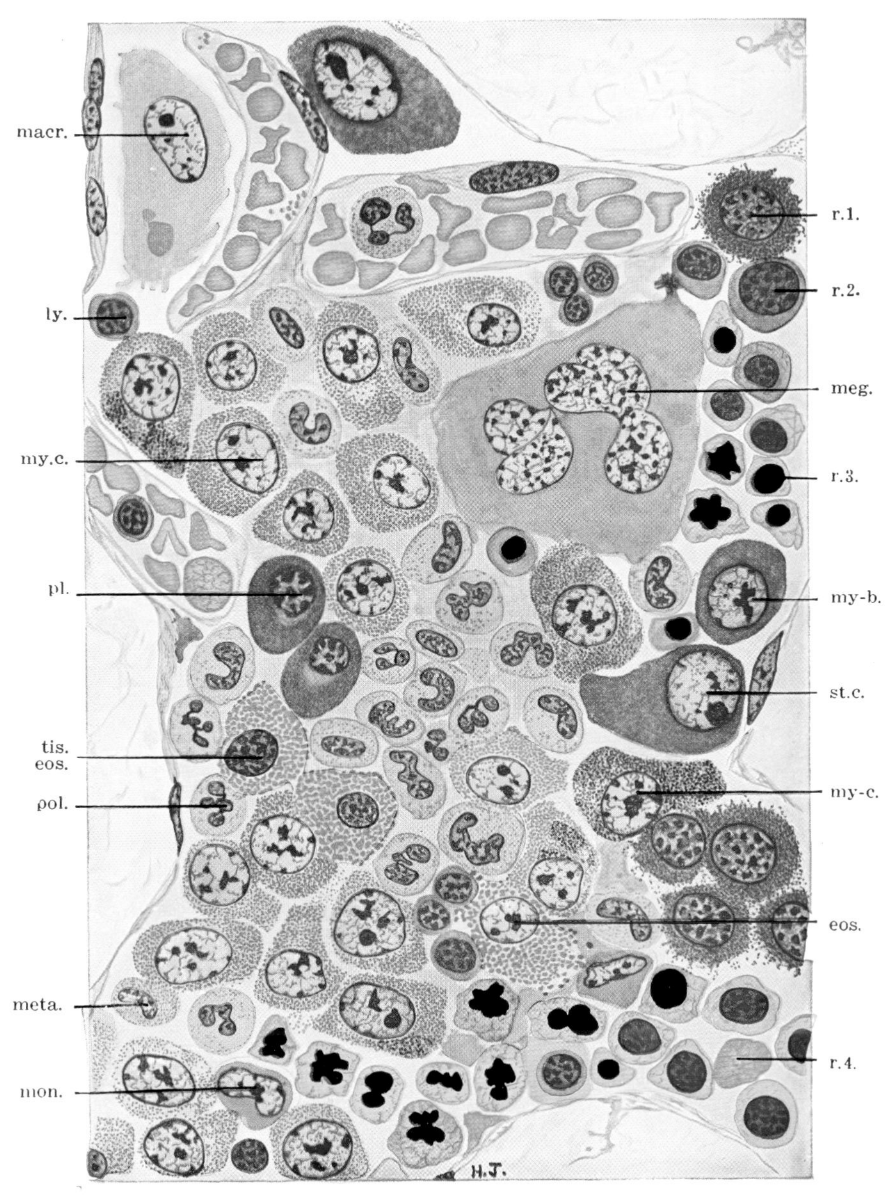

Plate 2

Normal vertebral bone marrow, male adult. (Zenker fixation, decalcified and stained with phloxine-methylene blue.) In one field representative cells have been brought together in the proper proportion and relation one to another in order to illustrate typical normal picture. Zeiss ap. obj. 90, oc. 10. *eos.*, Eosinophil; *ly.*, lymphocyte; *macr.*, macrophage; *meg.*, megakaryocyte; *meta.*, metamyelocyte; *mon.*, monocyte; *my-b.*, myeloblast; *my-c.*, myelocyte; *pl.*, plasma cell; *pol.*, polymorphonuclear leukocyte; *r.1.*, *r.2.*, *r.3.*, *r.4.*, stages in red corpuscle formation; *st.c.*, stem cell; *tis. eos.*, tissue eosinophil. (From Bremer and Weatherford: A Text-Book of Histology, Philadelphia, 1948, The Blakiston Co.)

of the cell is pear shaped or polygonal, without cytoplasmic processes. The nucleus is large and is situated at the widest part of the cell. As the name implies, these are regarded as the cells from which the blood cells are derived.

Promyelocytes, myelocytes, metamyelocytes. There are three intermediate stages between the hemocytoblast and the granular leukocyte. They are characterized in general by the development of cytoplasmic granules which are neutrophilic, eosinophilic, or basophilic, according to the kind of leukocyte destined to develop from each. It is possible, with sufficient care, to recognize three main types or stages of this group. The youngest (promyelocyte) is a spherical cell with a basophilic cytoplasm much like that of the hemocytoblast except that it contains a few granules. The nucleus of the promyelocyte is large and pale. The second stage (myelocyte) is the most common of the group and is the most easily distingushed. The myelocytes divide rapidly, giving rise to successive generations of cells in which one may trace a gradual increase in the number of specific cytoplasmic granules and an accompanying loss of affinity for basic stains. Also as divisions occur there are slight loss of size and increase of density of the nucleus. The products of the last divisions of the myelocytes are the metamyelocytes. These cells develop without further division into polymorphonuclear leukocytes. Metamyelocytes are, in fact, early stages of granulocytes which are not sufficiently mature to enter the circulation under normal conditions.

Proerythroblasts, erythroblasts, normoblasts. The proerythroblast is the earliest recognizable stage in the development of the red blood cell. It differs from the promyelocyte in the following ways: It is slightly smaller and has a more chromatic nucleus; hemoglobin is beginning to develop in its cytoplasm; at this stage the cytoplasm is basic, like that of the hemocytoblast and the promyelocyte, but the presence of hemoglobin gives it a slightly purplish or grayish tinge. In the next stage, the erythroblast, a series of changes develops gradually as the cells divide. These changes are of two kinds: an increase in the amount of hemoglobin in the cytoplasm and a decrease in the size of the cell and its nucleus. The former change is expressed morphologically as a shift in color from the grayish blue of the proerythroblast toward the pink which is characteristic of the erythrocyte. When the pink color is fully developed the cells are called normoblasts. A normoblast is only slightly larger than an erythrocyte but differs from it in having a nucleus. Normoblasts undergo a number of divisions, during which their nuclei become progressively smaller and darker. Ultimately the nucleus of the normoblast is reduced to a compact, deeply staining mass, and when this is extruded from its surface the cell is a fully developed red blood corpuscle.

Giant cells or megakaryocytes. These are the largest cells of bone marrow and the most readily recognized. They have a rather dense reddish cytoplasm and a polymorphic nucleus. In size and color they resemble the osteoclasts which will be found at the margin of the marrow. Osteoclasts, however, have many separate nuclei (polykaryocytes), whereas the parts of the nucleus of a giant cell are connected by strands of nuclear material. It is from the cytoplasm of the giant cell that the blood platelets are formed, according to most authors. In addition to the cells just described above, all types of blood corpuscles are to be found in bone marrow.

Development of blood cells in embryo. While the most important permanent source of blood cells is the red bone marrow, there are several other sites of blood formation which occur during embryonic development. The cells which differentiate into blood islands in the extraembryonic mesoderm of the yolk sac give rise to hemocytoblasts. The liver and the spleen also have an important hemopoietic function during early embryonic existence.

GERMINAL CENTERS OF LYMPH NODES

In lymphoid tissue there are centers of lymphocyte production. These consist of areas which stain more lightly than the surrounding tissue because they are composed of large, pale cells with vesicular nuclei. These are hemocytoblasts, which differ from the hemocytoblasts of bone marrow in that they are destined to produce but one type of corpuscle, the lymphocyte. Some authors prefer to give to them the name lymphoblast on this account. Surrounding such a center of pale cells is a ring of densely packed lymphocytes which, with their deeply stained nuclei and scanty cytoplasm, form a marked contrast of color in the germinal center.

CHAPTER VI

Cartilage

In the connective tissues described in Chapter V the elements present consist of cells and fibers embedded in a viscid ground substance and tissue fluid. These elements are collectively known as the matrix. In the supporting tissues such as cartilage and bone the character of the matrix varies. In cartilage the ground substance is semirigid and contains a protein-carbohydrate complex known as chondromucoid. On partial hydrolysis the latter yields chondroitin sulfuric acid. Chondromucoid is PAS positive, basophilic, and stains metachromatically with toluidine blue. In older individuals mineralization of cartilage, for example, in the larynx, may occur and is usually accompanied by degenerative changes of the cells. Cations, for example, Ca and Str, are bound strongly to chondroitin sulfuric acid so that cartilage in these regions stains orthochromatically with toluidine blue and appears intensely basophilic with hematoxylin and eosin.

Cartilage forms the skeleton of the embryo and is exemplified in the adult by the tracheal rings. Throughout the matrix collagenous fibers interlace much as they do in the fluid matrix of areolar tissue. The cells lie in minute spaces in the matrix called the lacunae. These vary in shape according to their position in the plate of cartilage. The cells, originally stellate like other mesenchyme cells, have lost their protoplasmic processes and have assumed the shape of the lacunae in which they lie. Unlike connective tissue cartilage contains no blood vessels, so that nourishment must reach the cells by seepage through the matrix.

Cartilage develops from mesenchyme, as do the other supporting tissues. Mesenchyme cells first elaborate the fibers and later lay down the solid matrix upon them. Each cell forms a circumferential layer of matrix, thus enclosing itself in a lacuna. As growth and development proceed, the amount of matrix between cells increases, pushing them farther apart, so that ultimately the condition is reached in which the cells lie in lacunae scattered through a relatively large amount of intercellular substance. For a time, at least, after the embryonic period, growth may be effected interstitially by the division of cartilage cells and the laying down of matrix around each daughter cell. Later, however, the increasing solidity of the matrix renders this type of growth more difficult, and increase in the size of the cartilage plate is brought about by the addition of new layers at the periphery by the cells of the perichondrium (appositional growth). In adult cartilage one may, as we have said, find two or four lacunae close together separated by very thin walls of matrix. These and the lacunae which contain two cells indicate that interstitial growth is proceeding with difficulty.

Fibrocartilage

Cartilage occurs in three forms, fibrous, hyaline, and elastic, distinguished by the character of their fibers and the relative proportions of fibers and matrix. Of the three types, fibrocartilage most nearly resembles connective tissue (Fig. 22). In the intervertebral discs it blends on one side with connective tissue and on the other with hyaline cartilage, and, as we shall see, it is intermediate between the two kinds of tissue in qualities as well as in position. It consists of a network of coarse white fibers which take the usual red color when stained with eosin. These fibers are embedded in a solid matrix which fills the interstices between them. The extent of the matrix varies somewhat in different specimens. In some cases it replaces the fluid matrix only partially and appears merely as fine purplish lines between the red fibers and as thin capsules

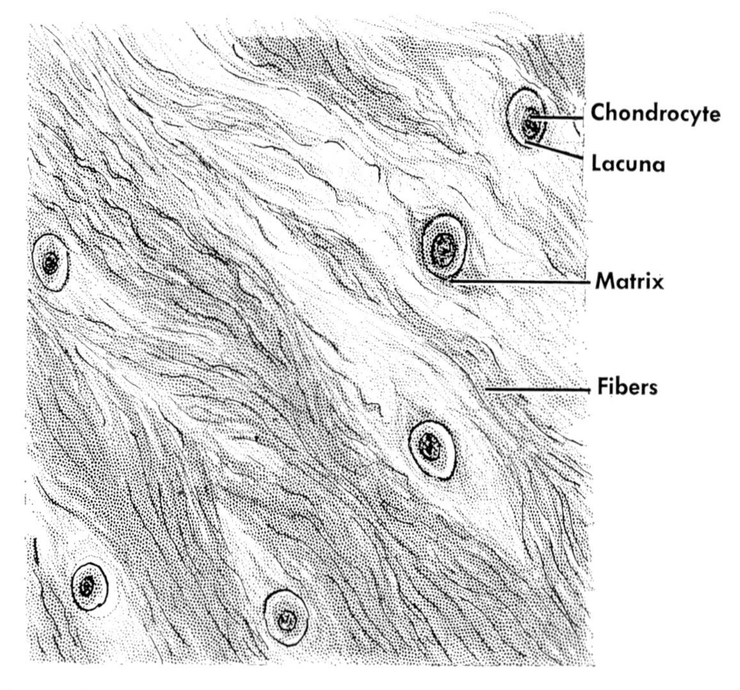

Fig. 22. Fibrocartilage.

surrounding the cells. In others its amount is greater and it forms darker lines among the fibers and definite branching islands containing lacunae. In the former condition it is not easily distinguished from dense connective tissue, but one characteristic feature is always to be seen: namely, the round or oval lacunae which contain the cells. In connective tissue the cells are flattened by the pressure of the surrounding fibers; in cartilage they are protected by the capsules of matrix in which they lie.

Hyaline cartilage

The collagenous fibers of hyaline cartilage are not gathered in bundles but are dispersed throughout the tissue in a fine, close network completely filled in by the substance of the matrix. The union is so close as to form a mass which, though pliable, is very firm. The fibers and matrix have, moreover, the same staining capacity and refractive index, so that in ordinary preparations they are not morphologically distinguishable. Hyaline cartilage is so called because the matrix appears clear (glasslike), and special techniques are required to demonstrate that the intercellular substance consists of fibers and matrix.

Hyaline cartilage occurs in the form of definite plates, in each of which the cells and matrix exhibit a definite plan of organization. If one studies a cartilage plate from the trachea, for instance, certain regions may be distinguished, and the plan will be found to be typical of all cartilage plates. At the periphery of the plate there is a fibrous layer, the perichondrium. This is, on the outside, similar to the surrounding areolar tissue with which it blends. It is well supplied with blood vessels. Toward the cartilage the perichondrium becomes more dense; that is, the fibers become heavier and more closely crowded, and the interfibrillar spaces containing the cells become smaller. The outer layer of the perichondrium is called the fibrous layer; the inner the chondrogenetic layer. At the inner border of the chondrogenetic layer a condition is reached in which individual fibers are no longer distinguishable, their identity being obscured by the solid matrix in which they are embedded. Both fibers and matrix are pink in this region in well-stained hematoxylin-eosin preparations. The cells are no longer free as in the fluid matrix of the perichondrium but are enclosed in spindle-shaped lacunae.

Toward the center of the plate changes occur in cells and matrix. The latter becomes chemically basic and accordingly stains blue instead of pink. The color is pale except immediately around the lacunae, where it is often very dark. The shape of the lacunae also changes toward the middle of the plate, and they become round instead of flattened. Often they are found in pairs or groups of four with the sides toward each other flattened. The cells occupying these central lacunae are spherical and in the living tissue fill the entire space. They are separated from the matrix

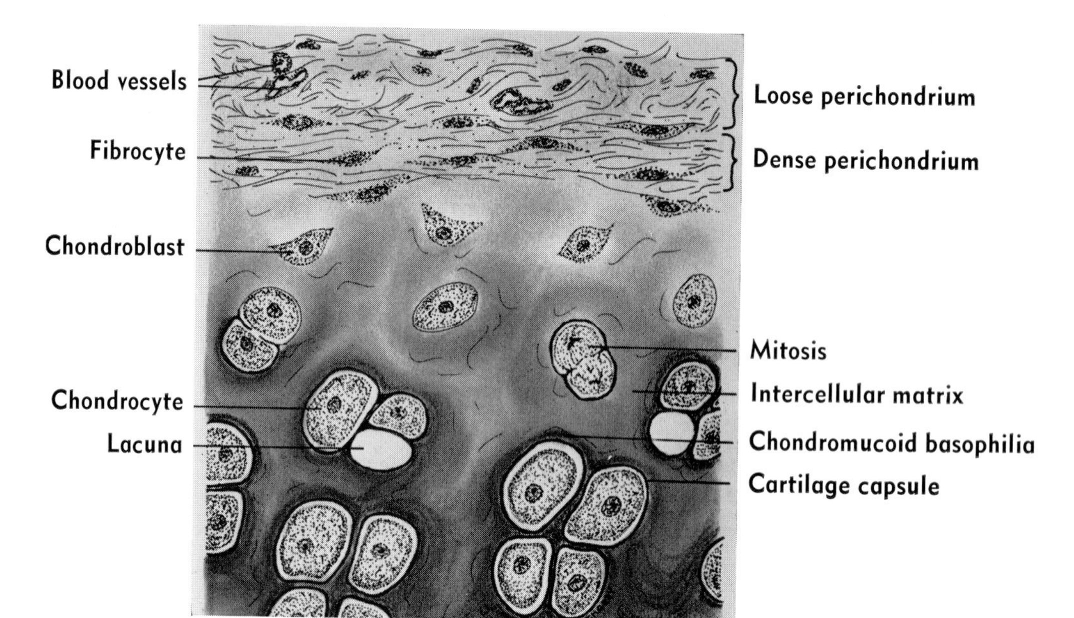

Fig. 23. Hyaline cartilage from trachea.

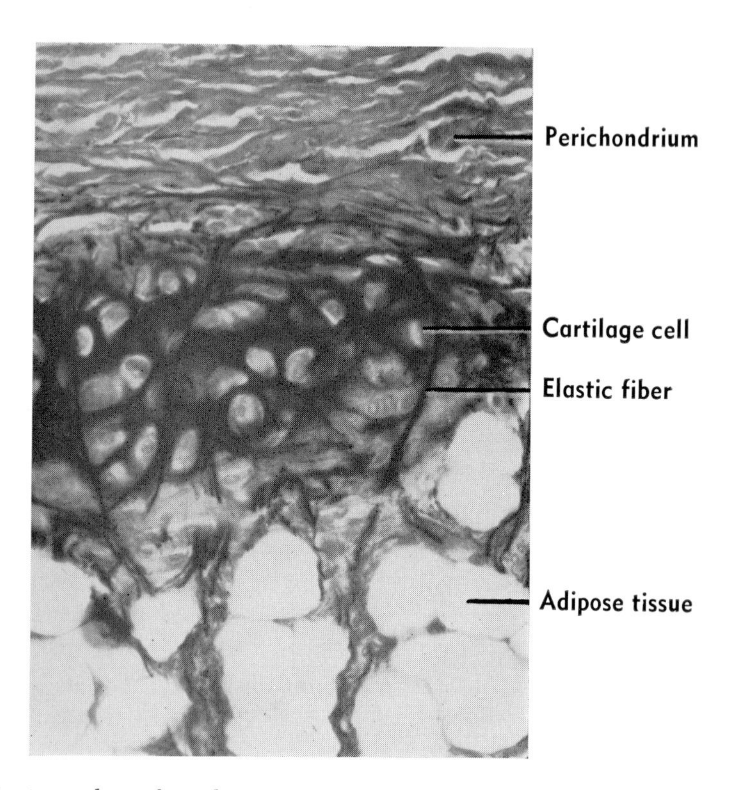

Fig. 24. Elastic cartilage of epiglottis, stained with resorcin to show elastic fibers.

by a fine capsule which may rarely be distinguished. In fixed preparations the cytoplasm is usually shrunken, and the only prominent feature is the nucleus. This is surrounded by an irregular cytoplasm. The shrinkage is due to the fact that fixatives penetrate slowly through the matrix and do not reach its center until after post-mortem changes have taken place there and also to the fact that cartilage cells contain large amounts of glycogen and fat which are lost in processing. The appearance of hyaline cartilage is illustrated in Fig. 23.

Elastic cartilage

Elastic cartilage is like hyaline in the arrangement of perichondrium, matrix, cells, and lacunae. The difference consists in the fact that elastic cartilage contains, besides the invisible collagenous fibers, a network of elastic fibers which may readily be demonstrated by the use of the appropriate stain. This type of cartilage occurs in the epiglottis and is present also in the external ear. It is laid down originally as hyaline cartilage and is later penetrated by the elastic fibers (Fig. 24).

The function of cartilage varies and serves the organism in many ways. Hyaline cartilage forms a large part of the temporary skeleton of the embryo in young individuals. This variety of cartilage makes up the articulating surface of movable joints: in this capacity it exhibits properties of unusual strength for support and also allows the bones to move freely. In the respiratory system the cartilage serves to prevent the collapse of passageways. Hyaline cartilage participates in and contributes to the growth and calcification of long bones. Nutritional and vitamin deficiencies and hormonal imbalance modify the normal participation of cartilage in bone development and result in the production of abnormalities of the skeletal system.

CHAPTER VII

Bone

The connective and supporting tissues hitherto described are found as components of various organs. Bone, on the other hand, forms a complete system of supporting structures, the skeleton. Like the other members of the group, it consists of cells and matrix. In this tissue the matrix becomes mineralized. The proportion of organic matter is greatly reduced so that when it is destroyed by drying the matrix appears but little altered from the living condition. Sections of bone cannot be made in the ordinary way because of the hardness of the matrix. Two methods are used to prepare bone for study: either it is softened by the use of acids so that only its cells and collagenous groundwork remain, or pieces are dried and ground very thin. The latter method destroys the cells; the former destroys the inorganic part of the intercellular substances.

Development

The subject of the development and adult structure of bone is complicated by the fact that there are two types of ossification and two kinds of arrangement of the tissue in its fully formed state. It is advisable to consider the interrelations of these before describing any of them in detail. Differences in development arise because in the embryo some of the bones are laid down in undifferentiated mesenchyme, whereas in other parts of the body a temporary supporting system of cartilages precedes bone formation. The first type of ossification (intramembranous) is comparatively simple. In the second type (cartilage replacement) stages of cartilage erosion and of bone formation are intimately associated and form a more confusing picture. The essential process by which a bony matrix is formed is, however, the same in both cases. The difference between intramembranous and cartilage replacement bone lies entirely in the tissue which precedes each in the place where it develops. The immediate result is also the same in both cases: namely, the formation of a mass of irregular trabeculae of bone penetrated by blood vessels and connective tissue. Such bone is called spongy or cancellous bone.

In whatever manner it has been formed, the newly developed spongy bone undergoes secondary changes. These consist of (1) erosion and (2) rebuilding. Differences in the manner and extent of rebuilding in different parts of the bone result in the development of two types of adult structure. In some regions the bone is eroded and rebuilt in its original form (spongy). In others rebuilding follows a new pattern and is more extensive so that the tissue has the arrangement which is called compact bone. Compact and spongy bone are alike in their essential elements but differ in the arrangement and relative amounts of matrix, blood vessels, and marrow spaces.

In the following outline the development of bone has been divided, for convenience, into four steps: spicule formation, confluence of spicules, erosion, and rebuilding.

A. Formation of spicules of matrix
   1. Intramembranous
      a. Spicules laid down directly in mesenchyme
   2. Cartilage replacement
      a. Bone formed around the outside of the cartilage (perichondrial)
      b. Erosion of the center of the cartilage
      c. Bone laid down on fragments of disintegrating cartilage (endochondrial)
B. Confluence of spicules to form spongy bone
C. Secondary erosion
D. Rebuilding
   1. In the form of new spongy bone
   2. In the form of compact bone

The division is arbitrary, and it should be remembered that different parts of the same bone may be in different stages of development at any one time and that the steps merge gradually into each other. Although all the processes involved are most active during fetal and early postnatal life, they continue slowly until old age is reached and any one of them may be accelerated by metabolic or traumatic changes. In the following account of the development of bone we shall trace the histogenesis of intramembranous bone and cartilage replacement bone, respectively, through the stages leading to the formation of adult bone.

Intramembranous bone. The regions in which this process occurs is determined by the presence of proximity of blood vessels. In an area where bone will develop mesenchymal cells differentiate to form fibroblasts. The cells are connected with one another by their processes and are surrounded by delicate bundles of reticular fibers. The cells and fibers are loosely arranged in a semiviscid ground substance.

The initiation of bone formation consists of the production of an increased amount of ground substance between the cells, often trapping some of the cells within it. At the same time the cells increase in size, assume a polyhedral form, maintaining meanwhile the numerous processes by means of which they are connected with adjacent cells. At this

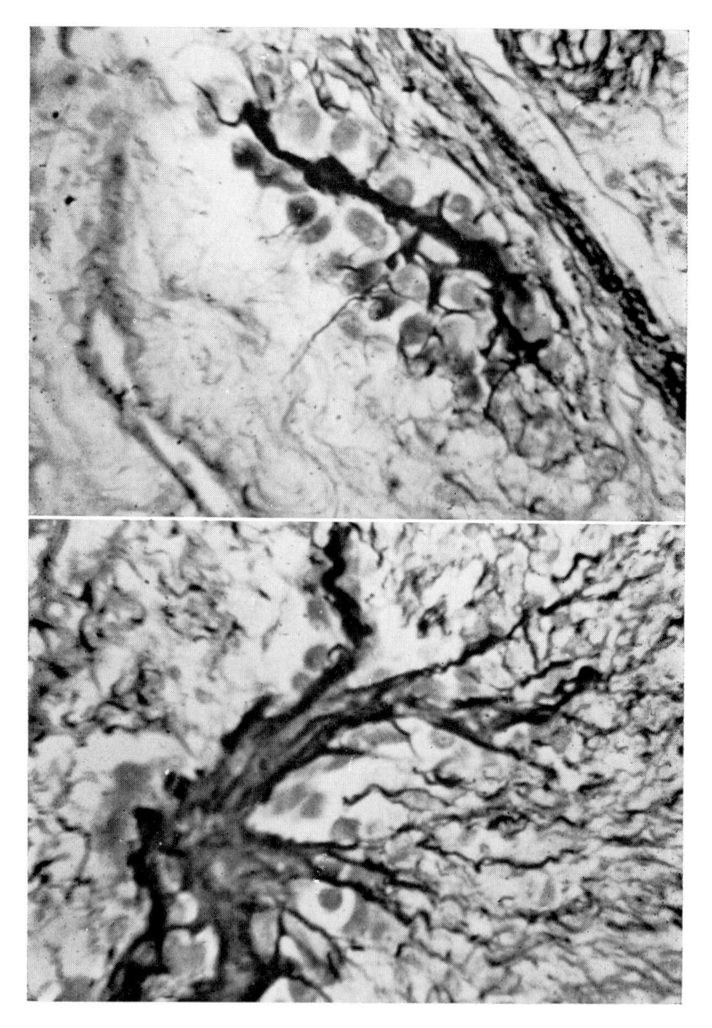

Fig. 25. Developing spicules of membrane bone, showing origin and incorporation of fibers before mineralization occurs. (Reticulum stain.)

stage they are known as osteoblasts (Fig. 27) and the bone in the non-mineralized state is sometimes referred to as osteoid.

When certain conditions are attained in the elaboration of this complex of cells and matrix the tissue undergoes calcification, that is, the mineral is deposited in the matrix in the form of hydroxyapatite $(Ca_3(PO_4)_2)_3$–$Ca(OH)_2$. In addition, bone mineral may contain other cations such as sodium, magnesium, carbonate, and citrate. The mineral or inorganic part of a bone may vary from 35 per cent dry weight in young bones to 65 per cent in adult bones.

The organic or interstitial component of bone contains numerous reticular fibers which are surrounded by an amorphous ground substance. In

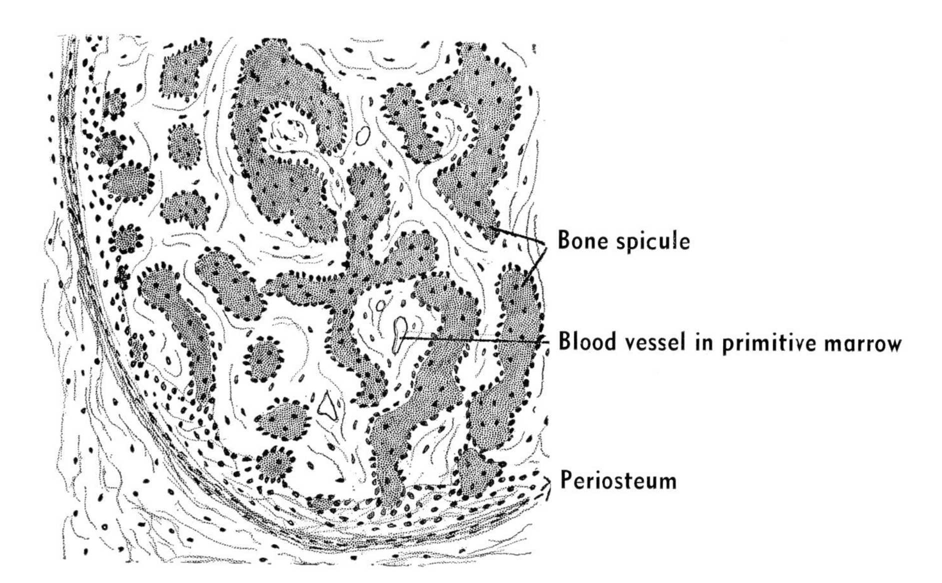

Fig. 26. Developing intramembranous bone of pig embryo. Spicules are uniting to form spongy bone.

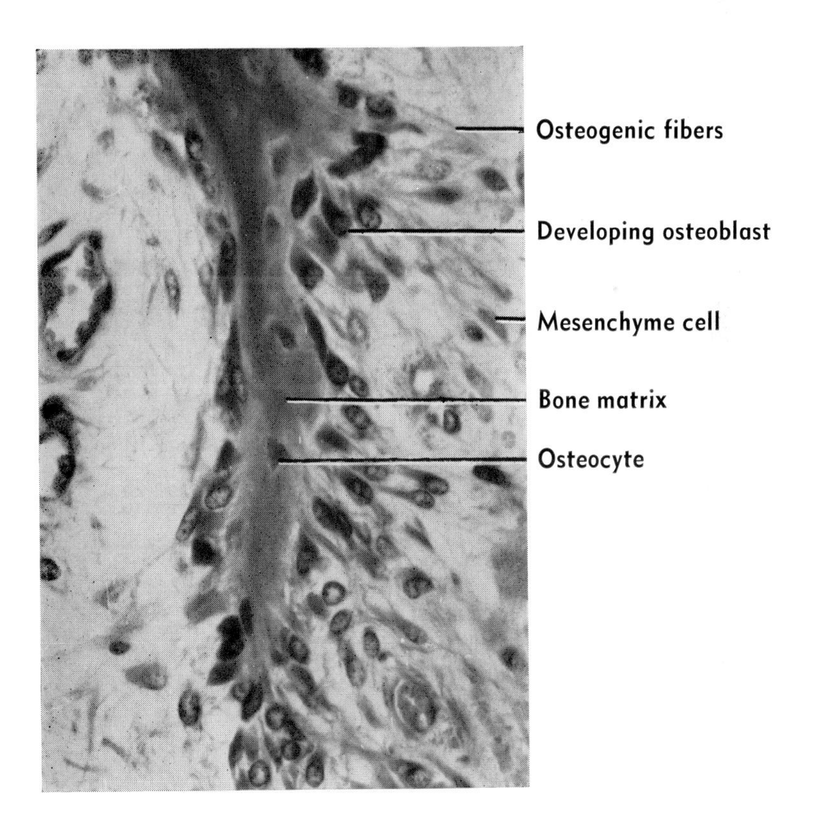

Fig. 27. Developing intramembranous bone. Note peripheral osteoid is lighter than central portion.

the embryonic state this substance is PAS positive and metachromatic, the latter property being correlated with the presence of a sulfated polysaccharide (Fig. 35).

Following the initial stages of bone formation just described, subsequent changes occur: osteoblasts arrange themselves on the surface of the developing bone in a continuous layer. Reticular fibers are added to the matrix from the surrounding mesenchyme to give rise to the so-called osteogenic fibers upon which calcification subsequently takes place. As mineralization occurs these fibers become collagenous. The bone increases in thickness by adding successive layers of matrix resulting from osteoblastic activity. During this process some of the osteoblasts with their processes become entrapped in the matrix and when calcification occurs they occupy a space in the matrix known as lacuna. These are the true bone cells or *osteocytes.*

An osteoblast, after it is surrounded by bone matrix, ceases to be active in the formation of new bone but remains in the tissue as a bone cell. The spicule thus formed contains all the essential elements of the bone: fibers, a calcified matrix, and cells situated in lacunae. It differs from cartilage in two respects: (1) in the chemical composition of the matrix and (2) in the shape of the lacunae. In cartilage the lacunae are round or oval and are entirely separate from each other. In bone each lacuna has a number of fine canals radiating from it and communicating with the canals of the other lacunae. The shapes of the cells in the two tissues correspond to their lacunae. In cartilage the cells are round or oval without processes, but in bone the osteocytes have fine processes which extend into the canaliculi. The latter cannot be traced for any great distance in the ordinary decalcified section of developing bone, but their points of departure from the lacuna give the latter a somewhat jagged outline. The spicule itself is irregular in shape and is surrounded by a more or less complete layer of osteoblasts.

As each spicule grows by the addition of new layers or lamellae of bone substance, it encroaches on the surrounding mesenchyme, and soon adjacent spicules come in contact and fuse with each other (Fig. 26). Thus by union of originally separate masses a lattice work of bony trabeculae is formed. It is characterized by the irregular shape and arrangement of its parts and of the enclosed spaces. The latter contain embryonic bone marrow which has developed from the mesenchyme in this region.

Cartilage replacement bone. Bone in the condition just described (spongy bone) is ready for the processes of erosion and rebuilding which may transform a part of it into compact bone. Before discussing these changes, however, we must consider the way in which spongy bone develops in situations where cartilage precedes it as a temporary supporting structure. In many parts of the embryo a sort of model of the skeleton

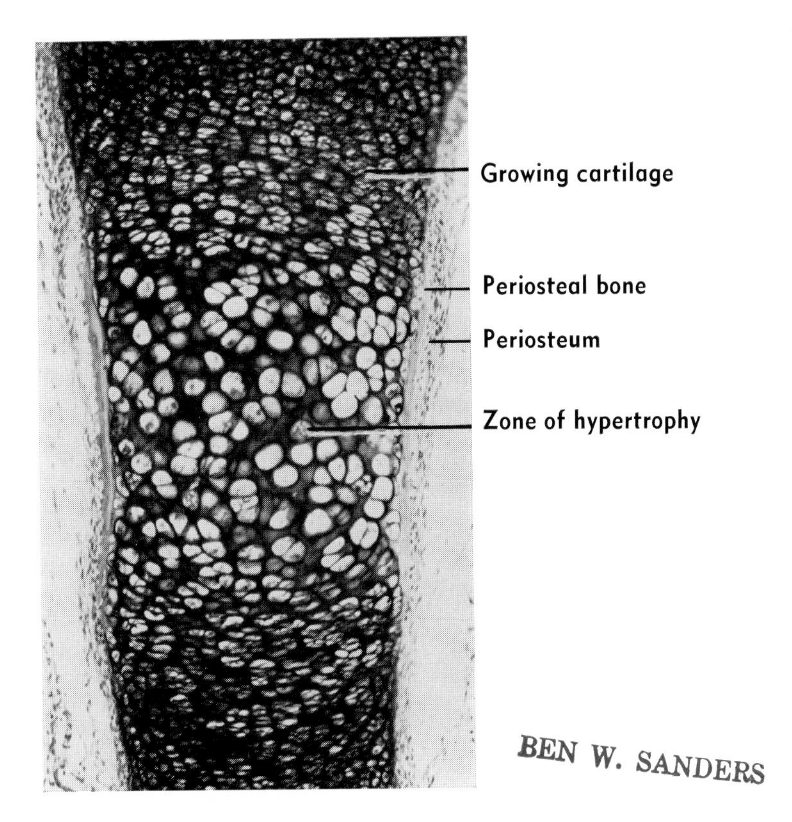

Fig. 28. Central part of shaft of developing long bone.

is laid down in cartilage. This must be replaced by bone in a gradual manner so that the part will not be left unsupported at any time. The process is well illustrated in the femur, which we may take as an example of a long bone. Before actual replacement of the cartilage is begun a cylinder of intramembranous bone is formed around its outside. This is the so-called perichondrial bone, laid down in a collarlike band around the shaft of the cartilage, the ends of which are left free for growth (Fig. 28). In longitudinal sections of a developing bone of this type the perichondrial bone appears as a fairly dense strip of bone on each side of the cartilage. As soon as the perichondrial bone is well established, changes occur in the part of the cartilage which is covered by it. A mass of mesenchymal tissue called the periosteal bud invades the cartilage, breaking down the matrix as it grows. The periosteal bud contains blood vessels, osteoblasts, and osteoclasts. By its action on the cartilage matrix it forms a cavity in the central portion of the model which is the primitive marrow. Jagged spicules of cartilage matrix are left projecting into the cavity, and it is along these that the osteoblasts line up and begin the formation of bone which, because it lies within the outlines of the cartilage model, is called endo-

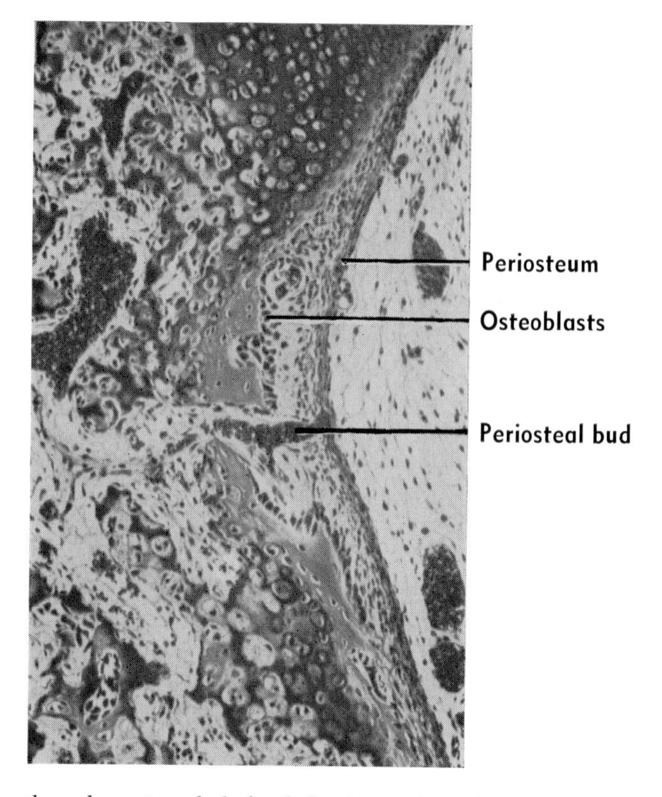

Fig. 29. Section through center of shaft of developing long bone, showing periosteal bud and associated structures.

chondrial bone. The essential process of endochondrial bone formation is like that occurring in intramembranous bone. Fibers are formed and matrix is deposited upon them, giving rise to separate spicules which later become confluent, resulting in a mass of bony trabeculae. The difference between the spicules of the two kinds of bone is that in endochondrial ossification each spicule is laid down around a fragment of calcified cartilage matrix which may be seen at its center for some time after bone formation has begun, while in intramembranous bone spicules no such substrate is present.

If one examines a section of a cartilage which is being replaced by bone, he will see zones which represent different stages of development (Figs. 29 and 30). At each end the cartilage is normal. Toward the middle, near the beginning of the region surrounded by perichondrial bone, is a zone of rapid growth, which is adding to the length of the model. This zone is characterized by the arrangement of the lacunae in rows lying in the long axis of the model. The lacunae in each row are flattened and separated from each other by thin plates of matrix, while the matrix between adjacent rows forms solid columns or bands. Still further toward the center the lacunae are enlarged, and at the border of the marrow cavity they are confluent and the matrix is reduced to jagged trabeculae. This is the place at which the erosive action of the invading marrow cells is apparent. The cartilage cells are said by some writers to be destroyed along with the matrix. Other workers claim that they are transformed into osteoblasts. Calcium salts are laid down in the remains of the cartilage matrix in this part of the model, with the result that it stains more deeply with hematoxylin than does the normal matrix in other parts of the section. It is upon the bits of calcified cartilage, as we have already said, that the bone is laid down. In properly stained sections one may see spicules of dark purple, partially calcified cartilage matrix coated with one or more layers of red bone. The whole is surrounded by osteoblasts.

The foregoing discussion describes the formation of the shaft or diaphysis of a long bone in which there is, at first, only one center of ossification. Later, however, new and independent centers develop in the ends of the cartilage model without the preliminary formation of perichondrial bone. These new centers, the epiphyses, spread radially. The growth

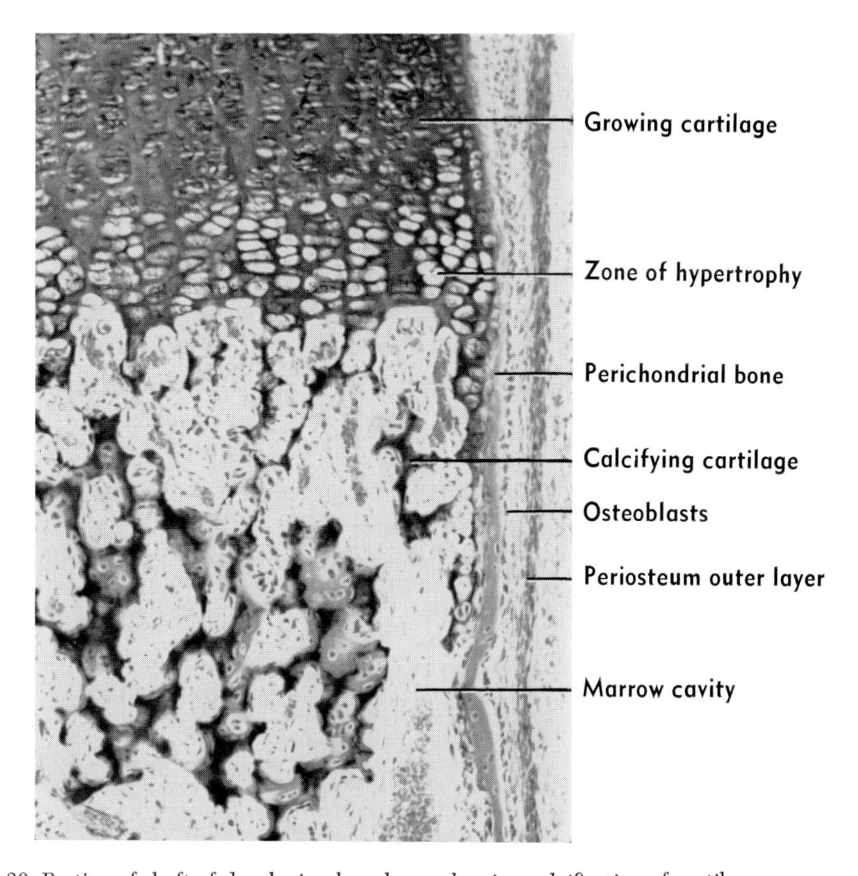

Fig. 30. Portion of shaft of developing long bone, showing calcification of cartilage.

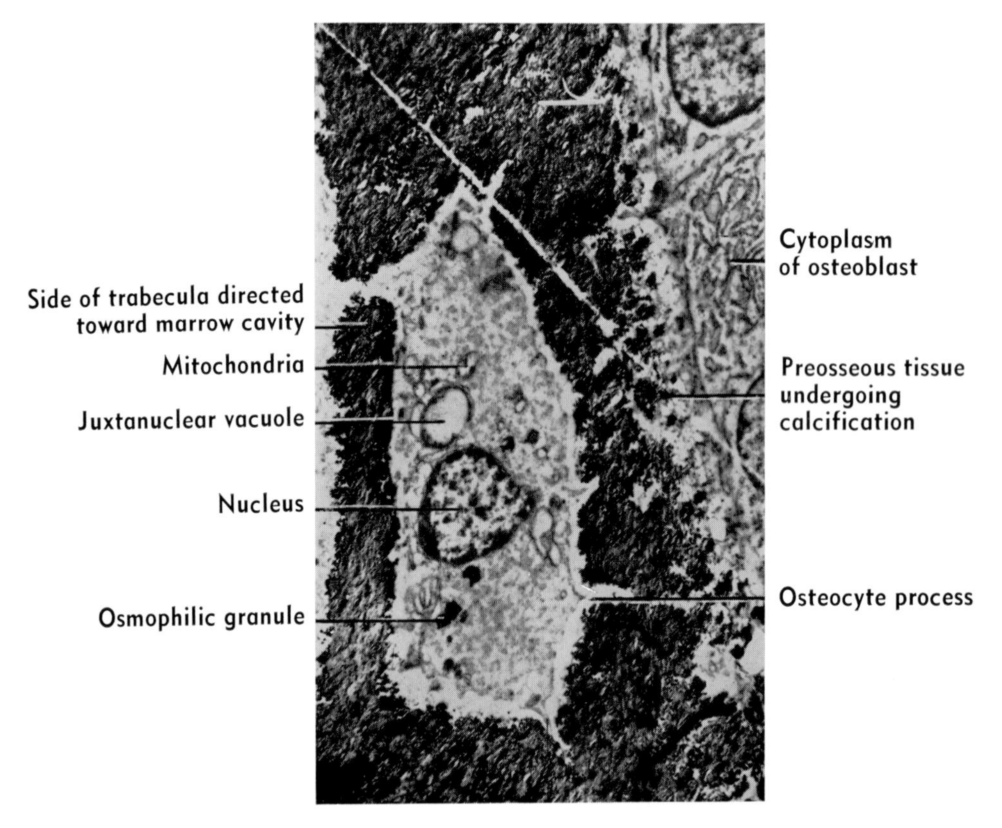

Fig. 31. Electron micrograph of osteocyte. (×7,000.) (From Knese and Knoop: Ztschr. Zellforsch. *48*:471, 1958.)

zone of the cartilage on which the increase in length of the bone as a whole depends thus comes to lie between two centers of ossification which encroach on it from opposite directions. The growth zone persists, however, during the early years of life, and so long as it remains the stature of the individual increases. Ultimately, at about the twentieth year of life, ossification outruns cartilage growth and the epiphyses and diaphysis unite. After this has occurred growth in length of bone ceases, but additions in thickness may be made by osteoblasts in the surrounding periosteum. The importance of this layer, as well as its structure, will be discussed in connection with the histology of the adult bone.

The process of erosion of bone actually begins soon after the first trabeculae of spongy bone have been laid down and continues actively as long as the bones are growing. It starts at the point where bone formation began, namely, at the borders of the primary marrow cavity. Thus, as mineralization of the diaphysis of a long bone moves toward the ends of the cartilage model, it is followed by a secondary breaking down and resorption of part of the newly formed tissue. The result is an enlargement of the marrow cavity which prevents the bone from becoming too heavy and solid.

The mechanism of erosion is not perfectly clear. It is generally believed to be accomplished by cells called osteoclasts. These are large cells in which the cytoplasm stains deeply with eosin and in each of which there are several nuclei. The osteoclasts lie along the margin of the bone matrix, sometimes partly enclosed in definite spaces (Howship's lacunae) which they seem to have hollowed out of it (Fig. 32).

Erosion of bone is not confined to the central portion of the bones where, as we have said, its effect is a progressive enlargement of the marrow cavity. It occurs throughout the mass of all bony tissue, but in all places except the marrow cavities it is followed by rebuilding. In the ends of the long bones and in the central portions of other bones the rebuilding keeps pace with erosion and follows the pattern of the original formation of the tissue, resulting in a renewal of spongy bone. In the peripheral parts of all bones, however, rebuilding is more rapid than erosion, and a compact layer of bone is established.

Formation of haversian systems. Compact bone is more regular in its arrangement than spongy bone. Its development may be described as follows: The marrow spaces, containing reticular tissue and blood-forming

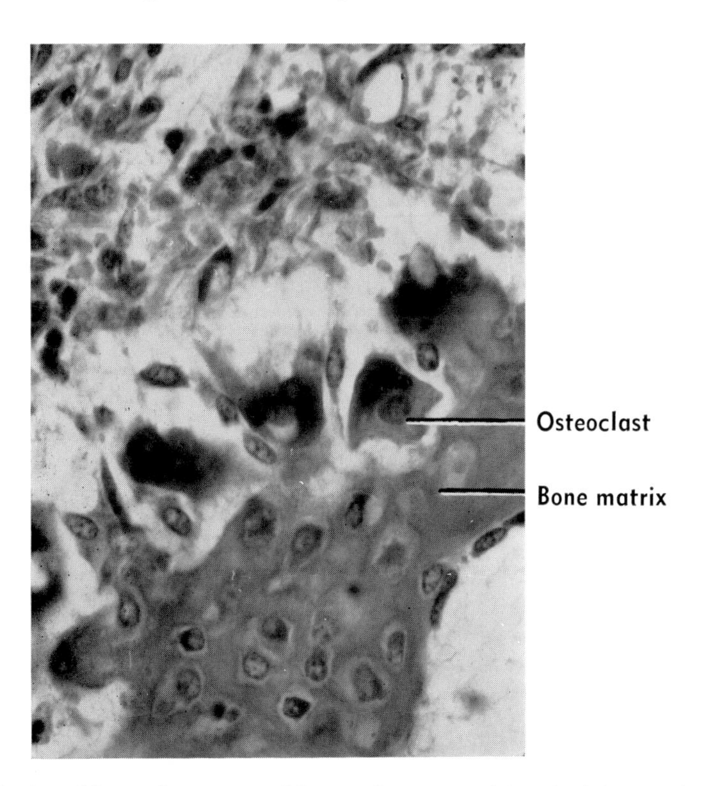

Fig. 32. Erosion of bone, showing osteoblasts in depressions (Howship's lacunae).

cells, are penetrated throughout by a rich vascular network. The vessels at the periphery of the bone follow a more or less regular pathway parallel to the surface. In long bones they run mainly in the long axis of the bone. In places where compact bone is to be formed, erosion follows a definite plan, rounding out the marrow spaces so that they form cylindrical cavities around the blood vessels. After the marrow spaces have been thus reshaped

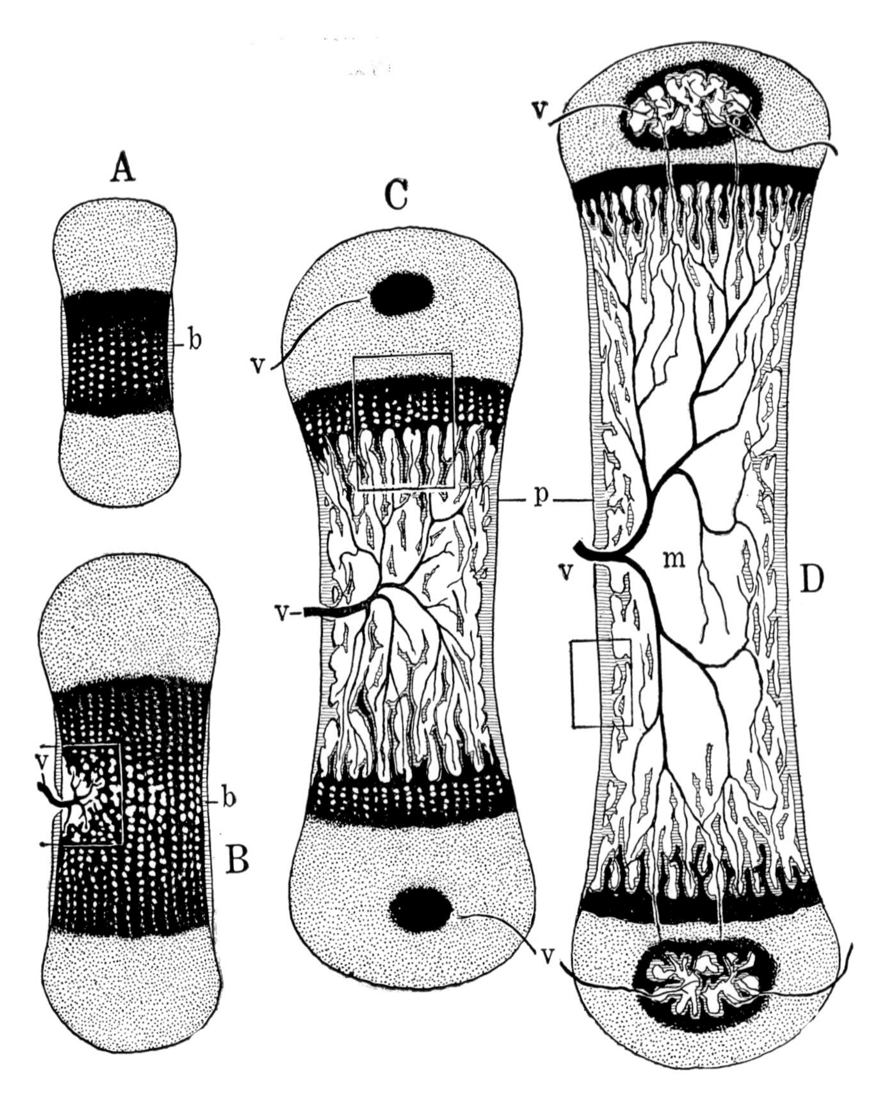

Fig. 33. Diagrams of ossification of a long bone. **A,** Early cartilaginous stage; **B,** stage of eruption of periosteal bone collar by an osteogenic bud of vessels; **C,** older stage with a primary marrow cavity and early centers of calcification in epiphyseal cartilages; **D,** condition shortly after birth with epiphyseal centers of ossification. Calcified cartilage in all diagrams is black; **b,** periosteal bone collar; **m,** marrow cavity; **p,** periosteal bone; **v,** blood vessels entering centers of ossification. (From Nonidez and Windle: Textbook of Histology, New York, 1953, McGraw-Hill Book Co., Inc.)

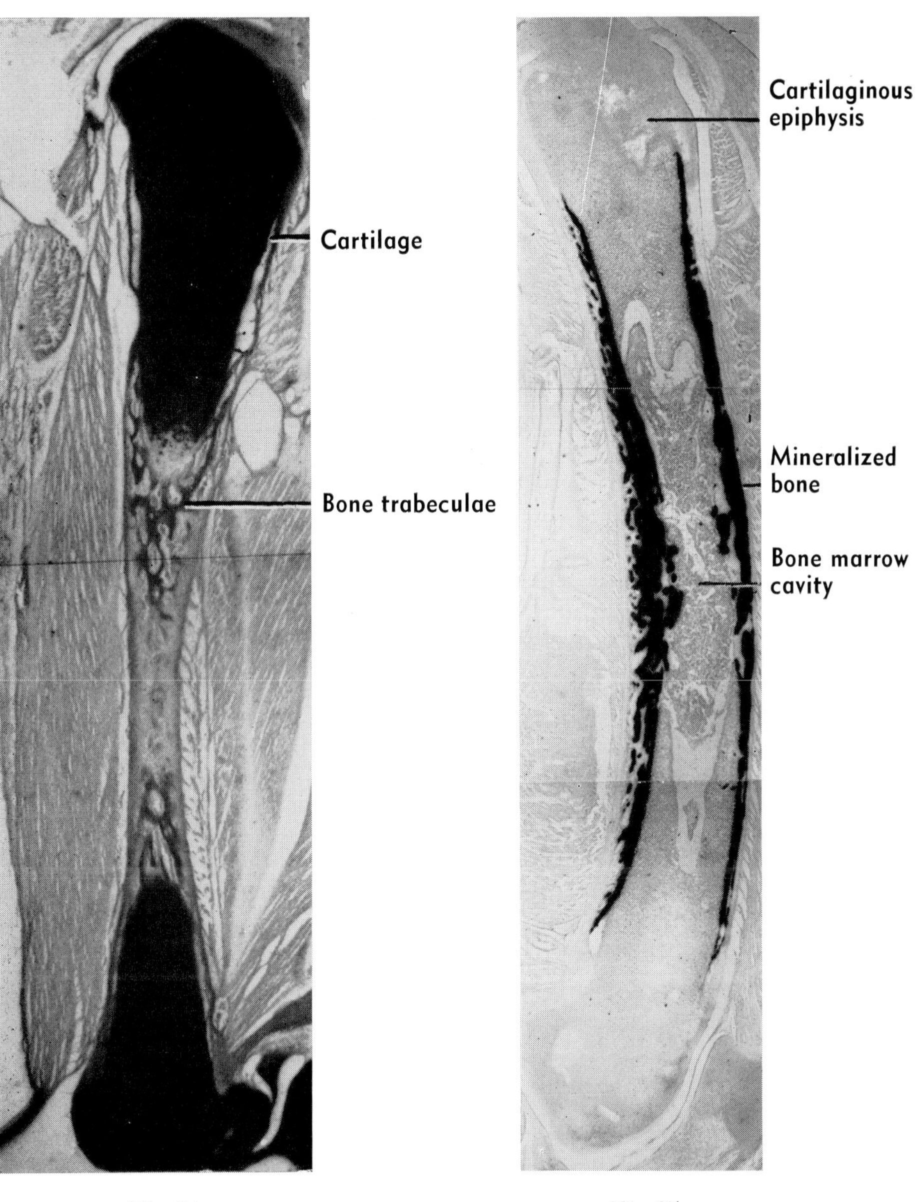

Fig. 34

Fig. 35

Fig. 34. Radioautograph of femur of fourteen-day-old chick injected on thirteenth day with S_{35}. Note uptake in cartilage matrix and to lesser degree in bone matrix. Black areas are also metachromatic. Compare with Fig. 35.

Fig. 35. Radioautograph of longitudinal section of femur of fourteen-day-old chick injected with Ca^{45} on thirteenth day. Black areas show regions of Ca^{45} uptake. There is practically no endochondral ossification in the chick bone at this time.

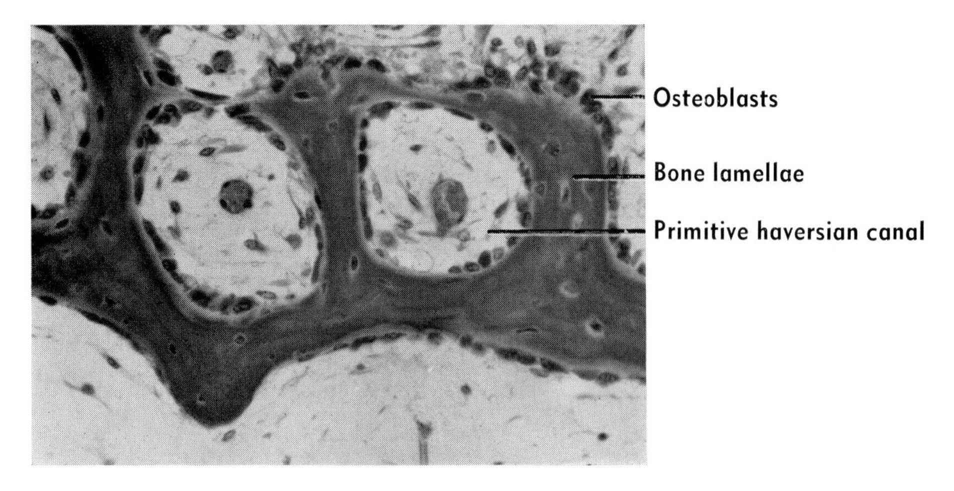

Fig. 36. Remodeling of bone to form haversian systems.

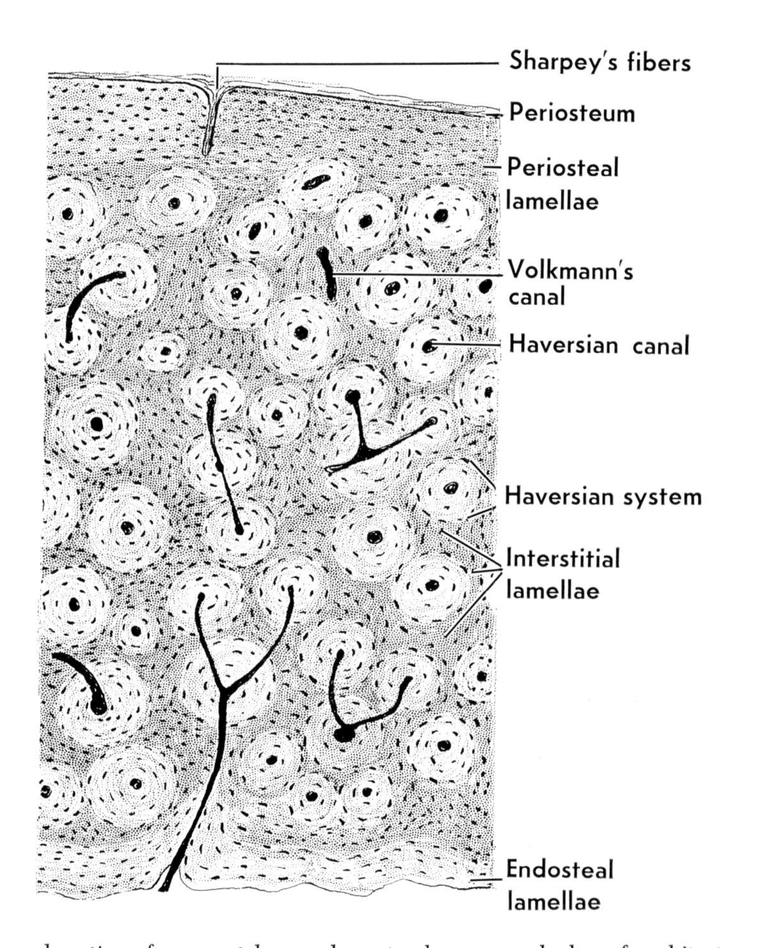

Fig. 37. Ground section of compact human bone to show general plan of architecture.

they are lined by successive concentric layers (lamellae) of new bone. The process continues until the space is almost filled with lamellae and it eventually persists as a central canal containing blood vessels and nerves. Such a grouping of layers of bone, with its central canal, is called a haversian system.

The remodeling of bone does not end with the primary haversian systems are laid down but continues into adult life. The primary systems are partially destroyed to make room for new ones in response to changes in mechanical requirements. The final result is a mass of bone composed of secondary and tertiary haversian systems embedded in the remains of earlier systems. The lamellae which form the background for the haversian systems, holding them together in a solid mass, are called interstitial lamellae. The surface of the bone is formed by circumferential lamellae which have been laid down by the osteoblasts of the periosteal tissue. This region contains no haversian systems. Endosteal lamellae of the same character line the shaft where it borders the marrow cavity (Fig. 37).

Adult bone

Since the development of bone has been so fully discussed, little remains to be said about its adult structure. Gross examination of adult bone which has been sawed in half will show that it is composed of both spongy and compact tissue. In the long bones the spongy arrangement is confined to the epiphyses and inner part of the shaft, and there is a central marrow cavity entirely devoid of bone matrix. In flat bones the spongy

Fig. 38. Ground section showing haversian system (osteone) with concentrically arranged lamellae and centrally located haversian canal.

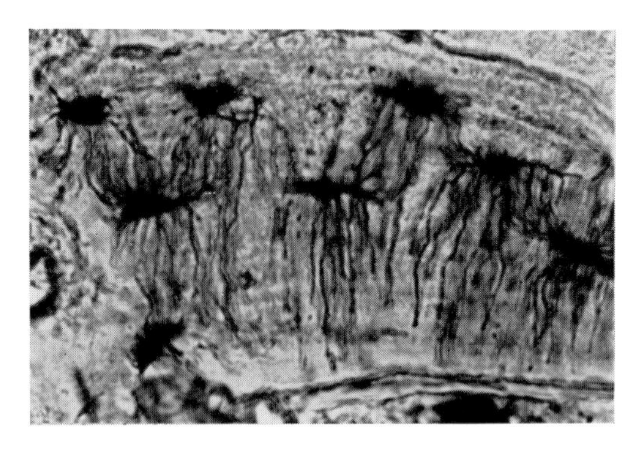

Fig. 39. Higher magnification of section of Fig. 38 to show detail of lacunae and canaliculi in bone matrix.

Fig. 40. Cross section of compact bone; ground section photographed in polarized light. This photograph indicates the high degree of orientation of the fibers and crystals of bone.

tissue forms trabeculae crossing from one side to the other, so that there is no large marrow cavity but a number of small irregular marrow spaces. Either form of bone has an outer layer or cortex of compact tissue which is, in turn, covered by a tough fibrous coating called the periosteum.

Microscopically, sections of decalcified spongy bone present a picture much like that of developing intramembranous bone except for the greater extent of the trabeculae. Osteoblasts and osteoclasts are less common but may be found in portions of the tissue which are undergoing changes in arrangement. The matrix stains red with eosin and is lamellated; the cells are dark in color and disposed, one in each lacuna, between adjacent lamellae. With special techniques one may demonstrate the canaliculi and the fibers on which the matrix was deposited, but these are not ordinarily visible in hematoxylin-eosin preparations.

Ground sections of bone do not show the cellular elements of the tissue, since these are destroyed in the making of the preparation. Such sections are useful in studying the architecture of compact bone. In transverse ground sections the following features are to be noted (Figs. 37 and 40): the haversian canals appear as empty circular spaces, each of which is surrounded by from six to fifteen concentric lamellae of matrix. The lacunae and the canaliculi radiating from them are readily visible. Between haversian systems is the packing of interstitial lamellae, and a piece taken from the periphery of the bone will contain periosteal lamellae. Canals running diagonally or at right angles to those of the haversian systems are the canals of Volkmann. They provide for transverse connections and anastomosis between the blood vessels and are distinguished from haversian canals by their direction through the tissue and by the fact that they are not surrounded by concentric lamellae. The vascular pattern of bone is best seen in longitudinal sections, in which, however, the concentric arrangement of lamellae is not to be observed. The appearance of decalcified bone is shown in Fig. 41.

It will be seen from the description of bone that in spite of its physical rigidity it is a tissue which retains considerable ability to respond to environmental changes. The most obvious of these are traumatic changes

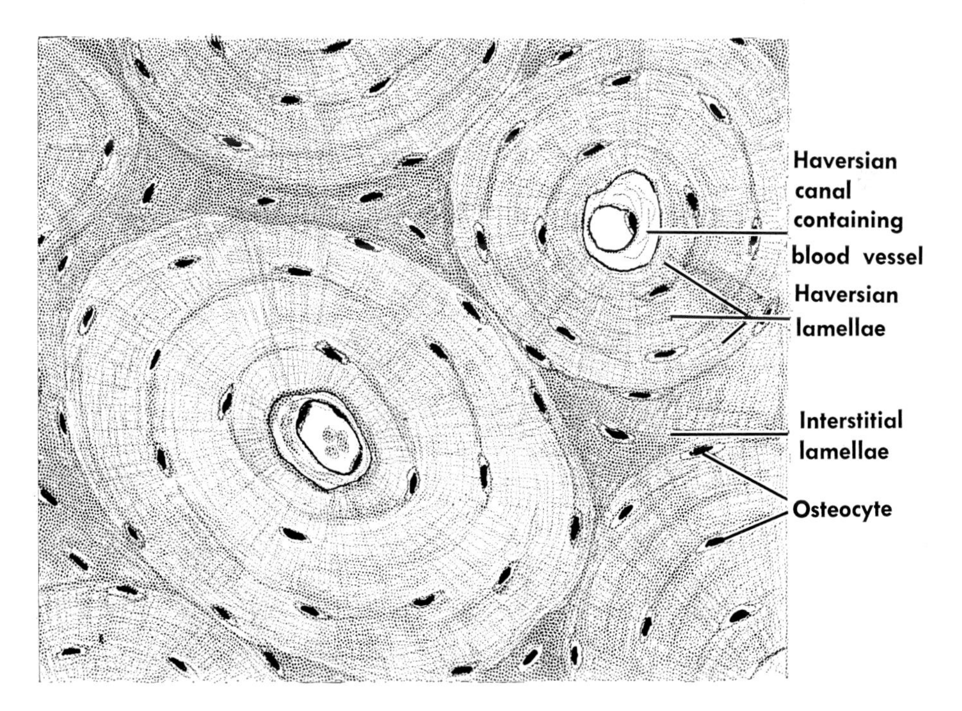

Fig. 41. Compact bone decalcified, showing organic constituents.

such as fractures, which are repaired by the osteoblasts in the periosteum and at the border of the marrow cavity. Some disturbances of the ductless glands provide a stimulus to the osteoblasts of the periosteum which results in the laying down of additional cortical layers of bone (acromegaly). Also the skeleton serves as a storehouse for calcium, and the rates of erosion and rebuilding respond to variations of the mineral metabolism of the body. It is essential to life that a certain amount of calcium be present in the body fluids. When this amount is not supplied by the diet it may be withdrawn from the bones, or, conversely, excess of calcium may be stored in them.

Periosteum

The periosteum is a connective tissue layer covering the bone except at the articular surfaces. It is divisible into two layers. The outer of these is a network of densely packed collagenous fibers with blood vessels. The inner layer provides the penetration fibers (of Sharpey) which are inserted into the bone and attach the periosteum to it. In the inner layer of the periosteum one may also find fine elastic fibers loosely arranged. Osteoblasts occur here also whenever appositional growth of the bone is taking place. The endosteum is a thin layer of connective tissue lining the marrow cavity and the smaller cavities within the bone.

In addition to the more obvious function which the periosteum performs, such as anchorage for tendons and ligaments, it is also concerned with repair and regeneration of bone. Whereas this is a somewhat disputed function, there seems to be little doubt that the osteogenic tissue which initiates bone repair is actually the inner component of the periosteum. The outer fibrous part of the periosteum is also important in bone repair inasmuch as it acts as a limiting membrane which restricts the extent to which new bone formation occurs.

Blood supply and nerves

The blood supply of bone comes by two routes. Near the middle of the shaft there is a medullary or nutrient canal which pierces the bone and leads to the marrow cavity. The nutrient artery passes through this canal, giving off branches to the haversian canals on the way. In the marrow cavity it divides into an ascending and a descending branch, both of which supply the marrow.

The other sources of blood for the bone tissue is by way of the numerous arteries of the periosteum. These enter the substance of the bone through Volkmann's canals which, in turn, lead to haversian canals.

Veins leave the bone through the nutrient canal, and it is here also that the medullated and nonmedullated nerves enter. The latter accompany the blood vessels into the haversian canals.

Marrow

Although marrow is not, actually, a part of bone as a tissue, it is included in sections of decalcified bone and should be mentioned here. It is of two kinds, named red and yellow marrow, respectively, according to their color in the fresh state. Both kinds have a framework of reticular tissue. Red marrow is the chief site of the formation of certain types of blood cells including the red corpuscles and contains a great number of blood vessels. The details of its structure have already been considered in a previous chapter. In yellow marrow the blood-forming elements have been replaced by adipose tissue and the amount of reticular tissue is reduced. Red marrow is present in the cavities of all bones during fetal life and early childhood. It is gradually replaced by yellow marrow and is found in the adult only in the epiphyses of long bones and in the ribs, vertebrae, cranial bones, and sternum.

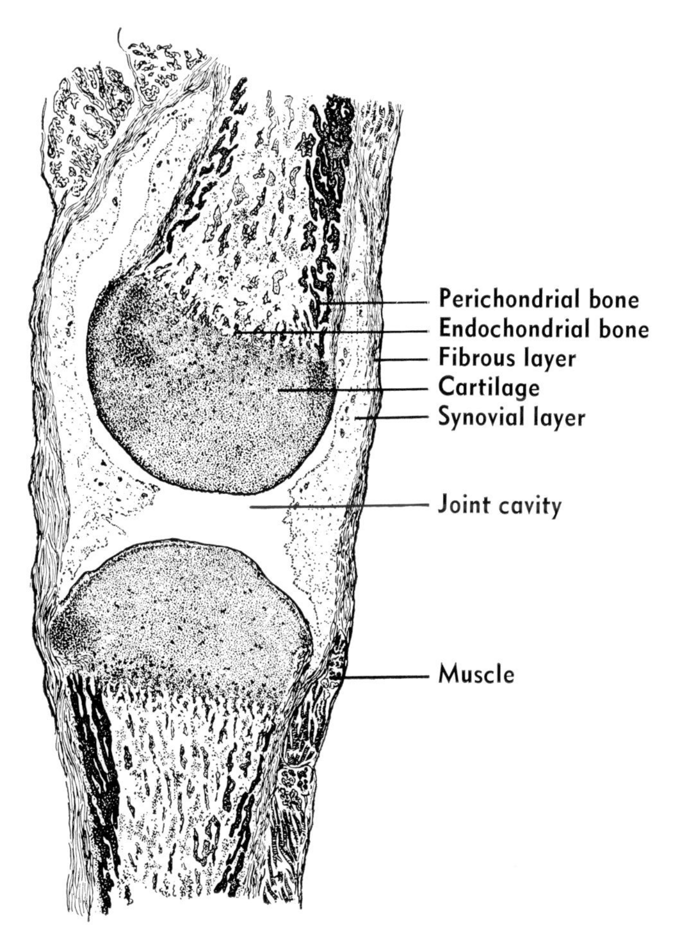

Fig. 42. Joint from finger of a newborn child. The process of cartilage replacement is still going on, and one may distinguish between endochondral and perichondral bone.

Joints

The bones are joined together to form the skeleton by a series of articulations, the structure of each varying with the degree of movability of the joint. Those articulations which are nearly or quite immovable are called synarthroses. In the skull, for instance, the bones are held together by ligaments composed of short fibers, of which some are elastic and others are continuations of the fibers of Sharpey. The vertebrae are less closely joined, allowing a limited amount of movement, and the spaces between them are occupied by intervertebral discs of fibrocartilage.

The movable joints or diarthroses are characterized by a space between the bones which is the articular cleft. Each bone bordering on this space has at its end a cap of articular cartilage, which is the remainder of the embryonic cartilage model of the bone. This cartilage is of the hyaline type but has no perichondrial fibrous layer (Fig. 42).

The capsule which encloses the articular cartilages and the space between them is two-layered. The outer part is the stratum fibrosum, composed of dense fibrous tissue continuous with the outer layer of the periosteum of the bones. The stratum fibrosum is blended with the tendons and ligaments of the muscles attached at this point. The inner or synovial layer is of looser and more vascular connective tissue. Where it borders on the articular cavity it is lined with the so-called mesenchymal epithelium. This consists of fibers and fibroblasts arranged around the border of the cavity. The synovial layer sometimes forms projections into the joint cavity which may contain fibrocartilage. The synovial fluid, or synovia, is believed to be secreted at least in part by cells of the synovial membrane. It is a yellow viscid fluid containing mucoproteins and cellular debris. It serves to lubricate and thus facilitate the smooth movement of the articulating surfaces.

CHAPTER VIII

Muscle

The fibers of muscle differ from those of connective tissue in structure and in function. In the connective tissues the fibers are intercellular, noncontractile, and serve the purpose of binding or padding. In muscular tissue the cells are called fibers and are composed of elongated cells in which the property of contractility is highly developed. The function of muscle is to move parts of the body by its contraction. Only a small amount of intercellular substance is present in muscle, except as it is intermingled with connective tissue cells and fibers.

The morphological characteristics common to all types of muscle are as follows: the cells are elongated with well-defined nuclei; the cytoplasm (sarcoplasm) stains red with eosin and contains fibrils (myofibrils) which run parallel to the long axis of the cell; and the fibers (cells)are surrounded by a limiting membrane, the sarcolemma. Three types of muscle are morphologically distinguishable: smooth muscle, skeletal muscle, and cardiac muscle. Of these the first and last are under the control of the autonomic nervous system and are called involuntary muscle. Skeletal muscle is innervated directly by the central nervous system and can, for the most part, be controlled by impulses from the higher centers of the brain. It is accordingly called voluntary muscle.

Smooth muscle

Smooth muscle is derived from mesenchyme, the cells of which are not originally different in their appearance from those which give rise to the connective and supporting tissues. The muscle-forming cell, however, soon assumes a peculiar shape. It elongates into a spindle, elaborating at the same time a small amount of intercellular substance. At an early stage in the development of the connective tissue cell fibers are visible along its border, to which the name fibroglia is given. In a similar way the developing smooth muscle cell is seen to have fibers along its border, here called myoglia. But whereas the border fibrils in connective tissue soon become separated from the cells, increasing to form the most conspicuous part

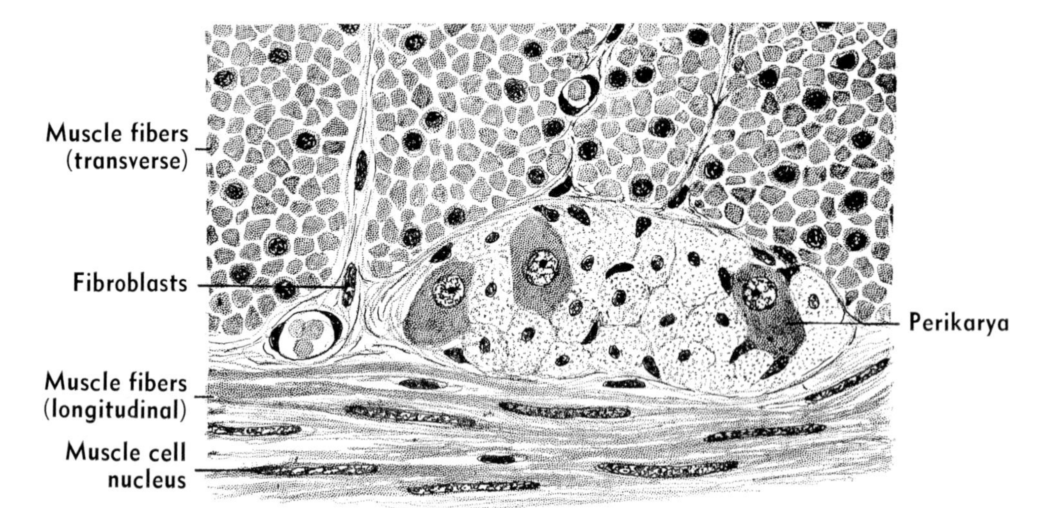

Fig. 43. Smooth muscle from wall of intestine of monkey, showing longitudinal and transverse sections of fibers. Compare nuclei of muscle cells with those of fibroblasts of connective tissue among muscle fibers. Also illustrated are perikarya, fibers, and supporting cells of Auerbach's nerve plexus.

of the tissue, those of smooth muscle remain in contact with the cell. They are said to persist throughout the life of the cell, connecting one fiber with another, although it is not certain that this is so. As the cells increase in size and become closely applied to each other, intercellular fibers become very difficult to demonstrate and will not be seen in ordinary sections.

Smooth muscle cells vary in length from 0.02 to 0.5 mm. and have a diameter at their thickest portion of about 4 to 7μ. From the middle they diminish gradually to a fine, rounded point at each end. The cells may be best seen in preparations made by shaking a bit of muscle in a weak acid solution. This dissolves the intercellular substance and makes it possible to study the form of the isolated fiber. The myofibrils in the cells of smooth muscle are fine and not easily seen. The nucleus of the cell is elongated and centrally located at the thickest portion of the spindle. It lies in a small area of granular cytoplasm and the myofibrils diverge to pass around this area. The sarcolemma is so thin that it is imperceptible in ordinary preparations. Branching fibers are very rare; they have been found in a few parts of the body but are to be regarded as exceptional.

Many of the features just described are imperceptible in longitudinal sections of smooth muscle (Fig. 43). The fibers normally occur in sheets, closely packed together, and it is seldom that an entire cell can be seen. In thick sections it is often difficult to make out the boundaries of adjacent fibers, since several of them are included overlapping in the depth of a section. One may see only the long nuclei and the cytoplasm faintly marked by the myofibrils. Longitudinal sections are best studied at the edge of a band or sheet where the muscle shades off into the surrounding connective tissue, and individual cells may be distinguished.

In transverse section the smooth cells appear as discs of cytoplasm having various diameters. The largest of the discs are cut through the middle of the fibers and include the nucleus of the cell. The smaller sections pass through the ends of the fibers and therefore have no nuclei in them. The characteristics peculiar to smooth muscle in cross section are the small size and round shape of the individual fiber, the homogeneous appearance of the cytoplasm, and the fact that the nuclei are centrally located in the cells (Fig. 43). Smooth muscle occurs in bands or sheets surrounding glandular organs and forming a part of the wall of tubular organs. Such sheets are not surrounded by definite coverings but mingle with the areolar or reticular tissue around them. Isolated fibers of smooth muscle may also be found occurring in the tunica propria of the digestive tract.

Skeletal muscle

Skeletal muscle or striated voluntary muscle presents a different appearance from the type just described. It develops from solid masses of mesoderm, unlike the loose mesenchyme which forms smooth muscle. In the development of a striated muscle fiber nuclear division occurs without cytoplasmic division; the fiber of adult skeletal muscle is therefore multinucleate. It is longer and thicker than the smooth muscle cell and maintains a uniform diameter throughout its length, ending bluntly. Early in the development of the fiber the nuclei migrate from the center to the periphery of the cell where they are to be found in adult muscle of this type. The sarcolemma, which in smooth muscle is only a fine limiting mem-

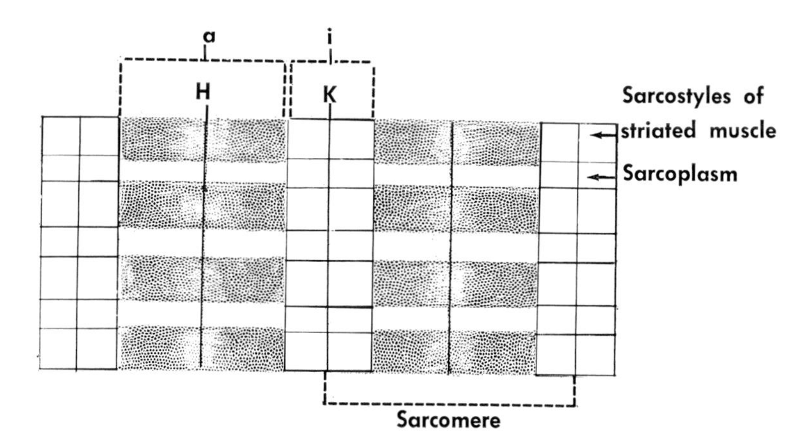

Fig. 44. Diagram of four sarcostyles of striated muscle. **a**, Anisotropic or dark band, bisected by Hensen's membrane, **H**; **i**, isotropic or light band with Krause's membrane, **K**. Space between sarcostyles is filled with sarcoplasm.

brane, is thicker in skeletal muscle and may easily be seen as a structureless sheath around the fiber. The most striking morphological characteristic of striated muscle, to which it owes its name, is the transverse marking of the myofibrils. These fibrils are thicker than those of smooth muscle and are called sarcostyles. Each sarcostyle is composed of a succession of bands of different and alternating refractive indices. One set of these is anisotropic and appears as a dark band in stained preparations; the other is isotropic and has a paler color. The position of the dark band on one sarcostyle exactly corresponds with that of the dark band on the adjacent one. Since the sarcostyles lie close together and since the depth of a section usually includes several overlapping sarcostyles, the effect of a continuous band of darkness traversing the entire fiber is produced. The dark bands alternate regularly with light bands, giving the muscle its characteristic transversely striated appearance. (Figs. 44 and 46.)

Although the light and dark bands do not cross the protoplasm (sarcoplasm) from one sarcostyle to the next, there are fine membranes running from side to side of the fiber, dividing both the sarcostyles and the sarco-

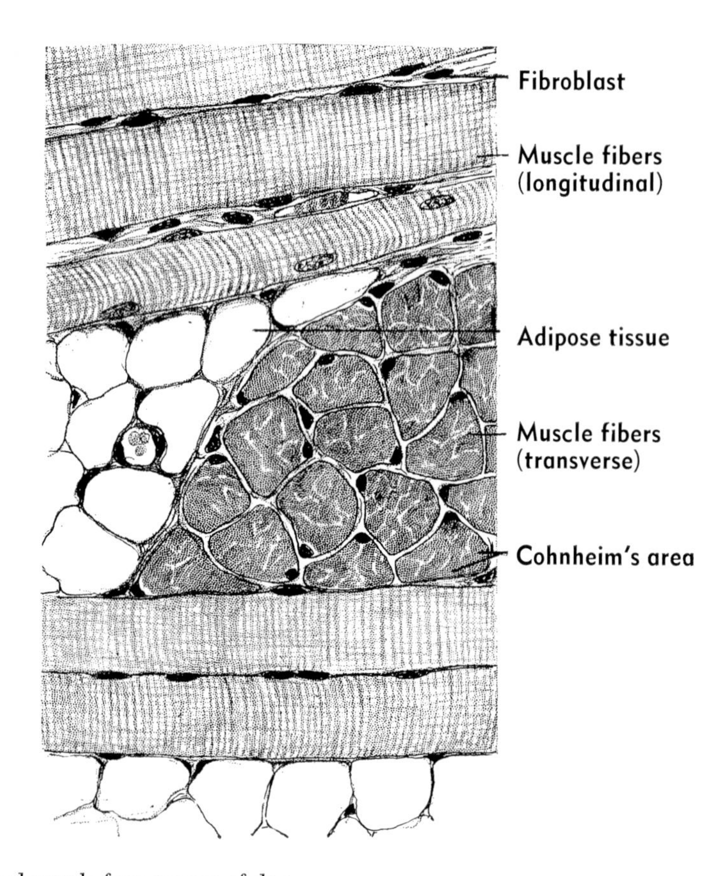

Fig. 45. Striated muscle from tongue of dog.

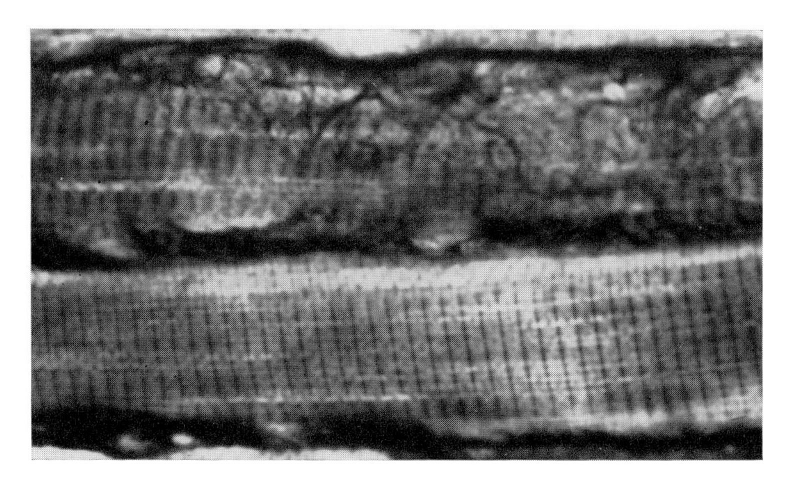

Fig. 46. Longitudinal section of striated muscle; upper fiber shows arrangement of reticular connective tissue. (Silver stain.)

plasm into a series of discs. There are two series of these membranes which are placed alternately, like the bands of the sarcostyles. Hensen's line, or the median membrane, bisects the dark region, and Krause's line crosses the middle of the lighter area. Of the two Krause's line is the more easily demonstrated; it divides the fiber into equal segments called sarcomeres. Often neither line is visible in sections, but they can usually be found in thin sections stained by the iron alum-hematoxylin method.

The appearance of ordinary sections of skeletal muscle is represented in Fig. 45, and the important points are as follows: in longitudinal section the myofibrils are marked by alternating light and dark transverse bands. There are many nuclei in one fiber, lying at its periphery immediately beneath the sarcolemma. Occasionally one sees a nucleus which seems to be in the center of a fiber. Careful focusing of the microscope will show, however, that in such a case one is looking down on the surface of a tangential section and that the nucleus is on the outside of the cell. In transverse sections it is apparent that the fibers are larger than those of smooth muscle, having diameters which range from 17 to 87μ. Their shape is round or polygonal, and the peripheral position of the nucleus is noticeable. It is also possible to see the cut ends of the sarcostyles which give the cytoplasm a finely stippled appearance. In transverse section one may see that the myofibrils are gathered in groups instead of being evenly distributed throughout the cytoplasm. Some writers use the term sarcostyle to describe such a group of myofibrils, but the name is usually applied to the myofibril itself. Large fibrils are sometimes called a muscle column of Kölliker. In a cross section of a muscle fiber one may sometimes see such a group of fibrils separated from adjacent groups by clear sarcoplasm. Such cross sections of muscle columns are called Cohnheim's areas.

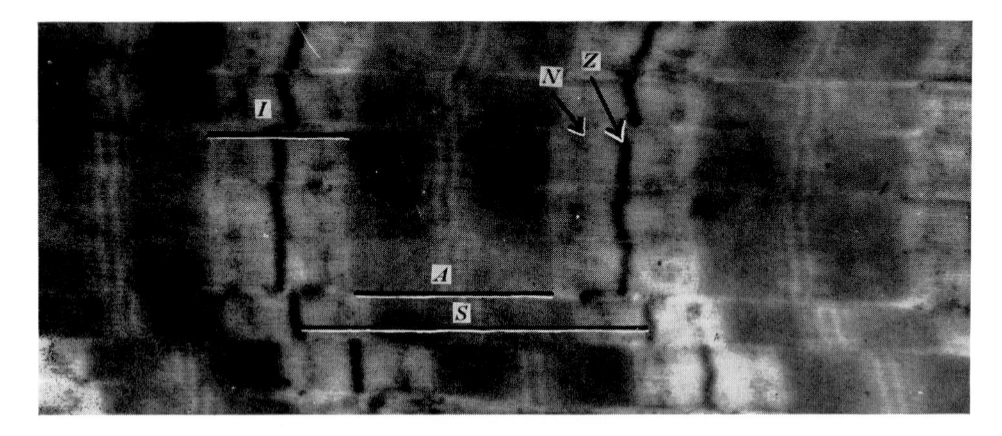

Fig. 47. Electron micrograph of striated muscle. Longitudinal section of rest length of rabbit psoas. **I,** I band; **A,** A band; **N** and **Z,** discs, respectively; **S,** sarcomere. Note fibrillae in myofibrils. (×45,000.) (Courtesy Dr. D. Spiro, Boston, Mass.)

Skeletal muscle, as the name implies, is attached to the bones, the attachment being made through the tendons. At the point where the muscle joins the tendon the nuclei are especially numerous, indicating that this is the region of the most rapid growth. The sarcostyles may be traced to the sarcolemma which covers the end of the fiber, and tendon fibers may be seen in close contact with the outside of the membrane. It is thought by some writers that the tendon fibers actually pierce the sarcolemma and are continuous with the sarcostyles. Such a continuity cannot, however, be observed in ordinary sections, which give the impression that the muscle is attached to the tendon by its sarcolemma. Recent findings have demonstrated that the connective tissue fibrils insert into indentations in the sarcolemma.

The fibers which compose a muscle are gathered together in fascicles or bundles. Fine connective tissue surrounds the individual fibers; this is called the endomysium. The covering of a fascicle is the perimysium, and the sheath surrounding a group of such bundles is the epimysium.

Muscle of exactly the same morphological appearance as the skeletal muscle is found in various places where it is not attached to the bones. In such situations it has no surrounding connective tissue sheath but merges with the connective tissue about it. Such muscle is not truly skeletal, since it does not move parts of the skeleton. In the tongue, for instance, it is more accurately described by the name voluntary muscle. In other regions muscle of this type is not, strictly speaking, either skeletal or voluntary. The wall of the esophagus contains, in its upper portion, striated muscle which is not under the control of the voluntary centers of the nervous system or attached to bone. It is morphologically indistinguishable from skeletal muscle, however, and is therefore called by the same name.

Cardiac muscle

The third type of muscle is that of the heart. The functional peculiarity of cardiac muscle is its ability to contract rhythmically and continuously. The contraction is entirely independent of the will. Morphologically cardiac muscle may readily be distinguished from smooth and skeletal muscle, although it shares some of the characteristics of each.

The fibers branch freely and anastomose so that the whole forms a syncytium (Fig. 48). This arrangement is evident under the low power of the microscope. The nuclei of cardiac muscle are centrally located like those of smooth muscle. The myofibrils are transversely striated in somewhat the same way as those of skeletal muscle, but the striations are not

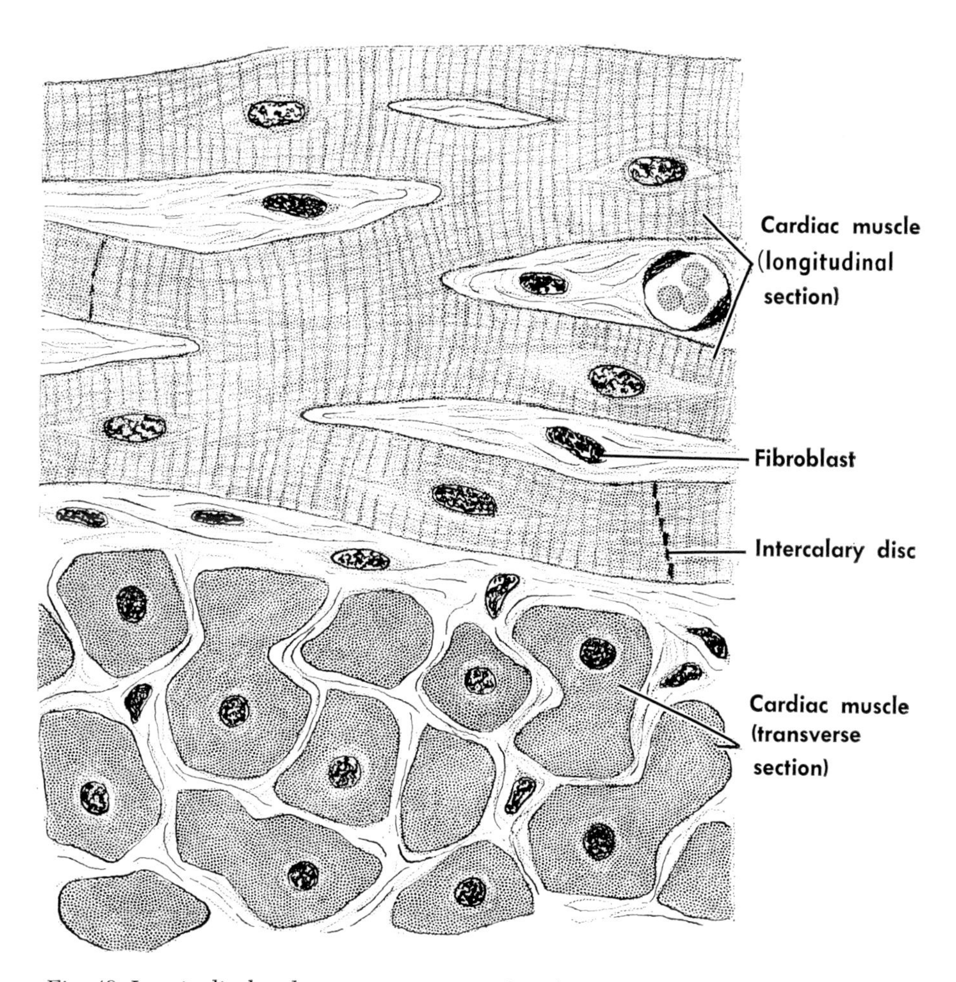

Fig. 48. Longitudinal and transverse sections of cardiac muscle of monkey.

so marked. The sarcolemma is also less noticeable than that of skeletal muscle. In longitudinal sections the fibers are recognizable because of their branching. They are distinguished from sections of striated muscle by the central position of their nuclei. In some preparations of cardiac muscle one may see transverse markings on the fibers which are different from the striations of the sarcostyles. These are the intercalary discs. They are fairly heavy lines sometimes running directly across the fiber or, more often, traversing it in a series of steps. The significance of these discs or lines is not known. They are often mentioned as a diagnostic feature of cardiac muscle, but, as special technique is required to demonstrate them, the student should not rely on their presence in distinguishing cardiac from other kinds of muscle. The presence of transverse markings on the sarcostyles, together with central nuclei and branching fibers, is a sufficient means of identification.

In transverse, as in longitudinal section, the postion of the nuclei differentiates cardiac from skeletal muscle (Fig. 48). In distinguishing cardiac muscle from cross sections of smooth muscle one must observe the extent and character of the cytoplasm. The fibers of cardiac muscle are thicker than those of smooth muscle, having diameters of from 9 to 20μ. It is possible to see in cross sections the cut ends of the sarcostyles, which give the cytoplasm a stippled appearance, except in the region immediately around the nucleus.

The most important diagnostic features of the three types of muscle are given in Table 2.

Table 2. Most important diagnostic features of muscles

Type	*Nucleus*	*Myofibrils*	*Sarcolemma*	*Shape and size*
Smooth				
Longitudinal section	Central	Faint; no striation	Very thin	Spindle
Cross section	Central	Invisible	Very thin	Circular, 7μ
Skeletal				
Longitudinal section	Peripheral	Well-marked striations	Definite sheath	Uniform thickness
Cross section	Peripheral	Visible as dots in groups	Definite sheath	Rounded polygons, 17 to 87μ
Cardiac				
Longitudinal section	Central	Lightly striated	Thin sheath	Branching
Cross section	Central	Visible as dots	Thin sheath	Round, 9 to 20μ

Circulation and innervation of muscle

All muscle has a plentiful supply of blood vessels and nerves. In striated muscle the network of capillaries is so extensive that each fiber lies in contact with at least one blood vessel. The innervation consists of myelinated fibers from the central nervous system, and each muscle fiber is in connection with a nerve fiber. In smooth muscle, which is composed of smaller fibers, the individual cell is not so well supplied. Capillaries ramify through the tissue but not to the extent of reaching every cell. Similarly the nerve supply does not reach every smooth muscle fiber.

The capillaries of cardiac muscle are supplied through the coronary artery. Its nerve supply is derived from the sympathetic and parasympathetic systems.

CHAPTER IX

Nervous tissue

The nervous system is divided into two parts: (1) the central nervous system (CNS), composed of the brain and spinal cord, and (2) the peripheral nervous system (PNS), consisting of all other nervous tissue, that is, ganglia and nerves. This system is composed of functional units known as *neurons* (nerve cells), which are arranged in chain formation extending throughout the body. Neurons are highly differentiated in that they are hyperirritable but have lost the ability to move and to reproduce and usually have limited powers to repair damage. It is this combination of irritability and arrangement which permits the nervous system to receive impulses, integrate them, and transmit them in such a way that coordinated activity occurs.

Neurons consist of a cell body or *perikaryon;* one or more branching afferent processes known as *dendrites,* which transmit impulses towards the perikaryon; and one efferent process known as the *axon,* which conducts impulses away from the perikaryon. The dendrites and axons are collectively called processes or *nerve fibers.* Branches occurring along the length of nerve fibers are called *collaterals,* those at the ends are called *terminal arborizations.* A *synapse* is a region in which the terminal arborizations of the axon of one neuron comes in close proximity to the dendrites or perikarya of succeeding neurons. Synapses are not regions of protoplasmic continuity, since minute but definite gaps between adjoining fibers are demonstrable.

PERIKARYON

The perikaryon is a cytoplasmic thickening which includes a nucleus (karyon). The nucleus is usually a large, lightly staining vesicular structure with a single prominent nucleolus and a number of fine chromatin granules (Fig. 50, *A*). The cytoplasm contains a conspicuous number of angular pieces of basophilic, metachromatic, RNA-containing, *chromophil substance,* usually referred to as Nissl or Tigroid bodies. With toluidine blue the Nissl substance stains a purplish color and gives the cytoplasm

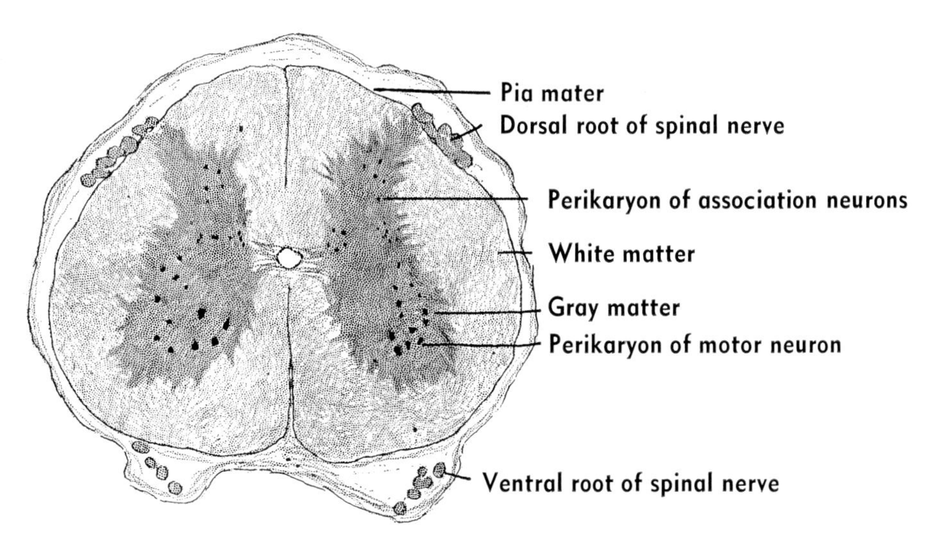

Fig. 49. Spinal cord of cat, low power.

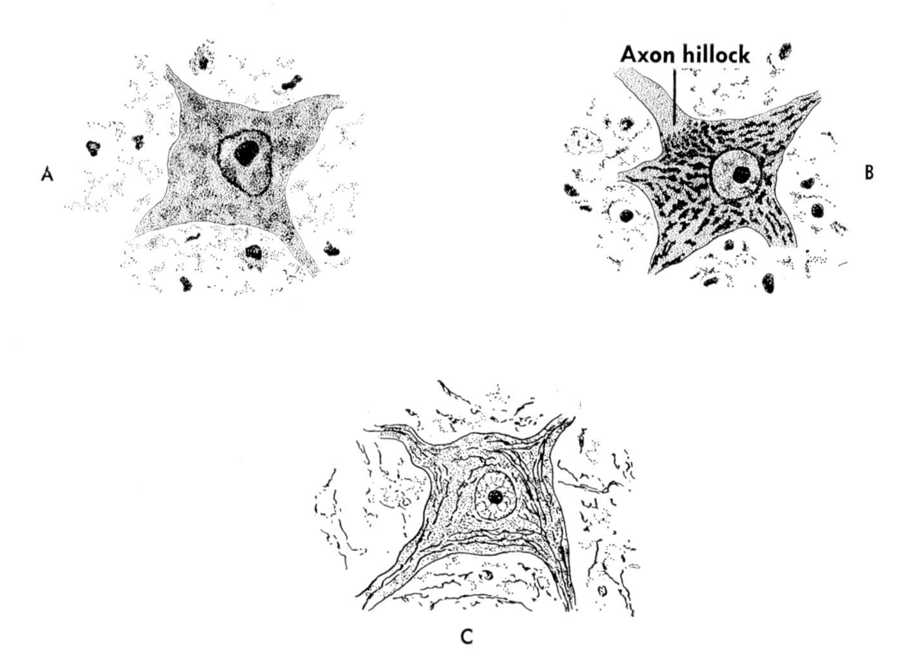

Fig. 50. Motor perikarya stained in three different ways: **A**, hematoxylin and eosin; **B**, toluidine blue, to show Nissl substance; **C**, silver nitrate, showing neurofibrils.

a mottled appearance (Fig. 50, *B*). Chromophil substance extends into the dendrites but is absent in a well-defined funnel-shaped area adjacent to the axon known as the *axon hillock,* as well as in the axon itself. The amount of chromophil substance in the perikaryon varies considerably, but recent research has failed to substantiate an older finding that this material decreases greatly in repeatedly stimulated neurons. By the use of special stains (for example, silver), minute *neurofibrils* (Fig. 50, *C*) may be demonstrated as a fine network embedded in the clear cytoplasm or *neuroplasm*. The neurofibrils are found in perikarya as well as in both dendrites and

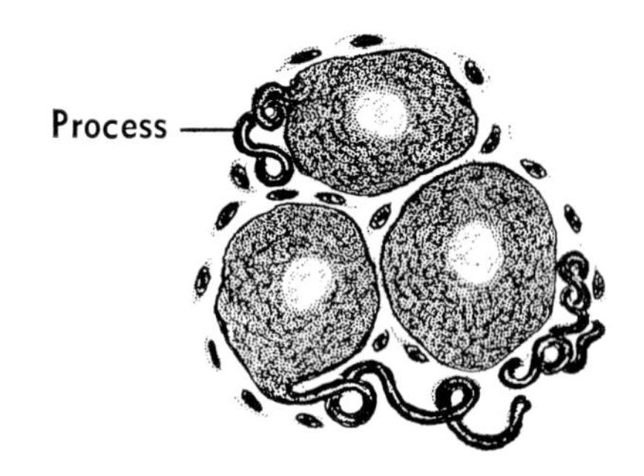

Fig. 51. Sensory neuron, Golgi method.

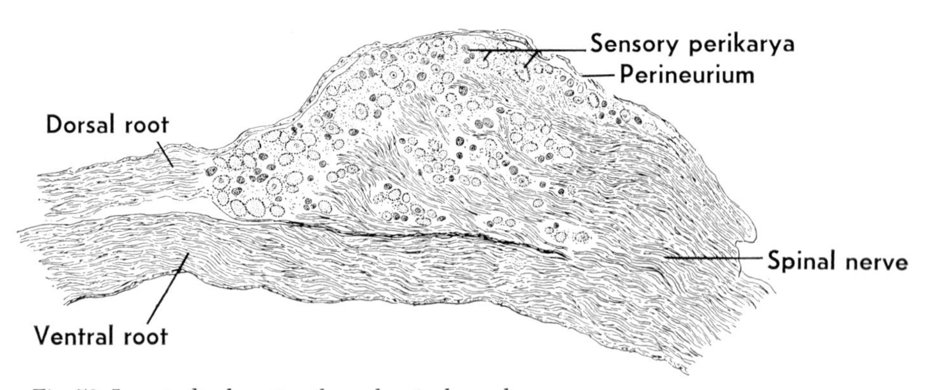

Fig. 52. Longitudinal section through spinal ganglion.

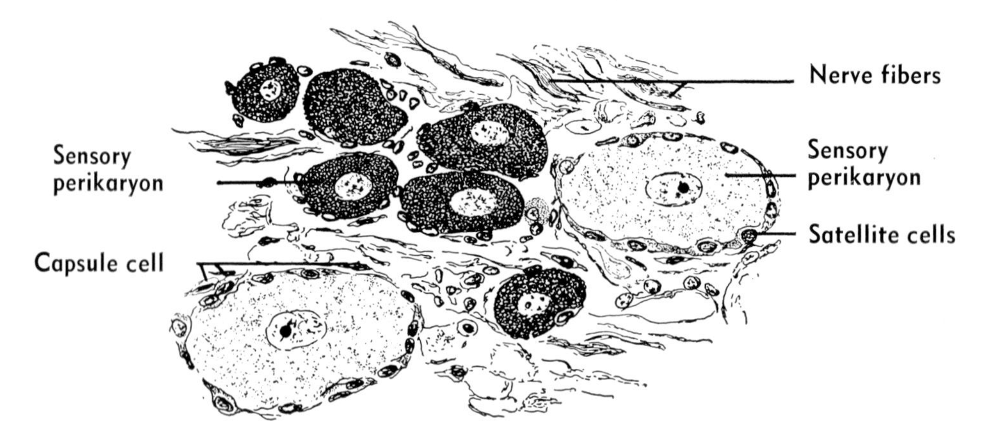

Fig. 53. Sensory cells from spinal ganglion.

axons. The fibrils are most readily visible in the axon hillock. With special techniques the Golgi apparatus and mitochondria may be demonstrated.

Perikarya are sometimes classified according to the number of processes they bear. The so-called *unipolar* perikarya found in the dorsal root ganglion of the spinal cord bear a single process which soon branches into an axon and dendrite (Fig. 51). *Bipolar* perikarya bear one axon and one dendrite as in the retina of the eye (Fig. 179). *Multipolar* perikarya bear several dendrites and one axon, as in the ventral horn of the gray matter of the spinal cord (Fig. 50). Perikarya occur exclusively in *ganglia* of the PNS (Figs. 43, 52, and 60) and in the so-called *reflex centers* of the gray matter of the CNS (Figs. 49 and 60).

NERVE FIBERS

Histologically, nerve fibers are of four types: (1) fibers without observable sheaths, (2) fibers with a prominent fatty myelin sheath only, (3) fibers with a cellular sheath, enclosing a minute quantity of myelin, and (4) fibers with a cellular sheath enclosing a thick layer of myelin.

Both axons and dendrites may or may not bear these sheaths and one cannot differentiate between these processes in routine histological preparations of nerves (PNS). By the use of Nissl body stains, for example, toluidine blue, one can frequently distinguish between axons and dendrites in the gray matter of the CNS. Because of this difficulty in histological identification it is customary to describe all "fibers" as one would an axon.

The axonic protoplasm itself is called the *axis cylinder* and consists of argyrophilic *neurofibrils* embedded in neuroplasm or *axoplasm*. The axoplasm shrinks badly in routine preparations so that it frequently appears as a thin acidophil structure with hematoxylin and eosin stains. The term *axon* is frequently used interchangeably with axis cylinder. In the gray matter of the spinal cord, where visible sheaths are absent, the axis cylinder is usually referred to as a *naked axon*. The axis cylinder also appears exposed, that is, without a visible covering, near the sites or within effectors (for example, muscles, glands, etc.). In gray matter freely branching dendrites may sometimes be distinguishable from the single axon. Naked fibers frequently give rise to collateral branches along their length and form the freely branching terminal arborizations.

In the white matter of the spinal cord the axis cylinder is surrounded by a *myelin sheath*, a phospholipid-containing component which appears black when treated with osmic acid (osmiophilia). The periodic acid-Schiff's test reveals that simple sugars are a component of myelin. When the myelin is removed by fat solvents, such as absolute alcohol or xylene, certain stains indicate that myelin is penetrated by a protein-containing network of *neurokeratin*. In longitudinal sections of these nerve fibers one may observe interruptions in the myelin sheath. They are known as the *nodes of*

Ranvier. In fresh tissue perparations myelin sheaths appear as white glistening coverings. It is the presence of this substance which gives the characteristic color to the white matter of the CNS.

In the autonomic division of the peripheral nervous system the so-called gray fibers contain only a small amount of myelin surrounding the axis cylinder. These are still referred to as "nonmyelinated" fibers. They are found in the vagus nerve, sciatic nerve, and the nerve plexi in the digestive tract and peritoneal cavity. These fibers are enclosed in a cellular covering known as *Schwann's sheath* and the cells are called *Schwann's cells.* In gray fibers the Schwann cells are flat and overlap each other so that the sheath appears discontinuous. In longitudinal sections the nuclei of these cells may be seen in irregular rows following the wavy contours of the axis cylinders. In hematoxylin and eosin preparations these nuclei may be confused with those of the surrounding connective tissue cells. The attenuated cytoplasm of Schwann cells is visible only in special preparations and is also known as the *neurilemma.* In cross sections through certain nerves several axis cylinders may lie in a small amount of myelin enclosed within one and the same Schwann cell. The latter are nevertheless considered nonmyelinated fibers.

The fourth type of fiber consists of a single axis cylinder surrounded by a thick myelin sheath, as well as a smooth, definitely delineated neurilemma (Fig. 56). This type of white fiber is found in the peripheral nervous system. As in all heavily myelinated fibers, there are periodic interruptions in the myelin where the neurilemma dips to touch the axis cylinder at the *nodes of Ranvier.* These nodes are observed only in longitudinal sections or in teased preparations. In routine preparations the nodes appear as slender transverse striations. In silver preparations a black precipitate forms on the node and on the axis cylinder for a short distance on each side of it, so that the fibers are marked at intervals by small black crosses. In osmium preparations the blackened myelin region is seen to be interrupted at the site of the node. When visible, the Schwann's cell nucleus may appear to lie in an indentation of the myelin. It is believed that myelin is a secretion product and an integral part of Schwann's cells. (The latter raises a question as to the origin of myelin sheaths in the white matter of the CNS where Schwann's cells are lacking.) In fibers bearing both myelin and a neurilemma, collaterals arise only at nodes, while branches of the axis cylinder may arise anywhere along a naked axon. We wish to reiterate that with rare exception the descriptive terminology set forth above in reference to axons is equally applicable in describing dendrites.

In passing it should be noted that some fibers are but a few millimeters long, while others are greater than 1 meter in length. The sum total of protoplasm in the fibers of a neuron is many time greater than the amount of protoplasm in the perikaryon. White or myelinated fibers conduct impulses at a higher rate than gray or slightly myelinated fibers. This would account for the fact that somatic reflexes (involving myelinated fibers and striated or skeletal muscles) are more rapid than visceral reflexes (involving slightly myelinated fibers and smooth muscle fibers). Fibers possessing a neurilemma can slowly regenerate if damaged, but the fibers of the CNS, lacking a neurilemma, do not regenerate.

NERVES

Nerves, or nerve trunks, are groups or bundles of fibers (axons, dendrites, and their collaterals) bound together by connective tissues and invested with blood capillaries. Nerves, *per se*, do not include perikarya. A single discrete bundle of nerve fibers and connective tissue is called a *fascicle* (Fig. 54). Some of the larger nerve trunks are composed of numerous fascicles, with an attendant increase in the amount of connective tissue and capillaries. The terminology used to designate the topography of the connective tissue associated with the nervous system is similar to that established for connective tissues found in skeletal muscles.

In nerve trunks comprised of several fascicles the entire structure is enclosed by a loosely arranged covering of collagenous and elastic fibers known as the *epineurium* (Figs. 54 and 55). In the large nerve trunks the epineurium is frequently prominent and contains many blood vessels. It may also give rise to extensions known as epineural septa occupying spaces between adjacent groups of fascicles. As the nerve trunk divides the epineurium is reduced until it can no longer be distinguished from fine areolar tissue (Fig. 55).

A single fascicle is held together by a concentrically arranged layer of dense collagenous fibers called the *perineurium*. The perineurium varies

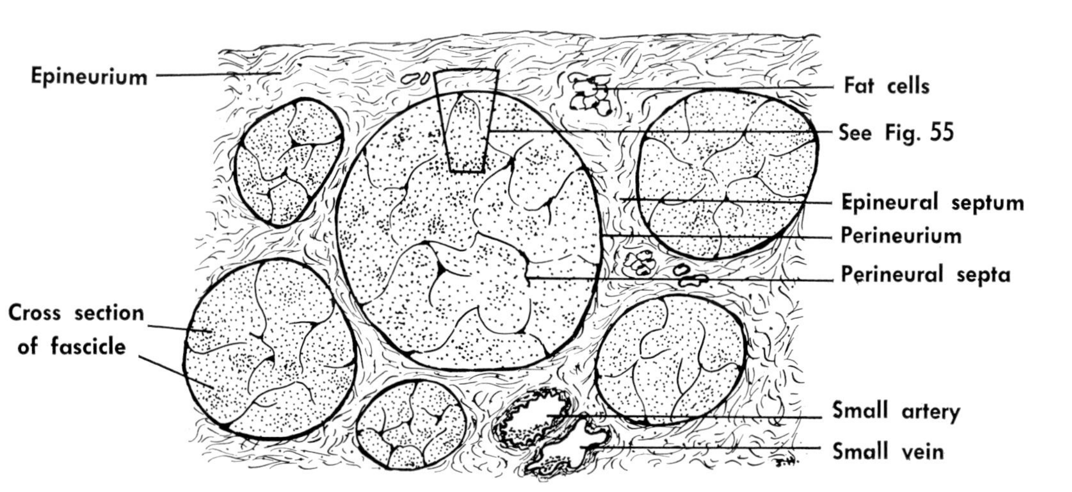

Fig. 54. Portion of transverse section of nerve trunk.

from a thick prominent structure in large nerves to a very thin one in small nerves. Branches or trabeculae of the perineurium (perineural septa of some authors) penetrate the fascicle and give rise to the *endoneurium* which in turn separates the individual nerve fibers. The endoneurium is composed of fine elastic tissue sheaths which completely enclose and are intimately associated with the neurilemma of individual fibers. These sheaths are known as the *sheaths of Henle* or *endoneural sheaths* (Fig. 56).

Small nerve trunks occurring in connective tissue are distinguishable from the fibers of connective tissue by the following features: in longitudinal section nerves appear as groups of fine fibers arranged regularly and parallel. The myelin sheaths may be completely dissolved, and, if this is true, each axis cylinder is then separated from its neighbor by a space bounded by the neurilemma sheath. The axis cylinder and neurokeratin

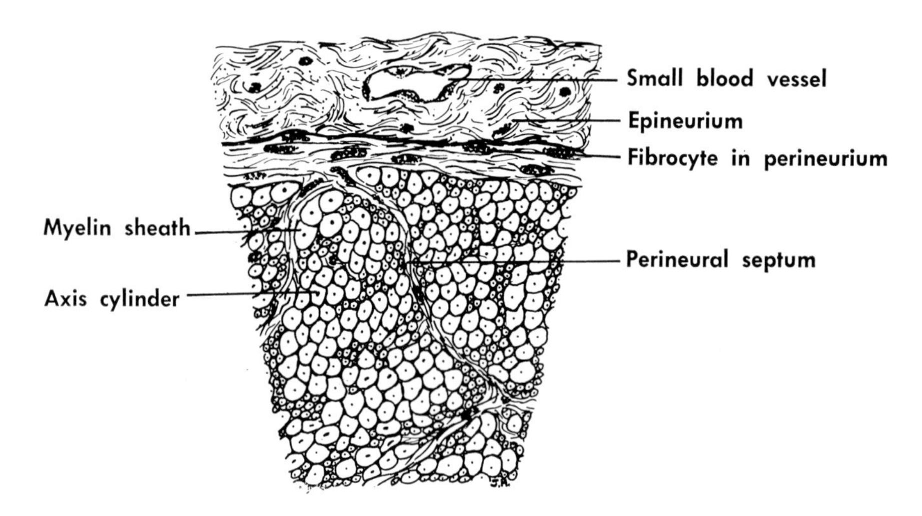

Fig. 55. Medium-power view of nerve fibers and surrounding connective tissue.

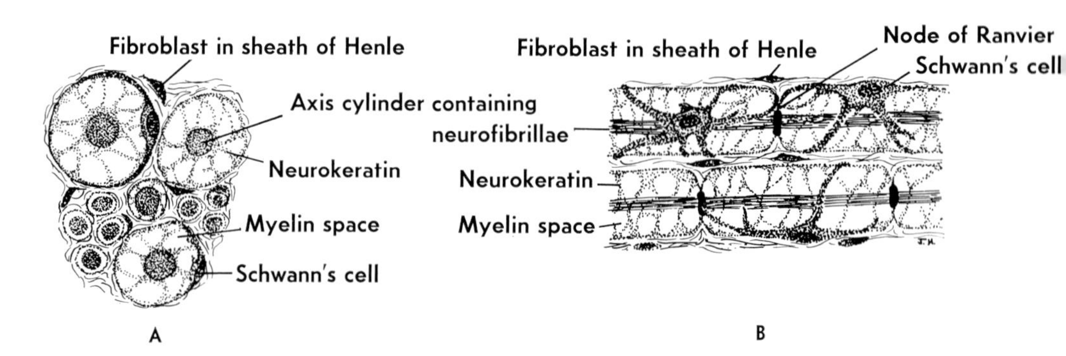

Fig. 56. Nerve fiber. **A,** Transverse section. **B,** Longitudinal section.

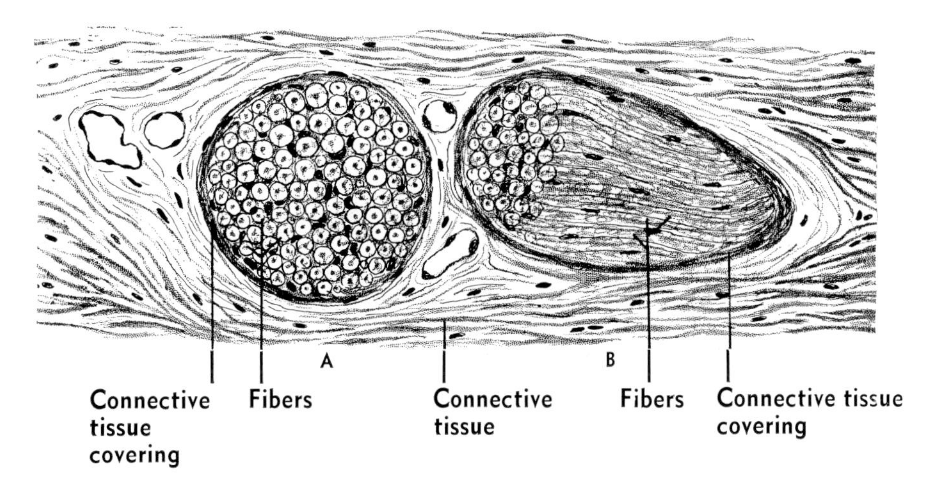

Fig. 57. Myelinated nerve fibers forming small trunks in areolar tissue. **A,** Cut transversely; **B,** cut tangentially.

are less eosinophilic (or more basophilic) than the surrounding connective tissue fibers. In transverse section a nerve is composed of one or more fascicles and is readily recognizable by the features presented in Fig. 57. Sections through nerves containing a majority of nonmyelinated fibers are somewhat more difficult to distinguish and may even be confused with smooth muscle fibers by the novice. In nonmyelinated fibers the neurilemma sheaths are irregular and nearly in contact with the somewhat basophilic axis cylinders.

NERVE FIBER ENDINGS

Motor endings

The motor endings are the terminal parts of the efferent neurons which are in contact with either muscles or glands. Striated muscles may exhibit two types of motor endings: (1) The motor end plate, shown in Fig. 58, consists of a terminal ramification of a naked fiber which ends in a mass of granular modified sarcoplasm. These structures appear in whole mounts as elevated areas which measure from 40 to 60μ in diameter. They are demonstrated with difficulty in sectioned material. (2) In some cases the motor terminations consist of a simpler bulblike arrangement of small loops which end within or on the surface of the sarcolemma.

The efferent fibers which supply cardiac muscle, smooth muscle, and glands are part of the autonomic nervous system. These fibers are usually nonmyelinated and often terminate in nodular thickenings. In muscle these terminations end near the nucleus of the muscle fiber: in glands the fibers reach to the base or sides of the gland cell where they end freely or penetrate the cell and end in an expanded terminal loop.

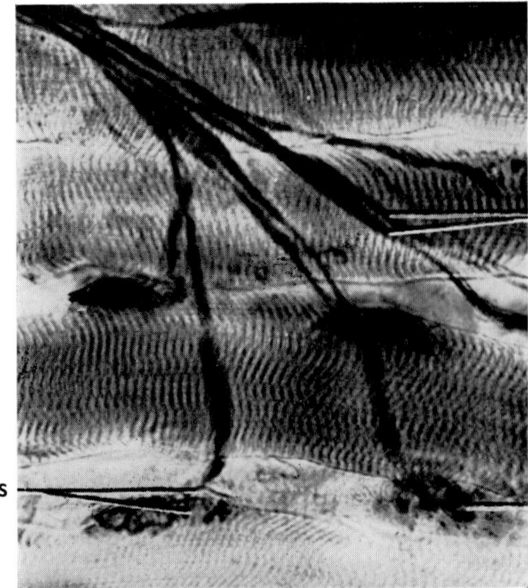

Fig. 58. Motor end plate. (Whole mount silver preparation.)

Sensory endings

Aside from those located in specialized organs, such as the eye and ear, the sensory endings consist of the following types: free endings, encapsulated endings, and muscle spindles.

Free endings. Free endings are the simplest type from the structural standpoint. They consist of terminal branches of delicate fibers which often show slight enlargements. These endings have been observed in stratified epithelia, tendon, and other connective tissue.

Encapsulated endings. Encapsulated endings are characterized by the presence of a central naked fiber or several branches embedded in tissue fluid which is enclosed within a connective tissue capsule. From their structure and location one may infer that these might function as pressure receptors. There are several varieties of encapsulated endings: (1) the tactile corpuscles of Meissner, (2) the genital corpuscles, (3) bulbous and cylindrical corpuscles of Krause, and (4) the lamellar corpuscles of Pacini (Fig. 59). The last named are so large as to be visible with the unaided eye.

Muscle spindles. Muscles have sensory fibers which terminate about slender bundles of muscle fibers which are poorly developed. The terminal parts of the nerve fibers are arranged spirally around these muscle cells. This complex of nerve and muscle is enclosed within a dense connnective tissue sheath and is known as a muscle spindle. Structures analogous to muscle spindles also occur in tendons.

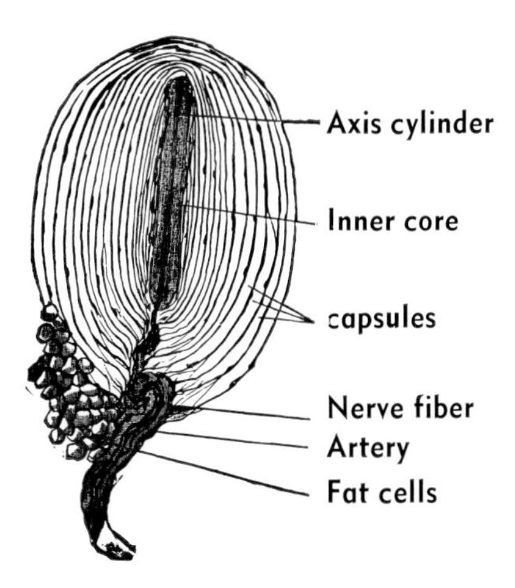

Fig. 59. Small lamellar corpuscle from mesentery of cat. The nuclei of the capsule cells appear as thickenings. The myelin of the nerve fiber may be traced to the inner core. (×50.) (From Bremer and Weatherford: A Text-Book of Histology, Philadelphia, 1948, The Blakiston Co.)

NEURON INTERRELATIONS

On the basis of function and anatomical relations neurons fall into three groups:

1. *Sensory* (first order or afferent) neurons, which are so situated and constructed as to respond to stimuli arising from within or outside the organism and to send impulses to association neurons.
2. *Association* (second order, intercalated, or internuncial) neurons, which serve as links between sensory neurons and neurons of the third group.
3. *Motor* (third order or efferent) neurons, which convey impulses to muscles or glands, stimulating them to action.

The most rapid responses to stimuli in higher organisms come about through the so-called reflexes which involve neuron pathways called *reflex arcs.* These are divided into two major kinds, *somatic reflexes,* resulting in contraction of skeletal or striated muscle, and several varieties of *visceral reflexes,* usually resulting in contraction of smooth muscle fibers associated with the viscera.

In the most common type of reflex arc all three groups of neurons are involved in sequence, that is, sensory, association, and motor. In the following paragraphs we shall proceed to examine several reflex arcs in detail.

Somatic reflex (Fig. 60, *D*)

Sensory neuron. If the somatic receptor is a lamellar corpuscle in the finger (Fig. 59), the axis cylinder represents the naked fiber of the dendrite

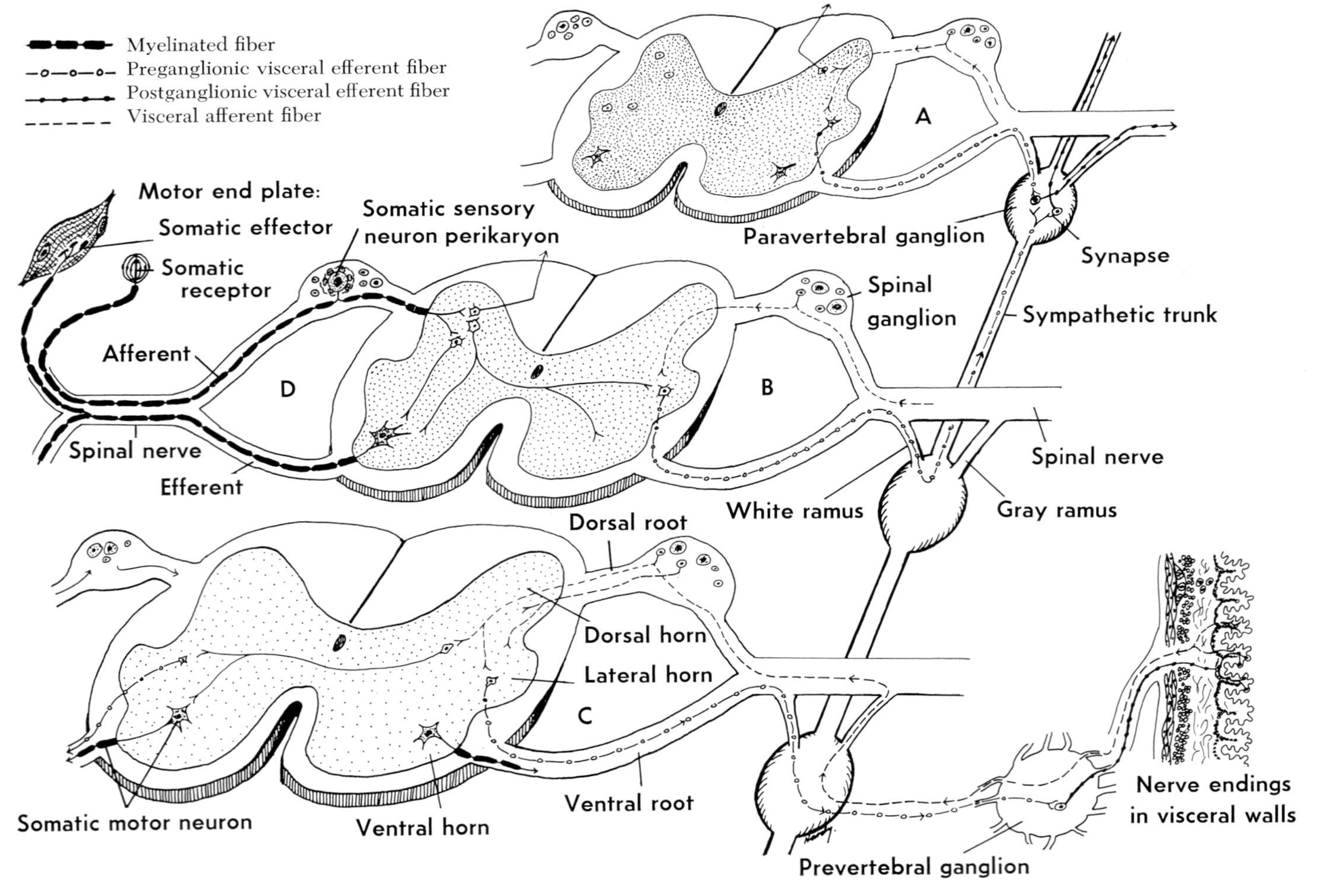

Fig. 60. Sympathetic and somatic reflex arc pathways. **A, B, C,** Alternate pathways of pregangionic visceral efferent fibers; **D,** somatic reflex arc.

of the sensory neuron. As the fiber leaves the inner core it becomes invested in Schwann's sheath and becomes myelinated. The dendrite runs through the finger, joining other fibers in small nerve trunks, then passes through the hand and arm in increasingly larger nerve trunks, until the fiber enters a spinal nerve. (The same type of myelinated dendrite arises from a number of other sensory endings.) The spinal nerve divides into a dorsal and a ventral root, but the dendrite enters only the dorsal root where it terminates in a large unipolar perikaryon within the dorsal root ganglion.

The perikarya of sensory neurons are located in the ganglia associated with the dorsal roots of all the spinal and cranial nerves, as well as in the special sense organs. They are usually unipolar, the single process borne by the perikarya apparently represents a union of axon and dendrite. This process winds about the perikaryon in a spiral fashion and then divides in T shape, one arm (the axon) extending toward the spinal cord; the other (the dendrite) has been described previously. The single process of such perikarya may be demonstrated by the use of silver salts (Fig. 51). In sections prepared to show the nucleus and cytoplasm, the cell body appears fairly round, without conspicuous projections. The characteristic vesicular nucleus and basophilic chromophil substance in the cytoplasm is shown to advantage. A spinal ganglion (Fig. 52) consists of a group of these perikarya, among which may be seen numerous myelinated fibers, nonmyelinated fibers, and supporting cells (Fig. 53). Individual perikarya are enveloped in a double layer of cells. The outer layer is composed of fibroblasts and connective tissue fibers. These fibers are continuous with those of the endoneurium. The cells just described are called *capsule cells.* The inner layer consists of a variable number of small stellate cells which may appear flat in profile and lie near the surface of the sensory perikarya. They are known as *satellite cells,* or amphicytes, and are not usually well preserved in routine preparations, and accordingly may not be observed in all preparations. Satellite cells are said to be analogous to the Schwann cells of other portions of the PNS.

The axon of the sensory neuron bears both a myelin sheath and neurilemma as it passes through the dorsal root of the spinal nerve. The perineurium of the dorsal root becomes continuous with the spinal meninges. The endoneurium and Schwann's sheath of the fiber are lost as the myelinated fiber enters the white matter of the spinal cord. In the white matter of the spinal cord the fibers remain myelinated, but upon entering the dorsal horn of the gray matter the axis cylinder is the only recognizable structure. Along its path the axon may give rise to a number of collateral axons which generally follow four routes in the CNS. (1) The myelinated collaterals in the lateral fiber bundles of the spinal cord (funiculi) pass from one segmental portion of the spinal cord to another and are known as *association* fibers, since the end result of their activity is coordinated contraction of muscles in several adjacent body segments (somites). In these adjacent segments the fibers lose their myelin as they enter the gray matter and synapse with association neurons. (2) The fibers may remain in the white matter and transmit stimuli to the higher centers in the brain where the impulse is registered as sensation. (3) The nonmyelinated collaterals in the dorsal horn of the gray matter may give rise to terminal arborizations which end in minute bulblike synapses on the dendrites and perikarya of one or more association neurons. (4) A few axons or their collaterals may pass from one side of the gray matter to the other where they synapse with association neurons. These fibers are known as *commissural fibers.*

Association neurons. Association neurons, as this term implies, serve to integrate impulses from the sensory neurons and to disttribute them to motor neurons in several adjacent segments. They are located within the gray matter of the CNS, and in the spinal cord they are found in the dorsal horn (Fig. 49). The processes are not sheathed, that is, they lack both myelin and Schwann's sheath. The dendrites may be relatively inconspicuous, and the axon branches frequently to yield a number of collaterals. The axonic fibers may be of either the association or commissural type. In the simple reflex arc illustrated only one association neuron is included, but more often three or more association neurons at different levels may receive impulses from one sensory axon. In addition the processes of association neurons frequently synapse with other association neurons, or with several motor neurons, perikarya of which are located in the ventral horn of the spinal cord.

The processes of association neurons, lacking a neurilemma, do not regenerate. Whereas fibrocytes, capsule cells, and fibers are lacking in the central nervous system (with exception of the connective tissue surrounding blood vessels), the nuclei of perineural satellites, forming part of the so-called *neuroglia,* are observed near perikarya.

Somatic motor neurons. In the ventral horn of the spinal cord terminal arborizations of association neurons synapse with both the dendrites and perikarya of one or more motor neurons. The prominent dendrites are entirely lacking in sheaths and frequently branch near their origins on the perikaryon. The motor paryikarya are the largest cell bodies in the spinal cord (Figs. 50 and 60, *D*). The axon is usually the thickest and most prominent process of the perikaryon. Arising in the gray matter, the axon is a naked fiber which gives rise to a few collaterals, similarly unsheathed. As the axon or axis cylinder enters the white matter in the spinal cord it acquires a myelin sheath and may give rise to one or two myelinated collaterals. As the axon enters the ventral root of the spinal nerve it acquires an endoneural sheath, as well as Schwann's sheath, and collaterals now arise only at the nodes of Ranvier.

Each of the axonic processes is enclosed in smaller and smaller nerve trunks and, just before reaching the muscle which it activates, a number of sheathed collaterals may arise. As the fibers enter the motor end plates they lose their sheaths and appear in the end plate as the axis cylinder (Fig. 58). The branching of the axon referred to above permits the simultaneous contraction of several adjacent muscle fibers. From the foregoing description of the axons and dendrites found in spinal nerves, it is obvious that it is impossible to distinguish between the two processes in routine histological preparations. A further complication is the presence of fibers within the same nerve trunk which may vary considerably in diameter and myelin content (Fig. 55).

Visceral reflexes

As indicated previously, the somatic reflexes result in the contraction of skeletal muscles, which are normally under volitional control. The function of the somatic reflex is to protect the organism against trauma by the introduction of a certain degree of automaticity. With certain rare exceptions the viscera, that is, the internal organs of the thoracic and abdominal cavities, are not under volitional control but under the control of hormones produced by endocrine glands or by a special division of the nervous system known as the autonomic system. While the hormones produced by endocrine glands form a gland-integrating mechanism classified under the endocrine system, certain hormones (for example, adrenin, oxytocin, etc.) are capable of acting directly upon smooth muscle fibers (for example, arterial blood vessels, uterus at term, gallbladder, muscularis of the gut, sweat glands, bronchi, etc.) and cardiac muscle. These and other visceral structures are also under the control of the autonomic system.

Visceral reflexes consist of an afferent flow to the central nervous system (visceral sensory neurons) and an efferent outflow (autonomic system). These reflexes involve extremely complicated pathways. It is beyond the scope of this book to describe in detail topics usually taken up in neuroanatomy and neurology, but a certain amount of description and discussion of some aspects of this subject appears desirable at this junction.

Autonomic system

The organization of the autonomic system is made on a functional rather than on a strictly morphological basis. Strictly speaking the visceral reflexes carried out by the *autonomic nervous system* involve only the efferent outflow from the central nervous system via the peripheral nervous system to the viscera. The autonomic does not include the visceral sensory neurons, even though these are involved in visceral reflexes. The processes or fibers which constitute the cranio-sacral outflow are known as the *paraysmpa-*

thetic system or division; those of the thoraco-lumbar region the *sympathetic* division.

Anatomic aspects of the sympathetic division. Distal to the point of fusion of its dorsal and ventral roots the spinal nerve leaves the neural canal (enclosed by the vertebra). Close to its point of emergence two communicating rami *(rami communicantes)* arise from the ventral surface of the spinal nerve (Fig. 60, *B*). The so-called *gray ramus* contain primarily the nonmyelinated or slightly myelinated fibers of the sympathetic system, whereas the *white ramus* contains both heavily and slightly myelinated fibers. At the distal ends both rami are fused with a so-called *vertebral ganglion* (paravertebral ganglion). The vertebral ganglia of adjacent somites are connected to each other via *sympathetic trunks.* In gross dissection these ganglia and sympathetic trunks appear like a strand of pearls on each side of and parallel to the vertebral column (Fig. 60). Nerve trunks arising from these ganglia, which fuse with trunks arising from ganglia of other somites, form huge masses of strands called *plexi.* Within these plexi (such as those in the abdominal cavity) one finds many small thickenings or knots of tissue containing perikarya of the sympathetic system. Relatively circumscribed functional groups of these thickenings are loosely referred to as *prevertebral ganglia* (Fig. 60, *C*). (For example, the three major groups found in the abdominal cavity are called the coeliac, superior mesenteric, and inferior mesenteric ganglia). A number of freely branching trunks arise from these "ganglia" and then enter the mesenteries to supply the abdominal viscera. These trunks, because of the low myelin content of their fibers, appear gray in gross dissection and are called gray nerves. The perikarya found in sympathetic ganglia are enclosed by satellite cells, a condition somewhat similar to that which is present in the dorsal root ganglia perikarya.

Anatomic aspects of the parasympathetic division. The preceding description does not fit the parasympathetic division, in which considerable variation exists in its different parts. Thus the vagus or tenth cranial nerve sends branches directly to the viscera involved, and plexi are formed either on or directly within the viscera involved. For example, the myenteric (Auerbach's) and submucosal (Meissner's) plexi, which form continuous networks of fibers along the whole digestive tract, are part of the parasympathetic system. These intravisceral plexi bear numerous relatively circumscribed ganglia containing perikarya, supporting cells (neuroglia), and fibers (Fig. 117). Much more complicated patterns are formed by the other cranial nerves. The sacral outflow of the urinary system follows the general pattern described for the gut, but that supplying the reproductive organs is poorly described in the literature.

"Local reflex" of the gut. Little is known about the origins and pathways of visceral sensory neurons in the gut. Some of them arise as free or naked fibers in the epithelial lining (mucosa) or subadjacent connective tissue (submucosa) of the digestive tract. These course through the enteric plexi where their perikarya may be located and give rise to nonmyelinated fibers which synapse with association neurons. The impulses are transmitted to several motor neurons with the resultant contraction of muscles in adjacent regions of the alimentary tract. It is thought by some authors that this type of "local reflex" accounts for continued contraction of the gut when the autonomic nerves are severed. These reflexes in turn are believed to be regulated by the competitive action of the two divisions of the autonomic system. The parasympathetic system, through the enteric plexi, produces a substance (choline esters) which brings about the contraction of smooth muscles in the digestive tract. The sympathetic system produces another substance (sympathin = adrenin?) resulting in relaxation of these muscle fibers. (In other organs the opposing functions of the divisions may be exchanged, that is, sympathin results in contraction and a choline ester produces relaxation).

Visceral sensory neurons. Visceral sensory neurons may arise as myelinated fibers from encapsulated end organs in the mesenteries, pancreas, skin, external genitalia, and many other locations. The myelinated fibers may pass through either a spinal nerve or via the prevertebral and vertebral ganglia through the white ramus to the dorsal root ganglion where unipolar perikarya are located (Fig. 60, *C*). The smaller and more basophilic perikarya in the dorsal root ganglion are said by some authors to represent visceral sensory perikarya (Figs. 53 and 60, *C*). The axonic process is myelinated but loses its Schwann's sheath as it enters the white matter of the spinal cord; it also loses its myelin as it enters the gray matter. These fibers present the same appearance as the fibers arising from somatic sensory neurons. Their exact pathway in the spinal cord is not well known and is at best inferential. It is thought that some collaterals transmit impulses via association fibers to the higher centers of the brain where the organism may become conscious of a disturbance in its feeling of "well-being," such as digestive or other visceral discomfort. The other axonic fibers are believed to synapse with the visceral motor perikarya of the sympathetic system in the lateral horns of gray matter in the spinal cord. The pathway from free endings in the gut appears to be essentially like that described above, except that the sensory processes are usually nonmyelinated, at least near their origins. (Other visceral sensory fibers arise in the mucosa of the gut, pass through the enteric plexi and through the vagus nerve, thence through the dorsal ganglion where the perikarya are located, and finally into the *medulla oblongata.*)

Sympathetic outflow. As indicated in the introductory paragraph of this chapter, the sympathetic division of the autonomic system involves only the visceral motor fibers (efferent outflow) from the perikarya located in the lateral horns of the thoraco-lumbar regions of the spinal cord. In the discussion which follows, only three relatively uncomplicated examples of efferent outflow will be considered.

All the axons arising from visceral motor perikarya in the lateral horn of the spinal cord are *preganglionic fibers.* They are nonmyelinated throughout their entire length and acquire a Schwann's sheath only on leaving the spinal cord. They pass through the ventral root to a vertebral ganglion via the white ramus (Fig. 60). (1) Some of these preganglionic fibers terminate synaptically with dendrites and perikarya in the first vertebral ganglion they enter (Fig. 60, *A*). These encapsulated perikarya give rise to nonmyelinated axons known as *postganglionic fibers.* These postganglionic fibers pass through the gray ramus to the spinal nerve and out to the periphery of the body where they innervate smooth muscles associated with hair, specialized contractile cells in the sweat glands, and various smooth muscles in superficial blood vessels. (2) Other preganglionic fibers (Fig. 60, *B*) may pass through the vertebral ganglion and out through a sympathetic trunk to an adjacent vertebral ganglion. They synapse with a neuron, which in turn produces postganglionic fibers which pass through a plexus and prevertebral ganglion to some effector in a visceral organ. (3) In the third major pathway (Fig. 60, *C*) the preganglionic fiber passes through the vertebral ganglion to a prevertebral ganglion where it synapses with a motor neuron, the postganglionic fibers of which proceed to innervate some effector as in the gut.

Summation

Complicated as the above description of somatic and visceral reflexes may seem, the vast majority of responses to external stimuli include much longer and more complicated chains of neurons than those described in this text. A single sensory neuron may transmit impulses to several association neurons, some of which may carry impulses to the brain where other association neurons are located. A single association neuron usually receives impulses from several sensory and association neurons, and in this manner single fibers may be under the influence of a number of different neurons. In the spinal cord and brain, impulses are received from various parts of the body and are integrated so that the outflow of impulses along the efferent neuron is adjusted to the needs of the body as a whole.

It is evident from the foregoing description that perikarya are not evenly distributed throughout the nervous system but are collected into groups. The largest collection of these groups are located in the so-called reflex centers in the gray matter of the brain and spinal cord, which contain the perikarya of somatic motor and association neurons as well as those perikarya which give rise to the preganglionic fibers of the autonomic nervous system (Fig. 60). Sensory neurons have their perikarya in the spinal and cranial ganglia, while the visceral efferent perikarya giving rise to postganglionic fibers are located in the autonomic ganglia. The axons and dendrites located outside of the ganglia in the PNS are found in bundles (fascicles) held together by connective tissue and supplied by blood vessels, thereby forming nerve trunks. The connective tissue sheaths of the spinal and cranial nerves are continuous with the meninges surrounding the CNS and terminate in these structures. (See discussion on meninges, p. 259.) The "internal support" of the CNS is described in the following discussion on neuroglia.

When the spacial relations of the nervous system and the various other parts of the body are considered, it is obvious that it would be impossible to study microscopically an entire neuron. For example, a motor neuron which sends impulses to a muscle in the foot has an axon which extends from the lumbar region of the spinal cord through the entire length of the leg. Other neurons, although not so extensive, have processes of such length that they cannot be dissected out and studied in their true relation of these parts to each other. The best methods of observing them involve utilization of very thick Golgi preparations or smears of gray matter stained with methylene blue.

NEUROGLIA (GLIA)

In addition to cells which are specialized for the transmission of stimuli, the nervous system contains a large number of nontransmitting cells. We have previously described the connective tissue framework of nerve trunks, but the central nervous system does not have such an internal support. On the other hand, the meninges and abundant arterial system (the latter containing relatively large amounts of elastic fibers and some collagenous fibers) form a tough external support for the CNS. Internally the support supplied by the presence of blood vessels is slight, and a type of interstitial cell known as astroglial cells form a pericapillary barrier which prevents the encroachment of blood vessel connective tissue on nerve cells. The astroglia form a part of the so-called internal support of the CNS collectively referred to as *neuroglia.* Another kind of neuroglial element, known as microglia, are believed by some authors to belong to the reticuloendothelial system and are inactive macrophages. The latter, however, do not seem to aid in support. Many investigators are of the opinion that the main internal support of the CNS is provided by the hydrostatic pressure of tissue fluid. This tissue fluid is believed to be eventually transformed to yield cerebrospinal fluid.

In addition to the interstitial tissue of the CNS, the term *neuroglia* is also sometimes used to include the cells of the neurilemma and the satellite cells enclosed in the capsules surrounding ganglion perikarya. In sections through the spinal cord, which have been stained to demonstrate perikarya and fibers, one may see the nuclei of neuroglia cells between the nervous elements. They are smaller than the nuclei of nerve cells and have no conspicuous nucleoli. The detailed study of this tissue involves the use of special methods and is not usually undertaken in a beginning course. The following discussion briefly summarizes the neuroglial elements.

Astroglia

The most common type of neuroglia cell is the astroglia. These are branching cells, some of which (fibrous) have along their borders, and in contact with their cytoplasm, fibrils which are similar to fibroglia and myoglia fibrils. Others (protoplasmic) lack these fibrils. In either kind of astroglia the cells have specialized processes which are in close contact with the walls of the blood vessels of the nervous system. These "sucker feet" have been thought to enable the cell to derive nourishment from the blood; it is also stated, however, that their function is to provide a special limiting membrane around the vessels (Fig. 61).

Oligodendria

A second type of neuroglia cell is the oligodendria (or oligodendroglia). These cells have short beaded processes and no neuroglia fibrils. Their nuclei are larger and paler than those of the astroglia cells. They are grouped around nerve cells in the brain and around fiber tracts in the spinal cord.

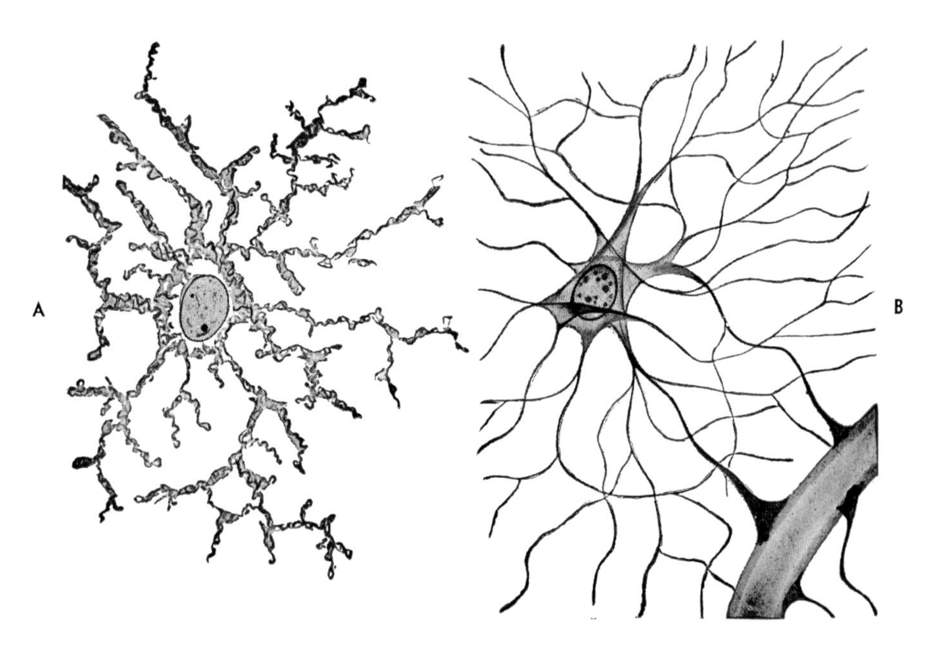

Fig. 61. **A,** Protoplasmic astrocyte. **B,** Fibrous astrocyte. (After Hortega; from Bremer and Weatherford: A Text-Book of Histology, Philadelphia, 1948, The Blakiston Co.)

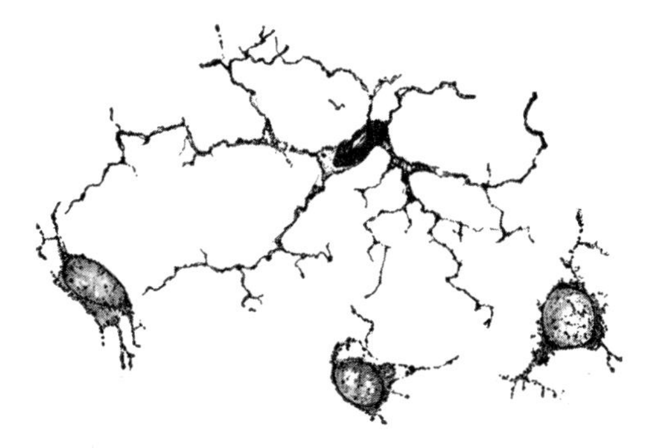

Fig. 62. Neuroglia cells from brain of rabbit. Microglia (above) and oligodendroglia. (Stained by Penfield's method.) (From Bremer and Weatherford: A Text-Book of Histology, Philadelphia, 1948, The Blakiston Co.)

Microglia

A third type is the microglia, the smallest of the neuroglia cells. They have deeply staining nuclei, are irregular in shape, and have no fibrils or "sucker feet." They are said to be phagocytic. Oligodendria and microglia are illustrated in Fig. 62.

Other types

The ependyma or layer which lines the central canal of the nervous system forms the fourth group of neuroglia cells. These are elongated cells which are arranged in a layer like columnar epithelium. They contain fibrils and are sometimes ciliated.

The neurilemma and capsule cells are sometimes considered as a fifth group of neuroglia cells.

It is of interest to note that these supporting cells, although they are similar in appearance and function to the simpler mesenchymal derivatives such as reticular tissue, are for the most part ectodermal in origin. This is certainly true of the ependyma and of the astroglia which form the greater part of the tissue. The microglia are probably mesodermal in origin; the oligodendria are said by some authors to be mesodermal but by others are said to be ectodermal.

CHAPTER X

Circulatory system

Blood and lymph are the carriers of nutritive substances, hormones, and the products of metabolism. The circulatory or vascular system is the means by which blood and lymph are distributed throughout the body. The system includes the blood vessels, the heart, and the lymphatics.

BLOOD VESSELS

The blood vessels may be conveniently divided into three main groups for study: the capillaries and sinuses, the arteries, and the veins.

Capillaries

The capillaries have but one coat which consists of simple squamous epithelium (endothelium). They are of fine caliber, some of them being so small that only one red blood cell at a time may pass through them. According to some authors the tubule is clasped at intervals by Rouget's cells. These are branching cells which are said to be contractile and to cause the constriction of the capillaries. They are not ordinarily seen, however, and it is doubtful whether they should be considered as a regular component of the capillary wall (Fig. 63). Most of the capillaries are surrounded by connective tissue, and they form the connecting vessel between arteries and veins. Their function is to provide a place for the exchange of oxygen and carbon dioxide; in them the blood changes from arterial to venous (or vice versa in the lungs). Physiologically they are, therefore, an important part of the blood-vascular system.

Some capillaries do not connect arterioles and venules, and the substances passing through their walls are not oxygen and carbon dioxide. An example of this kind of vessel may be found in the glomerulus of the kidney. The vessel in the glomerulus is, structurally, a capillary; however, blood passing through it gives off nitrogenous wastes but not oxygen. Other vessels consisting of endothelium only are called sinusoids. Their walls are in close apposition with epithelial tissue, from which the blood removes the secretion or to which it gives up substances for storage. Sinus-

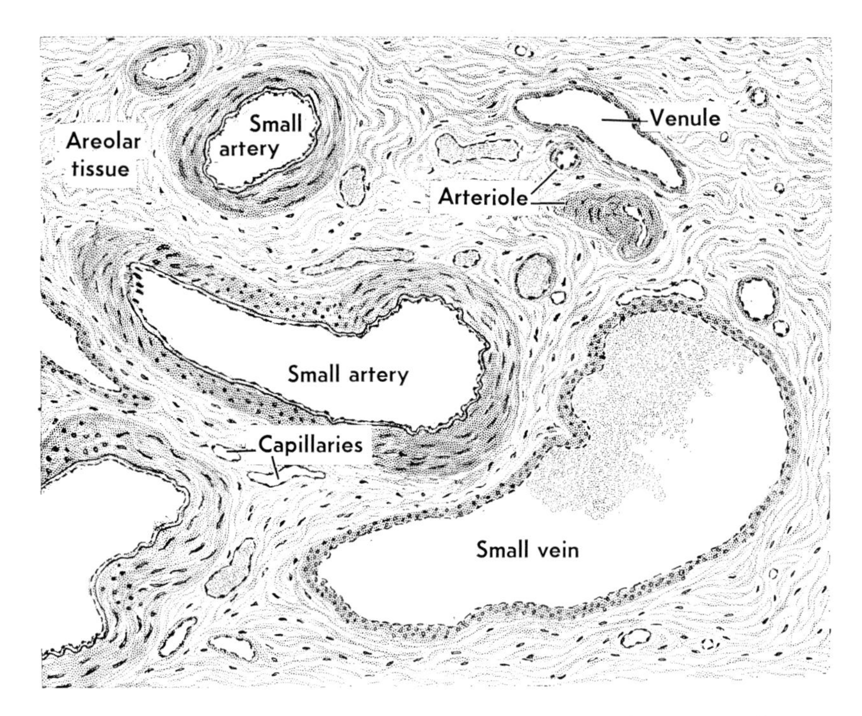

Fig. 63. Capillaries, arterioles, venules, small arteries, and small veins in submucosa of digestive tract.

oids are, morphologically, enlarged capillaries. Some of them are lined with an endothelium which exhibits the phagocytic properties of the reticuloendothelial system.

Arteries

Blood is carried from the heart to the capillaries by arteries. The wall of an artery is, in general, characterized by the presence of a coat of smooth muscle spirally arranged and by considerable amounts of elastic tissue. Because of this, arteries retain their shape after death and appear circular in transverse section. In this system of vessels there is a gradual change of structure as the caliber of the vessels diminishes. The changes in structure are nowhere abrupt, nor can they be accurately correlated with the size of the vessels. It is convenient, however, to select for study and description the following groups of vessels: aorta, medium-sized arteries, and small arteries and arterioles.

Aorta. The intima is lined with short polygonal endothelial cells. Below this lining there is a layer containing fine collagenous and elastic fibers and also a few scattered fibroblasts. The deeper portion of the intima also contains collagenous as well as longitudinally oriented muscle and elastic fibers. The internal elastic membrane consists of two or more lamellae which blend with similar membranes of the interna and media and is hence difficult to identify.

The second coat or media is by far the thickest layer, forming approximately four-fifths of the thickness of the wall. It consists of a mixture of circularly arranged smooth muscle fibers and elastic fibers. The latter predominate and mingle, on the one hand, with the elastic fibers of the intima and, on the other, with those of the outermost layer or adventitia. The smooth muscle fibers unite to form branching bands and like the elastic fibers appear spirally arranged. The muscle fibers are enclosed or surrounded by delicate reticular fibers.

The adventitia is a comparatively thin coat of connective tissue. Elastic fibers are concentrated at the outer border of the media, forming the external elastic membrane. Collagenous fibers merge with those of the connective tissue surrounding the vessel and are arranged in longitudinal spirals. In the adventitia and the outer portion of the media are small nutrient vessels (vasa vasorum) and nerves (nervi vasorum).

The aorta and a few other vessels like it are sometimes called the large arteries, or arteries of the elastic type. The common iliacs, axillaries, carotids, and pulmonaries belong in this group.

Medium-sized arteries. In the group of medium-sized arteries are included most of the vessels observed grossly in dissection to which names

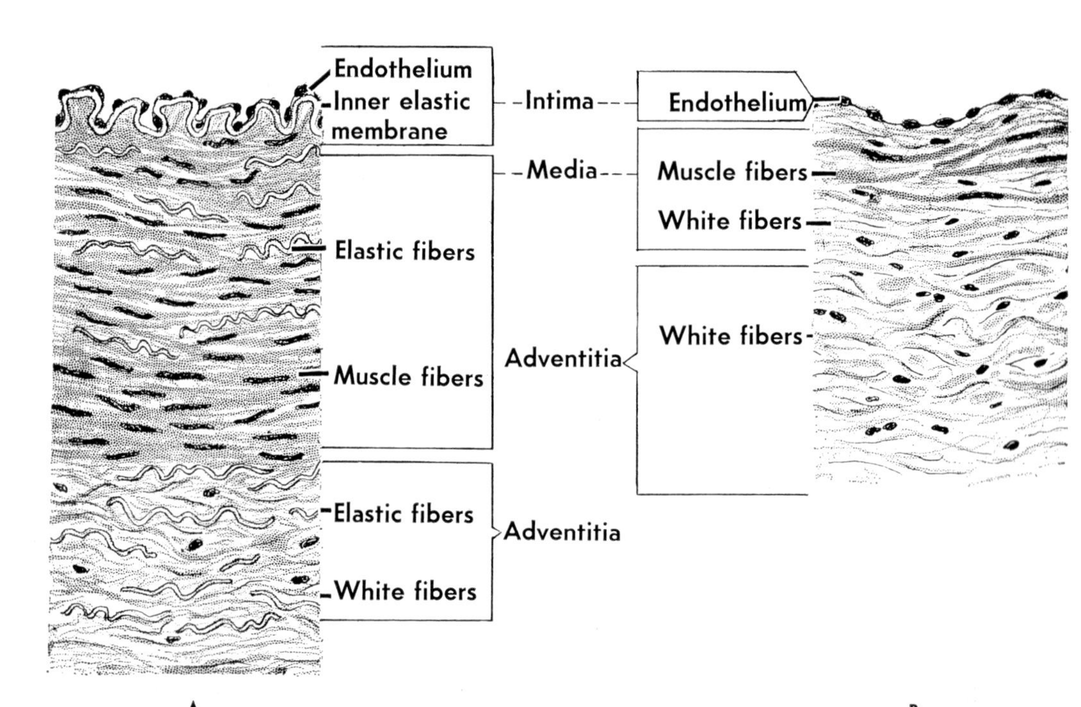

Fig. 64. Medium-sized artery, **A**, and vein, **B**, of dog.

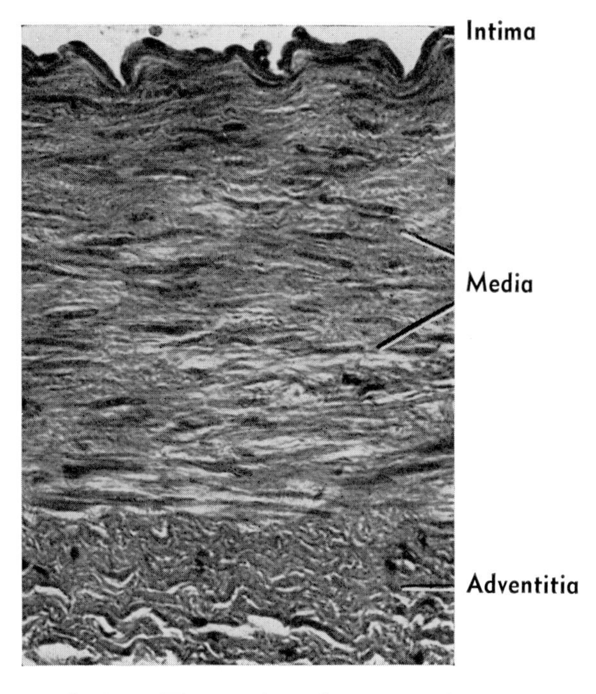

Fig. 65. Medium-sized artery. (Hematoxylin and eosin stain.)

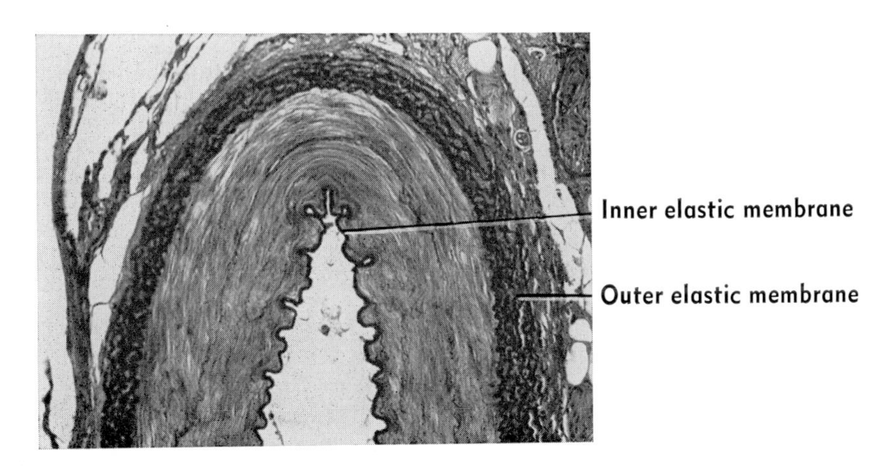

Fig. 66. Medium-sized artery, showing distribution of elastic tissue. Verhoff's method.

have been given. They are known as muscular or distributing arteries in contrast to those like the aorta in which elastic tissue predominates. They are characterized by a gradual change, as distance from the heart increases, from the elastic type to vessels having a wall composed mainly of smooth muscle. An artery of this group is shown in Fig. 64, and in it one may distinguish the following features: the intima consists of endothelium, a very small amount of subendothelial connective tissue, and elastic connective

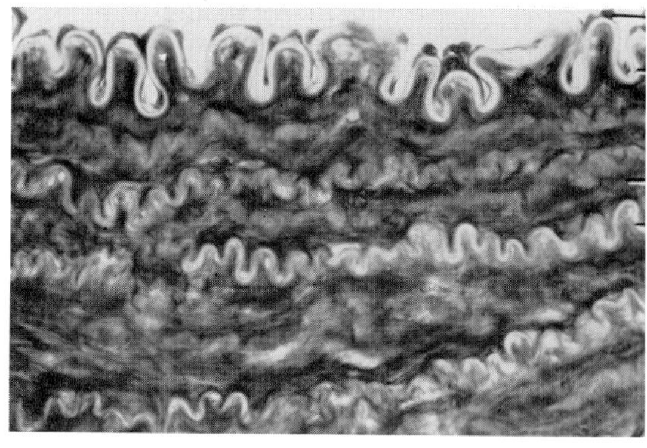

Fig. 67. Medium-sized artery, showing intima and media.

tissue. The latter is concentrated in a membrane known as the inner elastic membrane. In cross section this looks like a continuous sheet of elastic tissue, but in surface view it is seen to have open spaces in it (fenestrated membrane). Changes which occur at death cause the smooth muscle to contract, and this contraction throws the elastic membrane and its covering of endothelium into wavy folds. This results in a scalloped appearance of the border of the lumen, as seen in cross section of the vessel.

The media in vessels of this group, like that of the aorta, is the thickest of the three layers. It is composed mainly of smooth muscle circularly arranged. Interspersed among the muscle fibers are isolated strands of elastic tissue, distinguished by their wavy course and their highly refractive quality, as well as the presence of reticular and collagenous fibers and fibroblasts. The adventitia consists of an external elastic membrane and a layer of collagenous connective tissue containing small vessels and nerves. In some vessels of this group strands of smooth muscle longitudinally arranged are to be found in the adventitia.

The artery represented in Fig. 64 is fairly typical of the group. It must be emphasized, however, that a considerable variety of structure is included in the class of vessels which are called medium-sized arteries or arteries of the muscular type. A vessel may have considerably more or considerably less elastic tissue than the one represented and still belong to the same group.

Small arteries and arterioles. Small arteries and arterioles are the types of arterial vessels usually found in sections of organs. They present intermediate forms between the vessels just described and the capillaries or sinusoids which consist of a tube of endothelium alone. Elements are lost from the wall in the following order: first, the elastic fibers scattered through the media disappear, leaving a middle coat composed entirely of smooth muscle. Then the external elastic membrane is lost, and the adventitia becomes a covering of collagenous fibers hardly distinguishable

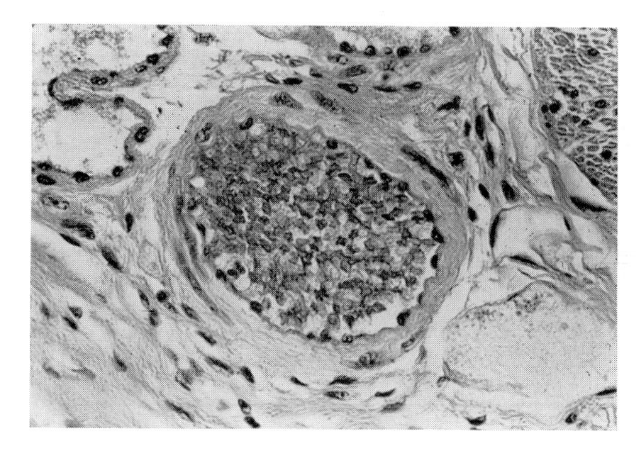

Fig. 68. Transverse section of small artery. (Hematoxylin and eosin stain.)

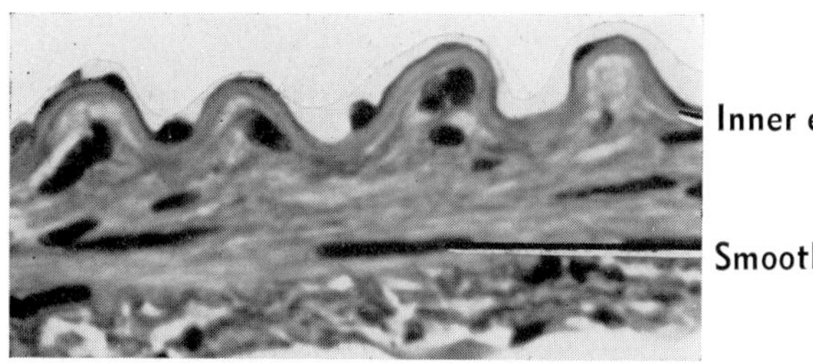

Fig. 69. Longitudinal section of small artery. (Hematoxylin and eosin stain.)

from the surrounding connective tissue. From this point on the vessel cannot be said to have the three typical coats, intima, media, and adventitia. In still smaller vessels the inner elastic membrane is first replaced by scattered elastic fibers and then disappears altogether. The muscle of the media also thins out to a few scattered fibers, and finally the blood passes into a tube consisting of endothelium alone. Precapillary arterioles and arterioles are vessels which have three distinct coats: the endothelium, a muscle coat several cells thick, and an external connective tissue coat. The so-called small arteries are recognized by having a larger diameter and a definite internal elastic membrane in addition to those components present in the arterioles.

Veins

The walls of the veins, by which blood returns from the capillaries to the heart, are composed largely of collagenous connective tissue, with muscle and elastic fibers much less prominent than they are in the arterial wall. Owing to the lack of elastic tissue, veins do not retain their shape after death and appear in sections as irregularly rounded structures. In

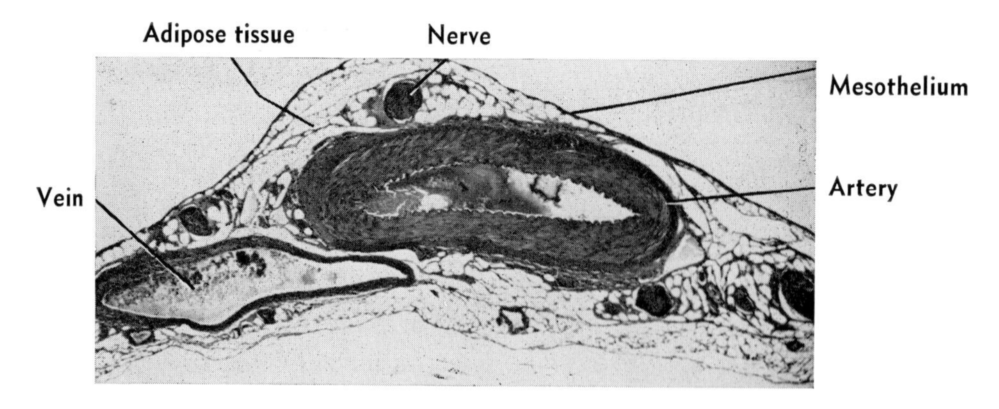

Fig. 70. Medium-sized artery, vein, and nerve. (Hematoxylin and eosin stain.)

general the wall of a vein is not so thick as that of the accompanying artery, but its lumen is larger.

The organization of the tissues in three coats is frequently indistinct. Tracing the system back from the capillaries toward the heart one may observe the following features:

Small veins and venules. Small veins and venules occur in the connective tissue of organs (Fig. 63). The first addition to the endothelium which changes the vessel from a capillary to a venule is not muscle but collagenous fibers. These and the accompanying fibroblasts are oriented longitudinally with respect to the vessel. As the caliber of the venule increases, its wall includes first muscle and then in still larger vessels scattered elastic fibers. The elements are arranged as in arteries but in different proportions. The larger vessels of this group have three coats: the intima consists of endothelium, subendothelial collagenous fibers, and scattered elastic fibers. The latter do not form a complete membrane and are not present in sufficient number to cause the scalloping of the border of the lumen which is characteristic of arteries. The media is a thin coat of muscle interspersed with collagenous fibers. The adventitia, which consists of white fibrous tissue, is the thickest of the three coats.

Veins of medium caliber. Veins of medium caliber exhibit many of the characteristics just described. The adventitia of collagenous fibers is the thickest of the coats. The muscle of the media and the elastic tissue of the intima increase somewhat in amount, but there is no inner elastic membrane. In some veins of this group longitudinal muscle fibers occur in the intima and in the adventitia. In the latter coat there may be a complete layer of such muscle fibers placed next to the circular muscle fibers of the media. This is not, however, of common occurrence.

A typical vein of this group is illustrated in Fig. 64. As in the case of arteries, the group includes a rather wide range of variation in structure.

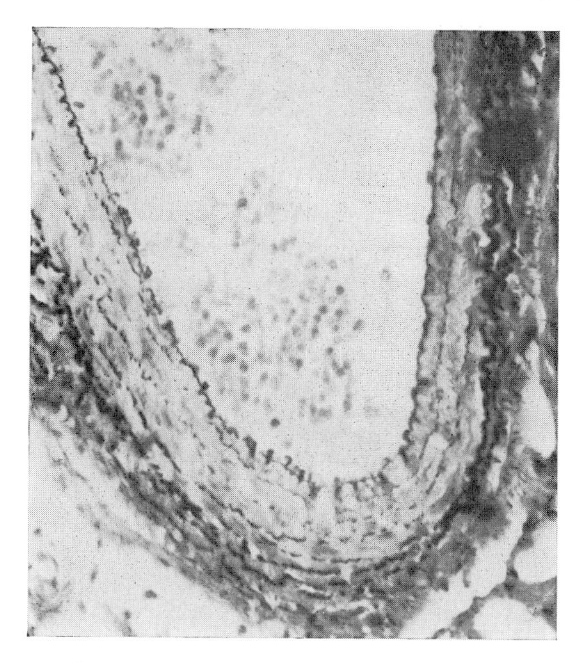

Fig. 71. Medium-sized vein, showing distribution of elastic tissue.

Large veins. Large veins show an increase in the amount of longitudinal muscle in the adventitia and a slight increase in the amount of elastic tissue in the intima. The elastic tissue, however, is not as prominent even in the largest veins as it is in quite small arteries. The circular muscle of the media is reduced in veins of this group and is lacking entirely in a few of them.

Some veins also contain valves, particularly those of the extremities. They consist of a thin connective tissue membrane. The surface of the valves are covered by endothelium which is reflected from the internal surface of the intima.

Comparison of veins and arteries

The difference between the smaller arterial and venous vessels lies in the amount of muscle and connective tissue present in each. Muscle is the predominant tissue in arterioles; in the venules there is little muscle and the walls consist mainly of endothelium and connective tissue. The larger vessels of the two groups may be distinguished by the following: intima, media, adventitia, size of vessels, and shape of vessels.

Intima. In arteries the presence of a complete inner elastic membrane is a distinguishing feature. This membrane contracts after death, throwing the intima into small folds and allowing the endothelial nuclei to project into the lumen of the vessel. In the veins the endothelium remains smooth. The entire intima of some veins extends into the lumen at intervals in large folds or reduplications which serve as valves to prevent the back flow of the blood.

Media. The media is the thickest coat of any artery and consists of muscle interspersed with elastic tissue. In veins the media is a thin coat of muscle; it usually contains all circular, but occasionally has longitudinal fibers. It has more white fibers than the media of an artery and includes elastic tissue only in the largest vessels of the system.

Adventitia. In arteries the adventitia is less important than the media. It contains the outer elastic membrane, and there are seldom any muscle fibers in it. The adventitia of the vein is its thickest coat and it often contains a large number of longitudinal muscle fibers.

Size of vessels. The lumen of the vein is larger than that of the accompanying artery, but its wall is thinner.

Shape of vessels. Because of the relatively large amount of elastic tissue, arteries retain their round shape in sections more often than do the veins. The latter are likely to be collapsed in section.

THE HEART

The heart is a specialized portion of the vascular system which develops from an enlargement of two veins in the embryo. It has three coats—endocardium, myocardium, and epicardium.

Endocardium

The endocardium, which corresponds to the intima of the vessels, includes an endothelial lining and a relatively thick subendothelial layer which is made up of connective tissue, smooth muscle, and elastic fibers. The valves of the heart are folds of the endocardium in which the fibroelastic elements are prominent. The annuli fibrosi are rings of elastic tissue which surround the openings from one chamber to another.

Fig. 72. Purkinje fibers in interventricular septum of heart.

Myocardium

The myocardium or muscular coat corresponds to the media of the vessels. It is made up of interlacing bundles of muscle. The tissue, however, is not like that of the media of the vessels. It is muscle of specialized type, cardiac, found nowhere else in the body. The nature of this muscle has been discussed in Chapter VII.

Epicardium

Epicardium is the connective tissue covering of the heart which corresponds to the adventitia of the vessels. It is bounded on the outside by the visceral pericardium.

In addition to the foregoing elements the heart includes a peculiar group of fibers known as the atrioventricular bundle of His and a similar collection called the sinoauricular node. These fibers are larger and paler in color than the cardiac muscle fibers. They were described by Purkinje and are hence often called Purkinje fibers. It is believed that this system of fibers correlates the contraction of different parts of the heart.

LYMPHATIC SYSTEM

The lymphatic system consists of lymph capillaries and vessels but is unlike the blood vascular system in that it does not form a complete circuit through which the fluid leaves and returns to a central propelling organ. Lymph capillaries begin blindly in the connective tissues from

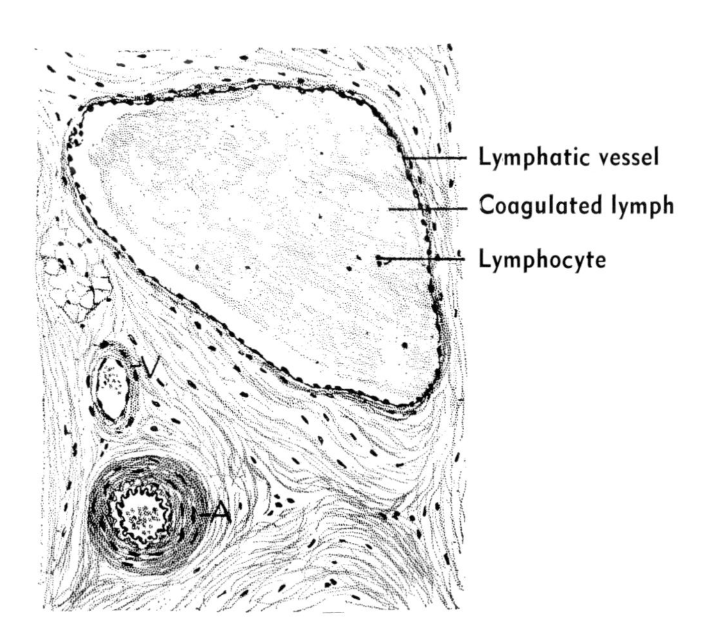

Fig. 73. Lymphatic artery and vein from hilum of lymph node. **V**, Vein; **A**, artery.

which they collect tissue fluid. The latter passes as lymph from the capillaries to larger vessels which join together, forming ultimately the thoracic duct and the right lymphatic duct. The thoracic duct is the larger of the two, since it alone receives lymph drainage from the abdomen. It empties its contents into the blood stream at the junction of the left internal jugular and left subclavian veins. In some cases there is a right lymphatic duct opening into the corresponding veins on the right side of the body, but the single duct on this side is often replaced by several smaller lymphatics.

Lymphatic vessels are thin-walled and are less conspicuous than the blood vessels (Fig. 73). The structure of the larger lymphatics most nearly resembles that of the veins, but instead of containing blood they are filled with a granular coagulum containing a few lymphocytes. The large lymphatics are composed of three coats: (1) an intima of endothelium and subendothelial tissue, (2) a media of circular muscle with little elastic tissue, and (3) an adventitia of loose connective tissue with scattered bundles of longitudinal muscle. They have numerous valves and are distinguishable from veins chiefly through the absence of blood in them.

CHAPTER XI

Lymphoid organs

In the group of lymphoid organs are included the lymph nodes, the spleen, the tonsils, and the thymus. Of these four organs the first three are composed of lymphoid tissue and form part of the defensive mechanism of the body. The thymus is placed with them tentatively because of a morphological similarity which may be deceptive. It is possible that this organ belongs, in fact, with the group of endocrine glands, but until definite evidence of its function is produced it is most convenient to study it in connection with the group of structures which it most nearly resembles. Lymphoid tissue consists of reticular tissue infiltrated with lymphocytes. The reticular tissue is fairly evenly distributed throughout the organs, but the lymphocytes are more concentrated in some regions than in others, such concentrations being known as nodules. These are to be found in the lymph node, the tonsil, and the spleen and are also widely distributed along the digestive tract, occurring singly or in groups.

Before considering the distribution and arrangement of lymphoid tissue in the organs just mentioned, it seems appropriate to point out that this tissue is widely distributed throughout the digestive and respiratory tracts and other parts of the body in a form not sharply outlined from the rest of the surrounding connective tissue. This is usually referred to as a *diffuse lymphoid tissue* in contrast to the denser form such as the lymph nodules in which the lymphocytes are more closely aggregated.

LYMPH NODE

A lymph node or gland is a mass of lymphoid tissue enclosed in a capsule of connective tissue. There are many such nodes scattered along the course of the lymph vessels of the body, the most conspicuous groups lying in the cervical region, the axilla, and the groin. Each node is a small, bean-shaped organ (from 1 to 25 mm. in diameter) having an indented hilum (Fig. 74). The nodes are whitish in color in the fresh specimen. When stained with hematoxylin and eosin a section of a node appears as a mass of purple tissue enclosed in a connective tissue capsule. The cap-

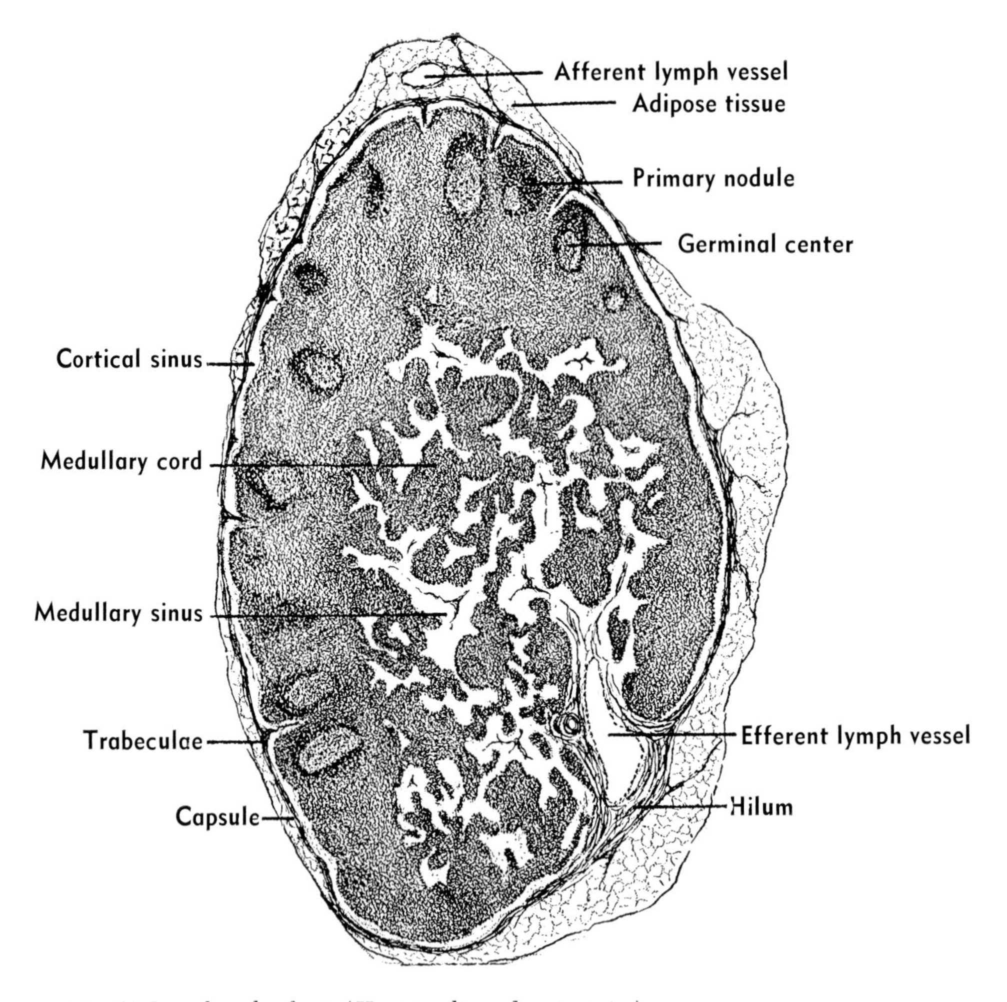

Fig. 74. Lymph node of cat. (Hematoxylin and eosin stain.)

sule sends trabeculae toward the center of the node from various points along its convex surface, and a group of branching trabeculae extends inward from the indented surface or hilum. Under the low power of the microscope it may be seen that the lymphocytes which give the organ its dark color are not evenly distributed. In the peripheral portion or cortex dense aggregations of lymphocytes appear which are known as nodules. When lymphocyte production is active the primary nodule has at its center a light area, the secondary nodule or germinal center. In the medulla of the lymph node the lymphocytes are collected in uneven clumps with no germinal centers. Between these central masses (medullary cords) there are areas of reticular tissue which are almost entirely free from lymphocytes. These are the medullary sinuses through which the lymph flows. Each sinus intervenes between a medullary cord on the one hand and a trabecula on the other. In a similar fashion one may see that there is a sinus interposed between the capsule and the cortex and that this peripheral sinus courses down along the trabeculae to join the system of anastomosing medullary sinuses. The cortical nodules are not sharply separated from each other or from the cords at the border of the medulla.

Afferent lymph vessels approach the convex surface of the node and pierce the capsule, opening into the cortical sinuses. From there the lymph passes to the medullary sinuses and is eventually collected at the hilum in the efferent vessels. Valves in both sets of vessels prevent the lymph from reversing its direction. Arteries enter the node at the hilum, run for varying distances in the trabeculae, and give off branches which break up into capillaries in the reticular tissue of the node, thus supplying nutriment to the organ. Veins return in the trabeculae and leave at the hilum.

The organization of the lymph node is illustrated in Fig. 75. A detailed

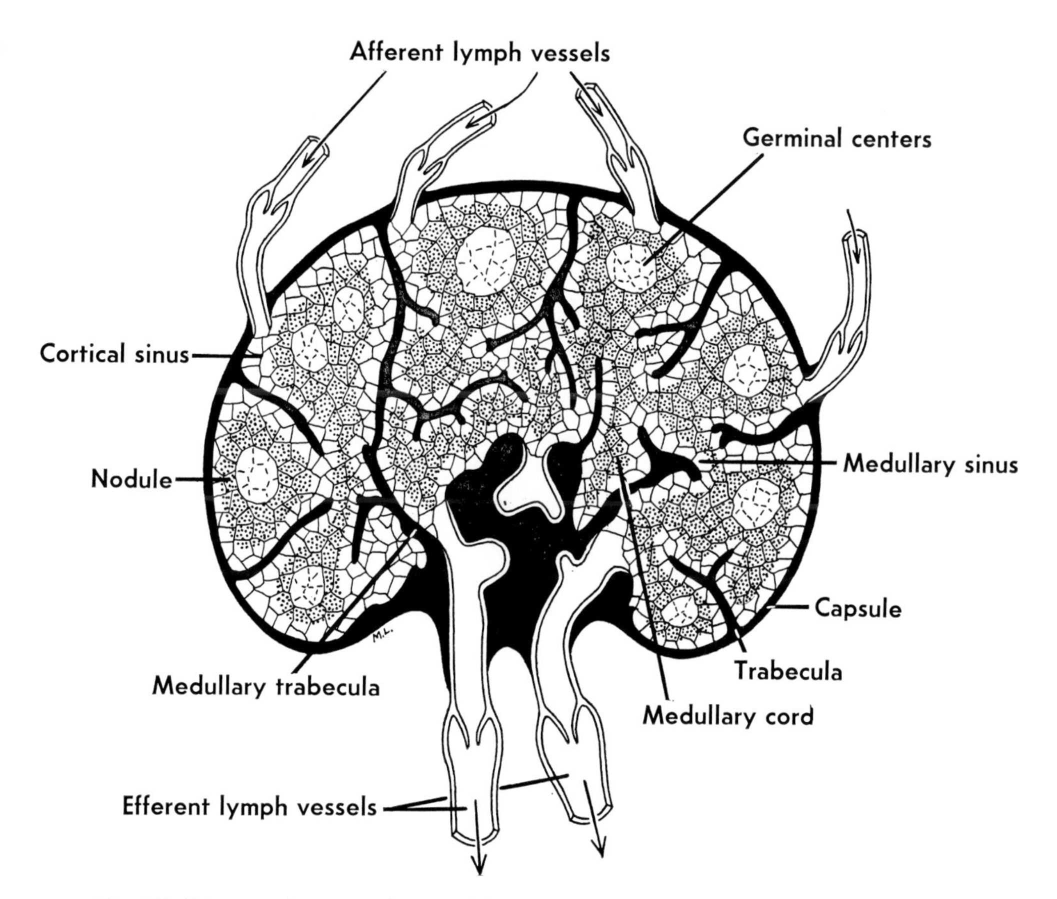

Fig. 75. Diagram showing relation of lymph node to lymphatic vessels. This diagram does not indicate arterial and venous supply of lymph node. (Redrawn from Maximow and Bloom.)

description of the various parts of the cortex and medulla of the lymph node as seen under high power follows.

Cortex

Capsule and trabeculae. The capsule and trabeculae are composed of dense white fibrous tissue with occasional elastic and smooth muscle fibers. In the capsule one may usually see the afferent lymph vessels, while the trabeculae contain small blood vessels.

Cortical sinuses. The peripheral sinus and those which course inward along the sides of the cortical trabeculae are not definite vessels enclosed in an endothelium. They are merely open spaces in the reticular framework of the node containing primitive reticular cells and macrophages but relatively few lymphocytes. The lymph seeps through the meshes of the reticular tissue in the sinuses.

Nodules. The nodules have a groundwork of reticular tissue like that of the sinuses. If secondary nodules are present they appear as regions of closely packed pale cells.

Blood vessels. Besides the vessels already mentioned as located in the trabeculae, the substance of the cortex contains numerous capillaries. These are so small that they do not form a prominent feature of the cortex.

Medulla

Medullary cords. The medullary cords are like the cortical nodules in the great number of lymphocytes present in them. They differ from nodules, however, in their irregular shape and in the fact that they do not at any time possess germinal centers. They are accompanied and surrounded by medullary sinuses.

Medullary sinuses. Medullary sinuses are like the peripheral sinus in structure and lie between the cords and the trabeculae of the medulla.

Medullary trabeculae. Medullary trabeculae are composed of dense white fibrous tissue and form a branching system radiating from the hilum which is part of the framework of the gland. Like the trabeculae of the cortex they include blood vessels. Efferent lymph vessels are prominent in the connective tissue of the hilum.

The lymph node has a dual function. It is a center for the production of lymphocytes and it is a phagocytic organ in which lymph is purified. The latter function is performed by the fixed macrophages of the reticular stroma.

SPLEEN

The spleen is the largest of the lymphoid organs. It is a mass of lymphoid tissue which in man is from five to six inches long and four inches wide. It has been shown that the lymph node consists essentially of a mass

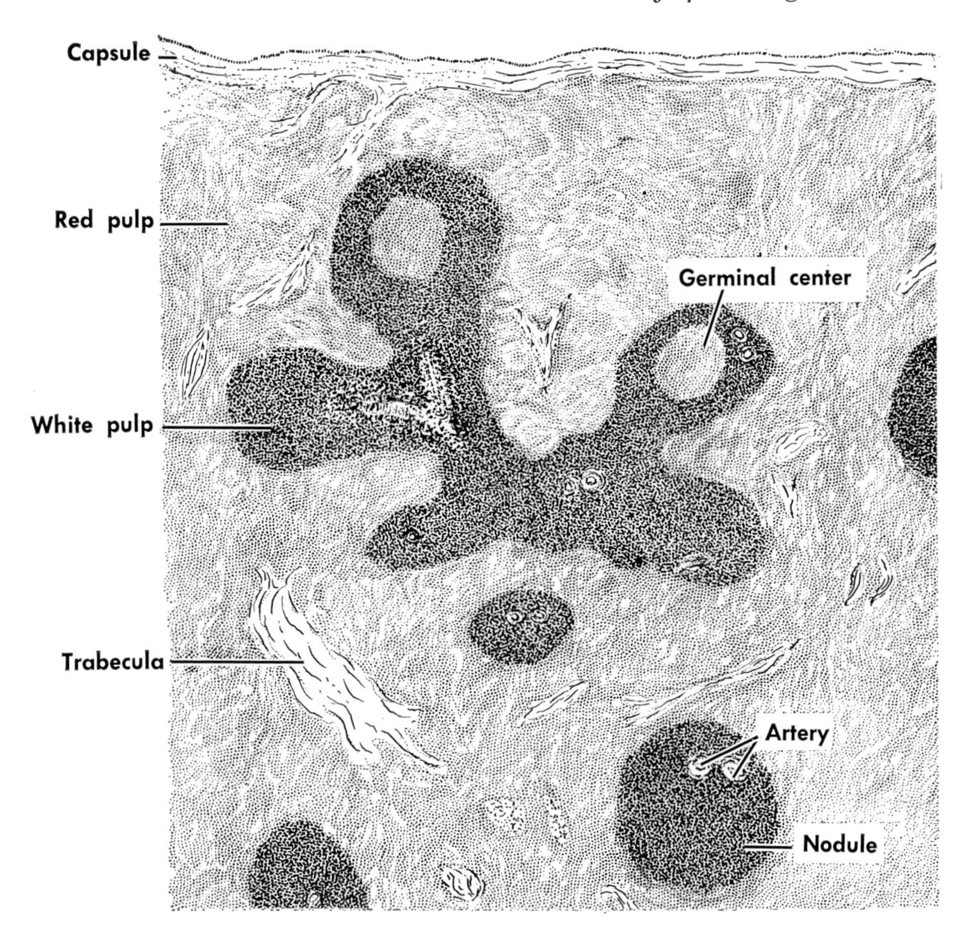

Fig. 76. Spleen of monkey. (Hematoxylin and eosin stain.)

of lymphoid tissue placed in the path of one or more lymph vessels, serving as a filter for lymph. In a similar manner the spleen is interposed in the blood vascular system to remove impurities from the blood. Under low power the greater part of a section of spleen is seen to be reddish in color when stained with hematoxylin and eosin. Scattered through this reddish tissue or pulp are areas of tissue stained a deep purple. This is the white pulp, which contains nodules. There is no regular arrangement of nodules about the periphery of the organ and no division into cortex and medulla (Fig. 76). The nodules are pierced by small arteries and lack germinal centers in adult man. The general arrangement of capsule and trabeculae is like that in the lymph node; that is, a series of trabeculae run in from the surrounding capsule on the convex surface, and a system of strands of connective tissue radiates inward from the hilum. Since sections of the spleen are usually prepared from small pieces of the organ, this arrangement of trabeculae is not seen in them.

Blood enters the spleen at the hilum, and the arteries run in the trabeculae for some distance. They enter the pulp, however, while they still have the coats common to small arteries: intima, media, and adventitia. In the pulp the vessels ramify, and it is usually at the point of branching that the nodules are to be found. After passing through the nodules the arteries emerge into the red pulp as the penicilli, in which three parts may be distinguished. The first part (arteriole of the pulp) is of fine caliber and the longest division of the penicillus. This divides into a number of vessels called the sheathed arteries, and these, in turn, divide into two or three branches of the structure of arterial capillaries which may connect with the venous sinuses of the red pulp.

There are several theories concerning the course of the blood after it passes through the arterial capillaries. According to one view it goes directly into the reticular meshwork of the red pulp instead of passing by way of a continuous endothelial tubule to the venules. This is the "open circulation" theory. Other workers believe that no such "dumping" of corpuscles into the reticulum occurs and that the arterial capillaries lead

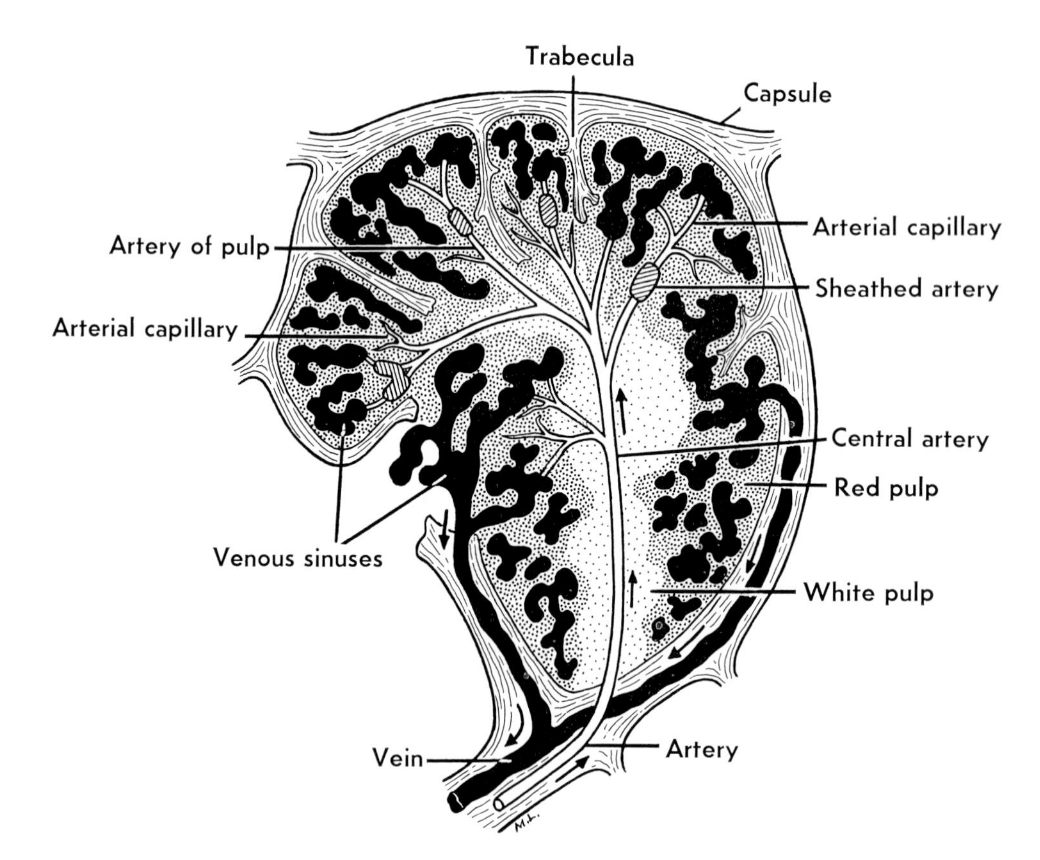

Fig. 77. Diagram to show circulation of blood in spleen. (Redrawn from Maximow and Bloom.)

to capillaries which, in turn, connect with the venules. This is the "closed circulation" theory. The third view is that some arterioles open directly into the pulp while others connect with venules through capillaries.

The venous circulation begins with the splenic sinus, which is composed of an openwork endothelium through which corpuscles may pass readily. From the splenic sinuses venules lead away and join each other, running back to the trabeculae. Blood leaves at the hilum. The circulation of the spleen is diagrammed in Fig. 77. Under the high power of the microscope the following details of structure may be seen: capsule and trabeculae, red pulp, and white pulp.

Capsule and trabeculae. The capsule and trabeculae consist of dense, white connective tissue with a few scattered elastic fibers and smooth muscle much like the corresponding structure in the lymph node. The capsule of the spleen, however, since the organ borders on the body cavity, is covered by mesothelium, which appears as a layer of squamous epithelium. This is often destroyed in preparing the specimen.

Red pulp. The framework of the red pulp is reticular tissue. It contains all types of blood cells which have passed into it either from the open ends of the arterioles or through the walls of the sinuses. The numerous erythrocytes which are present give this part of the organ its red color both in the fresh and stained specimens (Fig. 78).

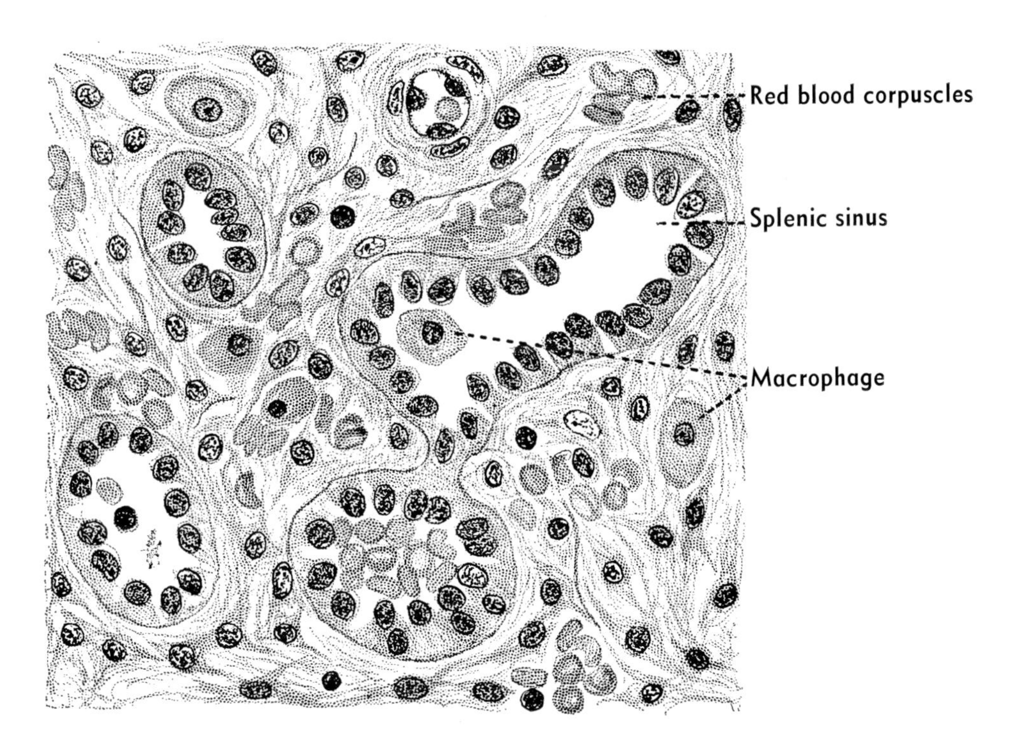

Fig. 78. Red pulp of spleen.

Among the reticular cells and corpuscles will be found free macrophages. These cells have vesicular nuclei and stain readily with eosin. They ingest fragments of worn-out erythrocytes which may be seen in their cytoplasm. The macrophages are distributed throughout the red pulp but are most easily distinguished among the blood cells in the lumen of a sinus. The name splenic cells, which is sometimes given to them, is misleading, as they are not different from other free macrophages found in organs other than the spleen. Two kinds of blood vessels in the red pulp are of unusual structure. The more prominent of these are the splenic sinuses. These vessels are the beginning of the venous system. They may be recognized as small spaces in the pulp surrounded by a ring of endothelial-like cells whose nuclei project into the lumina of the vessels. Ordinarily endothelial cells are closely joined and their nuclei are flattened so as to project only slightly into the lumen of the vessels they surround. In the splenic sinus these cells are loosely grouped and the lack of tension of the cytoplasm permits the nuclei to extend into the vessel. These cells are surrounded by a loose arrangement of reticular tissue forming a lattice work through which the corpuscles may pass. They are phagocytic and belong to the reticuloendothelial system.

The other type of blood vessel peculiar to the red pulp is the sheathed artery (second portion of the penicillus). Sheathed arteries are of capillary diameter and consist of endothelium plus a thin covering of concentrically placed cells which are probably reticular. The vessels are inconspicuous elements of the red pulp in human beings and require special strains for adequate demonstration.

White pulp. The white pulp, like the red, has a groundwork of reticular tissue but differs from it in containing large numbers of lymphocytes. It thus resembles the medullary cords of a lymph node. It surrounds the arteries from the point where they leave the trabeculae to their division into penicilli, actually invading and replacing the adventitial connective tissue of the vessels. Elastic fibers belonging to the walls of the arteries are scattered through the white pulp. At various points, particularly where the vessels branch, the white pulp contains nodules which form extensions of its substance asymmetrically placed with respect to the artery. In fetal life and childhood the nodules contain germinal centers, and these persist into adult life in some animals but not in man.

It will be remembered that all kinds of red and white blood cells are formed in the spleen during embryonic life. One would therefore find in embryonic spleens the precursors of the corpuscles, including giant cells. These, like the germinal centers of the nodules, may persist into adult life in some forms.

Function of the spleen. The spleen is known to have three functions. (1) It is of importance in the metabolism and distribution of the erythrocytes. It acts as a storehouse for healthy corpuscles, retaining varying numbers of them according to the demands of the body as a whole. The free macrophages of the red pulp ingest fragments of worn-out red blood cells, and the hemoglobin set free by the distintegration of corpuscles is stored in reticular cells. (2) It purifies the blood, since its phagocytes destroy infective agents. (3) It produces new blood cells. In this last respect the human spleen is most active during infancy and childhood.

TONSILS

Palatine tonsil

The tonsils are masses of lymphoid tissue embedded in the lining of the throat between the arches of the palate (Fig. 79). Their arrangement is best understood by reference to the structure of the wall of the pharynx. This consists of a layer of stratified squamous epithelium resting on a tunica propria of reticular or fine areolar tissue. Beneath this lies the submucosa of coarser areolar tissue, which contains scattered mucous glands. The tonsil develops between the tunica propria and the submucosa. As it enlarges it elevates the former and depresses the latter. The epithelium of the mucosa does not go smoothly over the surface of the tonsil but dips down in numerous deep pits or fossae. Under the low power of the microscope the tonsil appears as a mass of lymphoid tissue, bordered on

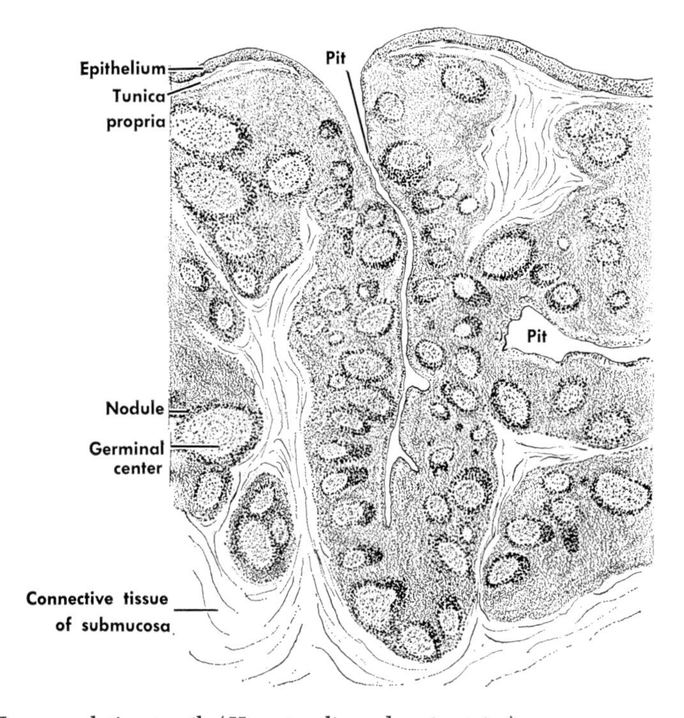

Fig. 79. Human palatine tonsil. (Hematoxylin and eosin stain.)

one side by stratified squamous epithelium and surrounded on the other sides by areolar tissue, which forms a tough capsule immediately around it. The mucous glands sometimes found in the areolar tissue outside the capsule are not part of the tonsil but belong to the pharyngeal wall. Noticeable features of the organ are its deep pits lined with stratified squamous epithelium and the presence of numerous germinal centers. The latter are usually grouped around the pits, but there is no division into cortex and medulla.

The pits (crypts) surrounded by lymphatic tissue are partially separated from each other by connective tissue derived from the capsule. Lymphocytes, mast cells, and plasma cells occur in this connective tissue; also heterophilic leukocytes may be present, which indicates a mild inflammatory condition. In the deeper regions of the crypts an infiltration of lymphocytes displaces the epithelium of the crypts to a considerable degree. Some of these cells pass through the epithelium and are eventually found in the saliva as the salivary corpuscles.

The lumina of the crypts often contain accumulations of living and degenerating lymphocytes, desquamated epithelial cells, detritrus, and microorganisms. These latter are said to cause inflammation and suppuration.

Pharyngeal tonsil

This is a median aggregation of lymphoid tissue which lies in the wall of the nasopharynx. In this region the epithelium, as is characteristic of the nasopharynx, is chiefly of the pseudostratified ciliated columnar variety. Patches of stratified squamous epithelium also occur and become more numerous in the adult. The lymphoid tissue is similar to that of the palatine tonsil. The capsule of this organ is thin and contains many fine elastic fibers which radiate into the core of the folds.

The tonsils generally reach their highest state of development in childhood and then usually undergo involution. Unlike the lymph nodes the tonsils do not possess lymphatic sinuses, and hence lymph is not filtered through them. They do, however, possess lymph capillaries which end blindly about the outer surface of the tonsil. The only established function of the tonsils is the formation of lymphocytes.

THYMUS

The thymus develops as an outgrowth from the pharyngeal wall of the embryo and has as a groundwork cells of epithelial (endodermal) rather than connective tissue (mesenchymal) origin. In later development the groundwork is infiltrated with cells which closely resemble lymphocytes in appearance and are probably derived from mesenchyme. It is claimed by some investigators that these small, darkly staining cells develop from the cells of the supporting framework and are, therefore, also endodermal

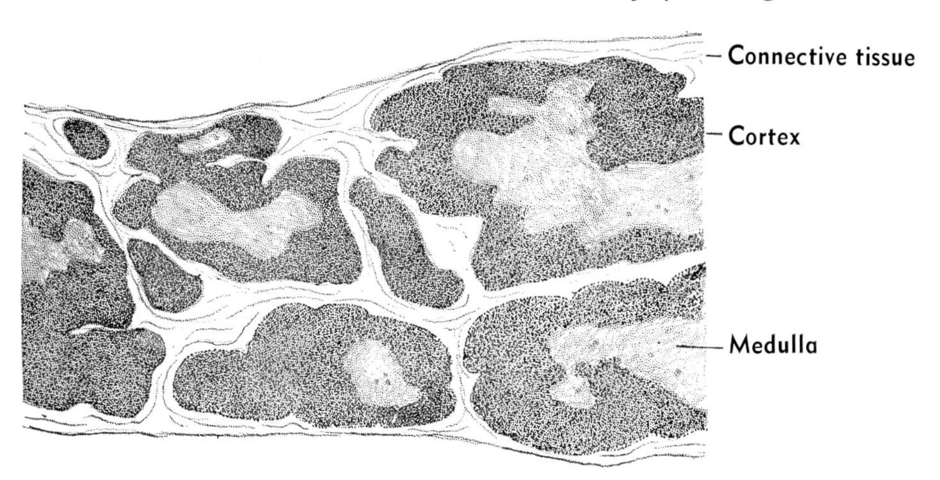

Fig. 80. Thymus of monkey. (Hematoxylin and eosin stain.)

in origin. The small cells are generally called thymocytes, a name which does not commit one to either view as to their origin.

The fully developed thymus (Fig. 80) resembles the other members of the lymphoid group with which it is here placed in having a groundwork of relatively large, branching cells infiltrated with small, deeply staining elements. It differs from them in that it contains neither sinuses nor germinal centers, so that there is no morphological evidence that it serves either as a filter or as a source of new lymphocytes.

Under the low power of the microscope the thymus appears as a mass of purple and reddish tissue embedded in a loose investment of connective tissue. The capsule and trabeculae are less definitely organized than are those of the lymph node and spleen. The organ is much lobulated and is divided into a cortex and medulla. Of these, the former is the more dense and is a deeper purple in color than the medulla, which is pink when stained with hematoxylin and eosin. The medullary substance extends from a central core into each lobule. Often a lobule is so cut that the connection of its medullary substance with the central core is not apparent, and it seems as if a mass of the lighter tissue were completely surrounded by cortical substance. If the lobule is small it may look like a nodule with a germinal center, an appearance which is deceptive, since there are no centers in the thymus.

Under the high power (Fig. 81) two types of cells may readily be distinguished in the medulla. They are (1) epitheloid cells, which have an irregular branching form like that of reticular tissue cells but are somewhat larger than the reticular cells of the lymph node; and (2) the thymocytes, which, as has been said, closely resemble small lymphocytes; they have dark nuclei and hardly any visible cytoplasm.

Some investigators believe that the thymus contains, also, true reticular

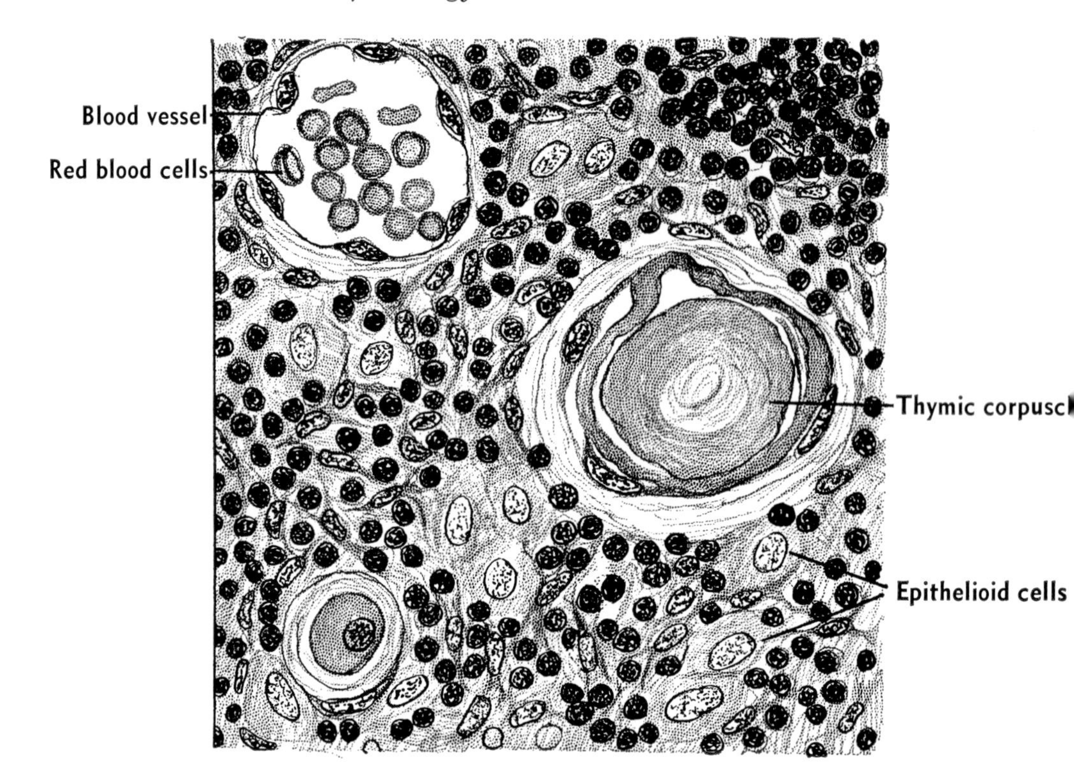

Fig. 81. Thymus medulla.

cells, which are found, together with reticular fibers, in the neighborhood of blood vessels. In other parts of the stroma there are few, if any, fibers. Another feature of the medulla of the thymus is the thymic corpuscle (Hassall's corpuscle). This is a group of cells ranging from 12 to 180μ in diameter. These corpuscles have a hyaline center staining red with eosin, which seems to be derived from degenerating cells, since it may contain several pyknotic nuclei. Around this center there are compressed cells concentrically arranged in a sort of whorl. Except for the hyaline center with its degenerating nuclei the corpuscle somewhat resembles the small arteries which ramify through the thymic medulla. The cortex of the thymus consists of epitheloid cells and thymocytes, but in this region the latter are so concentrated that they obscure the former.

It will be seen from the foregoing description that a section of the thymus stained with hematoxylin and eosin presents an appearance much like that of a section of a lymphoid organ lacking sinuses and germinal centers. When the organ is studied from the point of view of the origin and behavior of its cells, however, it seems doubtful whether it is, in fact, lymphoid.

The thymus has been considered by many investigators to be an endocrine organ. The reason for this opinion is its alleged behavior in relation to the reproductive system. The thymus continues to grow in the child up to the period of puberty. It then begins to degenerate in the majority of instances and is replaced by adipose tissue in adults. It has been found to persist in cases of infantilism (delayed sexual maturity) and in castrated animals, and this connection with the gonads has led to the belief that it is an endocrine organ. It has been shown, however, that the thymus may persist into adult life in sexually normal individuals, so that its connection with the development of the gonads is not invariable. In general it may be said that no definite proof that the organ secretes a hormone has been given, nor has it been shown that it does not do so. Its inclusion with the lymphoid group is based entirely on its morphological resemblance to the lymph node.

SUMMARY AND COMPARISON OF THE LYMPHOID ORGANS

Lymph node. The lymph node consists of a cortex and a medulla. The cortex contains nodules which may have germinal centers, a peripheral sinus, and sinuses beside the trabeculae. The medulla is composed of cords, sinuses, and trabeculae. The capsule and trabeculae are of dense connective tissue, with scattered fibers of smooth muscle in the former. The lymph node filters lymph, produces new lymphocytes, and has a phagocytic action, removing impurities from the lymph.

Spleen. The spleen is composed of red and white pulp and is not composed of cortex and medulla. The red pulp contains all types of blood cells and venous sinuses. The white pulp surrounds arteries and includes nodules which have no germinal centers in adult man. The spleen is phagocytic, forms new lymphocytes, and influences the metabolism and distribution of the erythrocytes.

Tonsil. The tonsil is a mass of lymphoid tissue embedded in the wall of the pharynx. It is covered by stratified squamous epithelium which dips into the substance of the organ, forming the pits. Lymph nodules with germinal centers are grouped around the pits. There are no sinuses. The tonsil forms lymphocytes.

Thymus. The thymus is divided into cortex and medulla and is composed of epithelioid cells and thymocytes which resemble lymphocytes. The medulla contains thymic corpuscles. The cortex is a dense mass of thymocytes and epithelioid tissue. The function of the thymus is not known.

CHAPTER XII

Glands

In the following chapters glands become a prominent feature of each of the several organs to be considered. Accordingly, a general survey and orientation of typical characteristics of glands will be discussed at this juncture.

Glands are composed of epithelial cells which perform the highly specialized function of producing *secretions.* These cells remove raw materials from tissue fluid or lymph, and from them synthesize substances which ordinarily are not utilized by the gland cell itself to any great degree. The secretory products are released upon free surfaces or into the blood-lymphatic complex of vessels for distribution to sites where the secretion products are utilized. Some glandular secretions are stored until the demands of the organism require the substance involved. In others the secretions are elaborated and released either continually or intermittently.

Excretion, sometimes used interchangeably with secretion, is a process by means of which the end products of carbohydrate, fat, protein, and mineral metabolism are removed from the internal medium of the organism. Thus liver cells can remove decomposition products of hemoglobin from the blood and convert them into bile salts and bile pigments, which are then passed into the bile system and eventually into the small intestine. Bile salts utilized in lipid absorption and digestion are resorbed and reutilized a number of times. Bile salts may accordingly be considered as secretion products. The bile pigments, by contrast, not utilized in the body are eliminated with the fecal mass. These pigments may be considered to be excretions produced by a secretory mechanism. Certain cells in kidney tubules are capable of adding substances to urine by secretory processes. The sweat glands secrete a modified tissue fluid which serves several functions, one of them at least being excretory in function. Even the salivary glands are partially excretory by virtue of their ability to remove salts, the thiocyanate ion, and urea from the body fluid. *Elimination* is the process by which excretions, secretions, and undigested food residue are expelled by the organism.

ENDOCRINE GLANDS

The endocrine glands, or glands of internal secretion, may have ducts in the embryonic state, but in the adult they are absent. They are accordingly classed as ductless glands. The secretions of endocrine glands may be stored or carried directly into blood capillaries, and it is by means of the latter that they are transported throughout the body to so-called target organs. The secretions of endocrine cells are called *hormones,* and in concert with the nervous system they regulate and coordinate the activities of all the cells in the body. In some instances hormones stimulate or suppress the activities of one or more specific glands or organs. In others, as in the case of thyroxin, they regulate the activities of *all* the cells of the body.

Hormones have a varied chemical composition. Some are proteins (insulin), some modified amino acids (thyroxin), while others are modified sterols (cortisone-like substances, estrogens, androgens), etc. Most endocrine glands have a dual function. The pancreas, for example, elaborates the hormone insulin as well as pancreatic fluid which contains a mixture of enzymes and sodium bicarbonate and is accordingly classed as one of the *mixed glands* (that is, both endocrine and exocrine in function).

In glands with known endocrine function there are three major cell arrangements: clumps, follicles, and cords.

Clumps. In the clump type of arrangement secretion and utilization are of approximately the same order of magnitude. The secretion is stored within the epithelioid cells themselves and is released upon demand into the abundant capillary network which permeates the clump. Examples of this type are the islets of Langerhans in the pancreas and the so-called interstitial cells in the testes. Clumps may be composed of small or large groups of irregularly shaped cells, but they do not form hollow spheres or tubes.

Follicles. A follicle consists of a cylinder or sphere of cells enclosing a cavity containing the stored secretion product. In the thyroid (for example, Fig. 163), consisting of many follicles, the cells are usually cuboidal, exhibiting a deeply staining secretion in the lumen called the colloid substance. Increased demand for the secretion results in a transfer from the lumen to the abundant capillary network surrounding each follicle. Depletion of the colloid reserves results in collapse of the follicle followed by the crowding of cells which appear columnar in transverse section (Fig. 164). Since it is thought that a depleted reserve results in active secretory activity by the cells, the columnar form is associated with the active or secretory phase of these glands. In the embryo the follicles originate as clumps of epithelioid cells. These cells produce more secretion than can either be utilized or stored within the cells. The secretion is accordingly stored in cavities formed between the cells, and thus gives rise to the space known as the "lumen" of the follicle.

Cords. In the cord arrangement the epithelioid cells are arranged in rows. The liver cords consist of two rows of cells closely aligned while the adrenal cortex exhibits many subparallel rows of cells. Secretions are stored within the cells and transferred to the abundant capillary network as required.

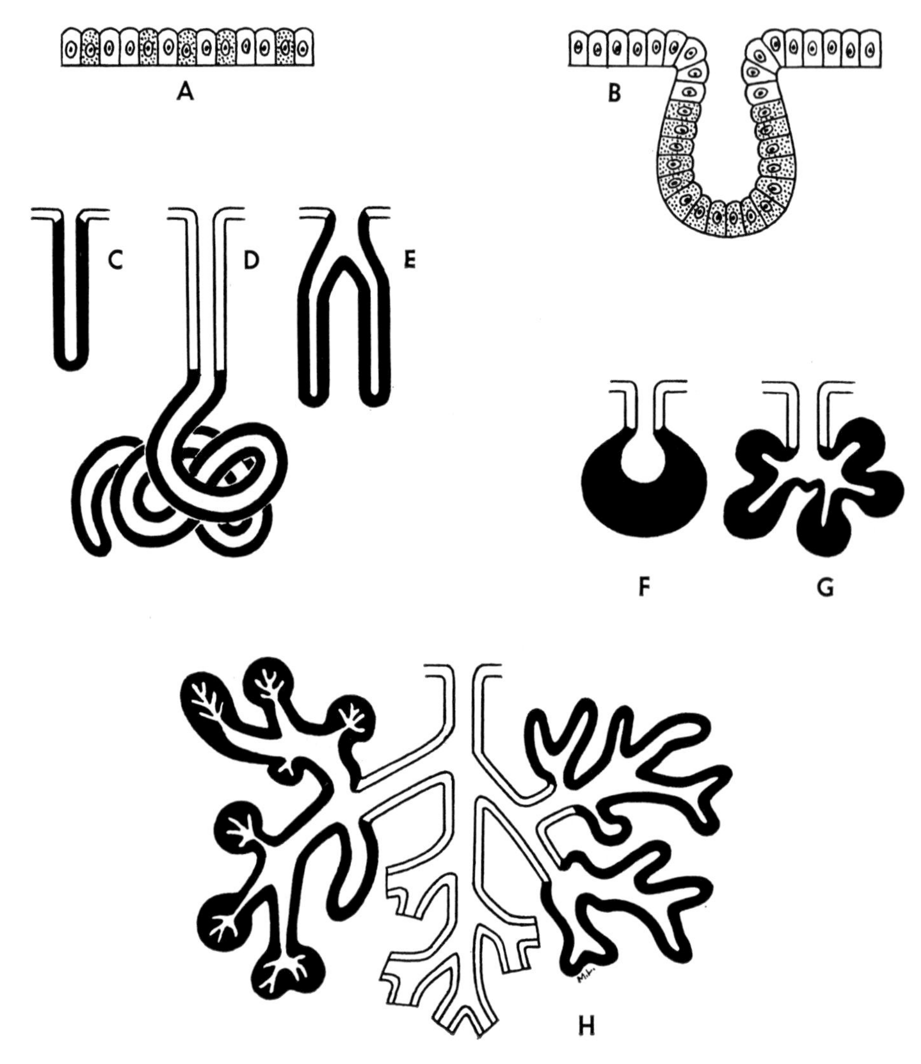

Fig. 82. Diagram showing different types of arrangement of glandular tissue. **A**, Glandular cells (granular) scattered among common epithelial cells (clear). **B**, Glandular cells forming saclike invagination into underlying tissue. **C**, Simple tubular gland. **D**, Simple tubular gland coiled. **E**, Simple branched tubular gland. **F**, Simple alveolar gland. **G**, Simple branched alveolar gland. **H**, Compound gland. (Redrawn from Maximow and Bloom.)

Epithelioid cells. By definition epithelia line cavities. With the exception of the follicular arrangement, endocrine gland cells do not line cavities. Prominent cuboidal or polygonal cells may occur in small or large irregular masses (Figs. 153 and 168) or in cords (Fig. 170) but invariably lack a cavity. For this special situation the term *epithelioid* (epithelium-like) was introduced. When epithelioid cells occur, one is led to suspect an endocrine function; however, physiological demonstration of endocrine activity is necessary before an endocrine role can definitely be ascribed to these cells. Cases in point are the thymus gland (Fig. 81) and the juxtaglomerular apparatus in the kidneys of rodents.

EXOCRINE GLANDS

Exocrine glands, or glands of external secretion, retain connections with surfaces. Unicellular glands, for examples, mucous cells, discharge their secretions directly on a free surface. Multicellular glands, for example, the salivary glands, discharge via a system of simple or branching ducts.

Ducts

There are several types of ducts: secretory, excretory, and intercalated.

Secretory ducts. One kind of secretory duct is lined by the glandular cells which produce the secretion (Fig. 86 and Fig. 82, *C*, *D*, *E*). In the salivary glands another type of secretory duct is found which contains glandular cells supplying additional substances to the secretion produced at some distance removed from the main gland cells. Special techniques demonstrate the presence of basal striations in these cells and hence they are frequently called *striated ducts.*

Excretory ducts. Excretory ducts are formed of simple epithelium which presumably conduct secretions without taking part in the elaboration of major secretory components (Fig. 82, *D*, *F*, *G*, *H*, and Fig. 118).

Intercalated ducts. Intercalated ducts (Fig. 118) are interposed between the glandular units and their conducting portions (for example, striated or excretory ducts.) The intercalated ducts are lined with flattened cells which presumably do not produce a secretion. The latter are found only in the larger glands (for example, pancreas and salivary glands).

Classification

The simplest glandular unit is the unicellular gland, which consists of a cell that forms part of a lining epithelium and also elaborates a secretion. The goblet cells scattered along the lining of the intestine and respiratory tract are of this type.

The next simplest type is the intraepithelial gland, consisting of a strip

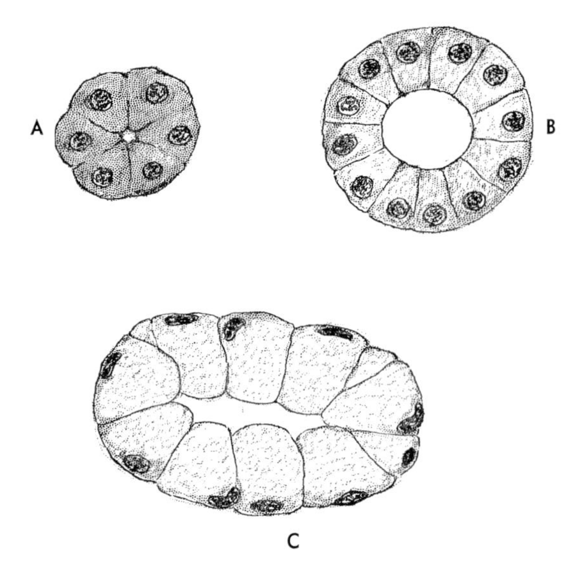

Fig. 83. Types of serous and mucus-secreting epithelium. **A,** Serous alveolus. **B,** Alveolus secreting thick mucus. **C,** Alveolus secreting thin mucus.

of consecutive glandular cells forming a slight thickening or pocket entirely within the limits of the epithelium. The lining epithelium of the gut contains fingerlike or tubular projections of glandular cells which are below the level of the epithelium in the underlying connective tissue (Fig. 82, *B, C, E,* and Figs. 105 to 115), maintaining their connection to the surface by means of a duct.

Another means of classifying glands is by the manner and degree to which branching of the excretory or striated ducts occur. If the ducts are absent (Fig. 82, *C, E*) or unbranched (Fig. 82, *D, E, G*) the glands are termed *simple.* If the ducts branch (Fig. 82, *H*) the gland is called a *compound gland.*

Simple and compound glands are further subdivided according to the shapes of the secreting portions as follows: tubular, alveolar (acinar), and tubuloalveolar. The name tubular is self-explanatory; an alveolar gland has secreting portions which are spherical or flask shaped, whereas the tubuloalveolar variety may exhibit glandular portions intermediate between the two types already mentioned (Fig. 82, *H,* left side). Another variety of tubuloalveolar gland consists of tubular units and alveolar units attached to the same excretory duct. The simple tubular gland is further differentiated into tubular, coiled tubular, or branching tubular (Fig. 82, *C, D, E*). Also illustrated in Fig. 82, *G,* is the branching alveolar type (compare Fig. 86, sebaceous glands). Other kinds of glands have been described such as those in the eyelid, but because of their highly specialized function and limited distribution they will not be discussed here. Other classifications depend on the mode of secretion (holocrine, merocrine, apocrine) and on the product of secretion (mucous, serous, mixed, zymogenic, etc.).

Secretions

The secretions of exocrine glands are varied, but at present none of these have been identified as hormones. (The case for parotin has not been confirmed as yet.) Mucigen, for example, is an inadequately characterized mixture of carbohydrate and protein; zymogen (a precursor of enzymes) is in part protein and forms an important component of many serous secretions; sebum and cerumen contain protein, carbohydrate, and much lipid; in addition, secretions produced by the sweat, lacrymal, and lactating glands are extremely varied and complex. Glands, such as the testes, ovaries, lymphoid, and myeloid tissues, are usually classed as *cytogenous glands,* since the chief activity of these glands is the production of living cells.

As indicated above, the modes of secretion are utilized in classifying certain glands. In the case of *holocrine* secretion, the secretory product is stored in the gland cell, and the entire gland cell is extruded and destroyed in the process of secretion. The sebaceous glands are of this type. In *apocrine* secretion (Fig. 162) the secretion accumulates in one or more large vacuoles below the free surface of the cell. During secretion a thin film of surface cytoplasm is removed with the secretory globules; the cell itself, however, is not usually destroyed in the process. In *merocrine* secretion there is a cyclic increase and decrease of the secretory product, which is more or less continually released into the lumen of the gland without, however, destroying the cell or depleting the cytoplasm. Typical of this variety are the glands of the oral cavity and digestive tract.

Unicellular glands

The simplest glands are composed of one cell, and the commonest representative of this group is the mucous or *goblet cell.* These cells are found in profusion in the digestive tract and in parts of the respiratory system. They are initially observed as tall columnar cells with elongate elliptical nuclei, distinguishable from their neighbors only by the absence of cilia or striated border. In the supranuclear position minute granules, then droplets of mucigen appear, which migrate and accumulate at the free border of the cell. As more mucigen droplets accumulate in the cell the nucleus is forced towards the base with concommitant changes in form from elliptical to a round and deeply staining conical form, until finally it appears as a flattened disc near the base of the cell. In addition, the apex of the cell expands laterally and distorts the neighboring epithelial cells. At this stage the cell looks like a goblet, with a narrow stem containing the nucleus and an expanded goblet-bell containing the nonstaining mucigen droplets in what appears to be a large cavity. In many instances the mucigen droplets nearest the surface are gradually released and dispersed in modified tissue fluid to form the viscid fluid known as *mucus.* In other instances the mucigen globules are released en masse, the goblet then collapses and appears as an irregularly outlined tall columnar cell consisting of a narrow strip of cytoplasm containing a deeply staining incredibly thin nucleus. The process of secretion is cyclic and may be repeated a number of times before the cell is replaced.

The presence of a large mass of nonstaining mucigen in hematoxylin and eosin preparations gives the impression of a large vacuole in cells filled with secretion. The principal ingredient of mucigen is a polysaccharide-containing protein called *mucin.* Aside from its adhesive properties it has the ability to combine with and coagulate in the presence of acids to form a protective coating on surfaces. The PAS reaction demonstrates the polysaccharide moiety as a red to purplish-red-staining region. Certain aluminum-containing stain mixtures (mucicarmine, mucihematin) stain mucigen droplets a vivid red or blue.

Multicellular glands

The usual example used to illustrate the multicellular variety are the salivary glands. In these and in other similar glands the cells are grouped into *secretory units.* These are of three types: mucous, serous, and seromucous or mixed units. They are usually arranged in alveoli (acini) and branched or straight tubules.

Mucous units are composed of a type of cuboidal epithelium, which is so disposed about a small lumen that the cells take on the form of truncated pyramids and are accordingly called pyramidal cells. At the beginning of a secretory cycle the nuclei tend to be round or ovoid and occupy a position nearer to the base of the cell rather than the center. As the mucigen globules accumulate near the lumen of the gland, the nuclei are displaced towards the base and are compressed to such an extent that they appear as flattened darkly staining rods in contact with the cell boundary. Some authors maintain that mucous units with rounded nuclei secrete thin mucus, but in view of their cyclic activity this contention would be difficult to verify. Since the mucigen takes up so much of the volume of the cytoplasm and does not stain with hematoxylin and eosin, the cytoplasm of these cells does not appear eosinophilic and may on occasion even exhibit a pale bluish color. In certain of the salivary glands the mucous units are easily detected under low power of the microscope as very pale areas. With PAS the mucigen stains such a deep purplish red that all cellular detail may be obscured. Although these cells exhibit cyclic activity, the release of secretion is gradual and typical of the merocrine type of secretion.

Serous units are also composed of pyramidal cells, but differ in that their nuclei are always centrally disposed in the cell. Their secretion granules are either slightly or extremely acidophilic and are primarily protein in character. Since these cells frequently elaborate enzymes (which are all partly protein) the secretion droplets within the cell are called *zymogen granules*. In many instances the granules are so small and so widely dispersed that the entire apex of the cell appears intensely acidophilic, while in other situations the granules are quite large and evenly distributed throughout the entire cell (Paneth cells). These cells produce an inactive precursor of the enzyme (zymogen). Zymogens are sometimes transported for a considerable distance before being activated. Since these cells are actively engaged in protein synthesis, the presence of large amounts of RNA or basophil substance in the perinuclear and subnuclear positions correlates well with their function. The serous cells of the pancreatic acini in well-stained hematoxylin and eosin preparations exhibit acidophilic apices and basophilic bases. The serous units of the salivary glands may be distinguished from the mucous units by the more central position of their nuclei and much greater affinity for dyes.

Mixed units are composed of both mucous and serous cells. The most easily demonstrated mixed units are found in the submaxillary glands of man. In one type of mixed unit the mucous cells form a tubular portion joining the duct, while the terminal portion consists of the more deeply staining serous cells. On occasion the mucous cells are so numerous they crowd the serous cells away from the lumen and form a crescentic cap of deeply staining cells or *demilune*. Occasionally a mucous cell is also extruded into the *demilune* complex. In section it is not always possible to distinguish between a "pure" mucous unit and the tubular portion of a mixed unit. A "pure" serous unit exhibits a small but distinct lumen in its center. In favorable sections through the terminal part of a mixed unit the serous cells are separated from the lumen by mucous cells. In tangential sections of a demilune one may observe serous cells only, a central lumen is usually lacking however. The student should be careful to distinguish between the mixed unit and the *mixed gland*, the latter being composed of both mucous and serous glands, and sometimes mixed units as well. Mixed glands of the type discussed here are also known as mucoserous or seromucous glands. The term mixed gland is also applied to glands which perform both an endocrine and exocrine function. (Compare pancreas, ovary, etc.)

Occasionally certain stellate contractile cells may be found between the secretory unit and its basement membrane. These cells are called basket or myoepithelial cells and contain thin prominent dark-staining crescentic nuclei. They are said to propel secretions into gland ducts as a result of their contraction.

A number of serous or albuminous cells of certain oral glands are slightly PAS-positive and from a histochemical point of view are termed mucoserous cells. They are not, however, morphologically distinguishable from serous cells and are accordingly classed with them.

Glands which are neither serous nor mucous do not, as a matter of fact, form a group united by similarities of function or morphology. They are mentioned here merely to point out that many glandular organs exist which are not to be classified as serous or mucous. They are so varied that no general statement regarding them can be made, and they will be discussed individually in later chapters.

CHAPTER XIII

Integument

The skin consists of an epidermal and a dermal layer (corium) and rests upon the subdermal connective tissue. The epidermis is a stratified squamous epithelium, modified in some portions of the body by the addition of a thick cuticular layer and in others by the development of the hair and nails. The corium is a layer of dense connective tissue in which are located the various glands of the skin and the hair follicles. The subdermal or subcutaneous tissue is also fibrous, but it is more loosely arranged than the corium and generally contains adipose tissue.

HAIRLESS SKIN

No hair grows on the palms of the hands or the soles of the feet. They are covered with thick skin, which consists of the following parts (Fig. 84): epidermis (stratum corneum, stratum lucidum, stratum germinativum, and stratum granulosum) and corium.

Epidermis

Stratum corneum. The outer layer of the epidermis or stratum corneum makes up about three-fourths of the thickness of the epidermis. It consists of cornified nonnucleated cells, the outer layers of which are detached from the surface in ragged patches (desquamation). The inner layers of the stratum corneum are compact and the outlines of individual cells are visible.

Stratum lucidum. Beneath the stratum corneum is the stratum lucidum, which consists of several rows of flattened nonnucleated cells. They form a hyaline, highly refractile band which appears homogeneous and stains deeply with eosin.

Stratum granulosum. The cells nearest the stratum lucidum are spindle shaped, with their long axes parallel to the surface of the skin. There are from two to five layers of cells in which the cytoplasm is full of granules which stain deeply with hematoxylin. These layers make up the stratum granulosum, which is prominent because of its color. On closer examina-

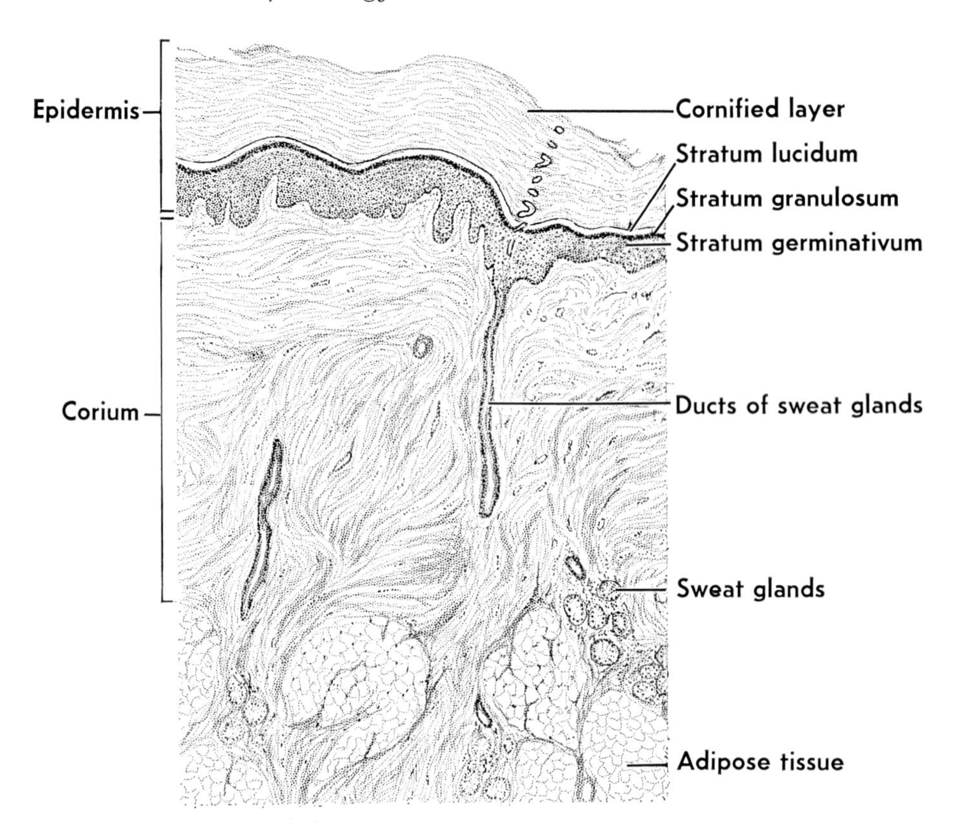

Fig. 84. Hairless skin from palm of hand.

tion it may be seen that the stratum granulosum differs from other epithelia in the arrangement of its cells. Instead of being closely applied to each other, they are separated by narrow spaces so that each is surrounded by a light line (in section). This is demonstrable in ordinary preparations. In exceptionally good preparations and under high magnification it may be seen that the polygonal cells below the stratum granulosum are also separated by clefts and that the spaces are traversed by minute cytoplasmic bridges, uniting each cell to its neighbors. The name prickle cells is sometimes given to the polygonal cells and those of the stratum granulosum because of these protoplasmic strands.

Stratum germinativum. The remainder of the epidermis constitutes the stratum germinativum and has many of the characteristics of the lower layers of stratified squamous epithelium. There are no very flat cells, such as one sees at the surface of the esophageal lining, since in the skin the surface cells have undergone cornification and form the stratum corneum.

The basal cells of the stratum germinativum are modified columnar cells with deeply staining cytoplasm and indistinct cell boundaries. The boundary between the epidermis and the corium is irregular, owing to the great number of papillae formed by the corium. Granules of pigment (melanin) are present in the stratum germinativum of the skin. In the white races melanin occurs in the basal cells only, except in deeply pigmented areas like the nipples and the circumanal tissue. In dark-skinned races it extends further into the germinativum. Some investigators believe that the epithelial cells elaborate melanin; others believe that it is formed and passed on to the epithelium by certain cells of the corium which are called melanoblasts. The melanoblasts lie directly beneath the epithelium and send projections into it between the cells.

Corium

The corium, or dermis, is a compact layer of connective tissue containing numerous collagenous and elastic fibers. In it are the sweat glands, which

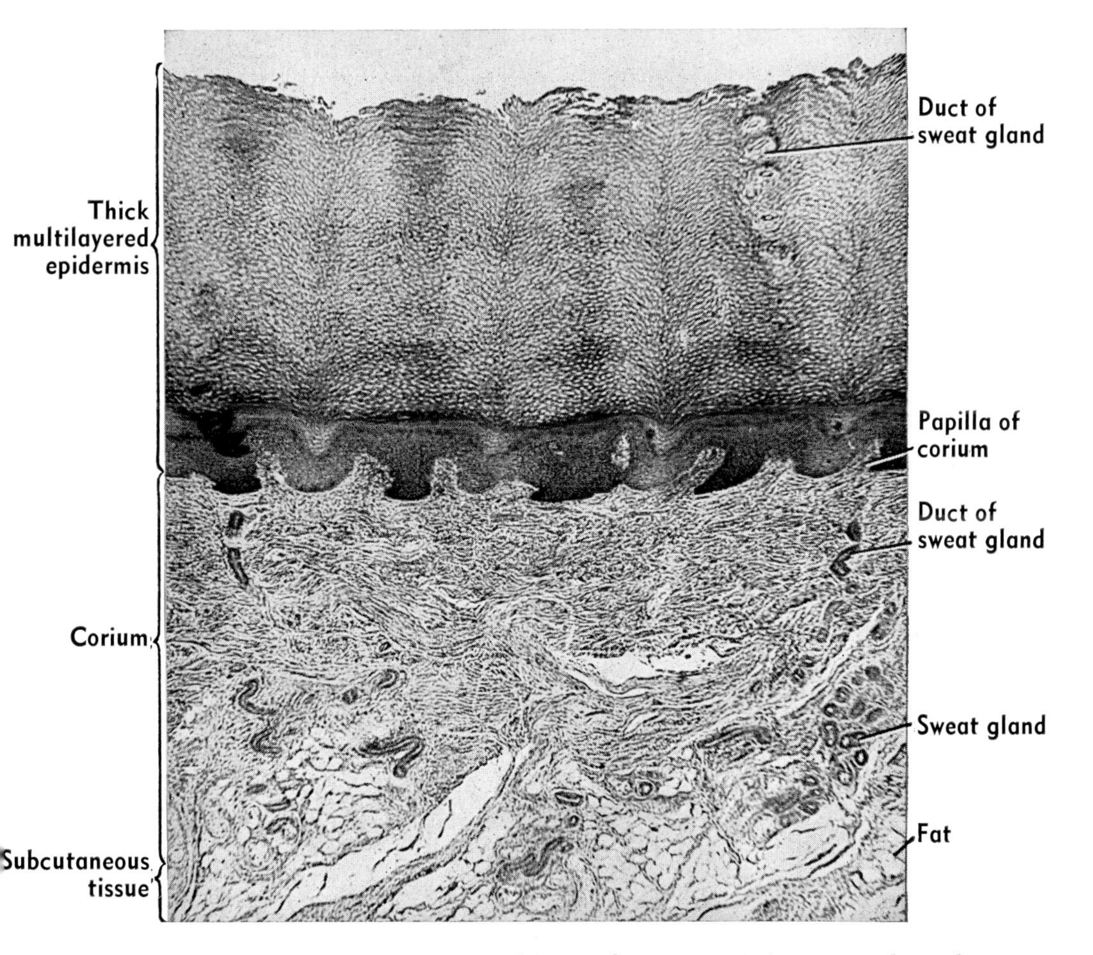

Fig. 85. Thick skin from plantar surface of human finger. (×50.) (From Nonidez and Windle: Textbook of Histology, New York, 1953, McGraw-Hill Book Co., Inc.)

will be described later. Some of the papillae which the corium sends into the epidermis contain capillary loops; others contain nerve endings.

HAIRY SKIN

In the skin of the greater part of the body the stratum germinativum of the epidermis extends into the corium to form hair follicles. These are most extensively developed in the scalp, which may be used as an example of hairy skin (Fig. 86). In this locality protection is afforded by the hair, and the cornified layer is much thinner than it is on the hands and feet. In some cases it is reduced to less than one-half the thickness of the germinative layer, the stratum lucidum is much reduced or entirely lacking, and there are but few granular cells.

A hair follicle has two layers. The outer layer is a poorly defined connective tissue sheath; the inner is a continuation of the germinative layer of the epidermis. At the base of the follicle the connective tissue forms a papilla which projects into the epithelium, and at this point also the epithelium is continuous with the hair shaft. This part of the follicle is enlarged to form the bulb.

A sebaceous gland and a strand of smooth muscle are associated with the

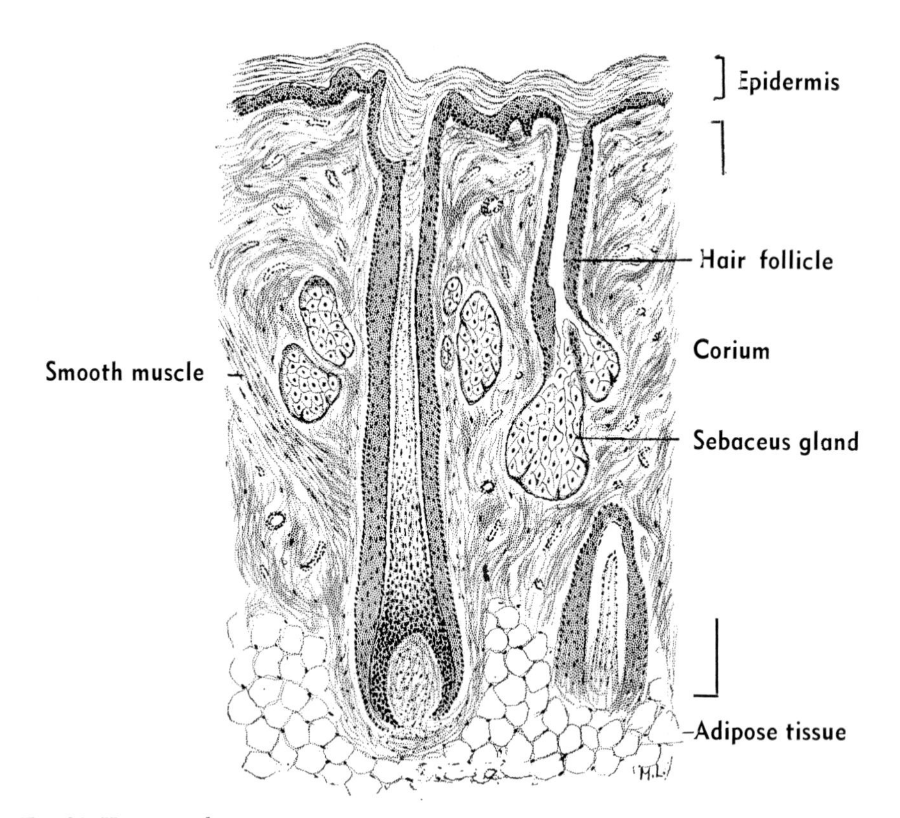

Fig. 86. Human scalp.

hair follicle. The axis of the latter is never exactly perpendicular to the surface of the scalp, and the muscle and gland lie in the wider angle of the two which the follicle makes with the surface. The hair itself is epithelial and under high magnification may be seen to consist of the following layers:

1. A cuticula of transparent overlapping scales.
2. A cortex of flattened cornified cells containing pigment.
3. A medulla of cuboidal cells, usually in two rows.

The follicle is composed of two sheaths, the outer of which is connective tissue, the inner epithelium. The former is divided into three layers:

1. On the outside there is a layer of loose connective tissue containing blood vessels. The fibers of this sheath, some of which are elastic, run longitudinally.

2. The middle layer consists of white fibrous tissue in which the fibers are circularly arranged.

3. The innermost layer is hyaline but may contain white fibers longitudinally disposed (membrana vitrea).

The epithelial sheath consists of two parts, outer and inner:

1. The outer epithelial sheath is an impocketing of the skin which grows thinner as it nears the bulb of the hair.

2. The inner epithelial sheath is still further subdivided as follows:
   (a) Henle's layer, located outside Huxley's layer, is composed of flattened or cuboidal cells having a clear cytoplasm. The cytoplasm contains longitudinal fibrils, and nuclei are present only in those cells lying deep in the follicle.
   (b) Huxley's layer lies outside the root sheath and is composed of several rows of elongated cells containing eleidin. Near the surface the nuclei of these cells are lacking or rudimentary.

Next to the hair there is a cuticle of nonnucleated cornified cells, the cuticula of the sheath.

GLANDS OF THE SKIN

The glands of the skin are of two kinds, the sweat glands and the sebaceous glands.

Sweat glands

Sweat glands are distributed over most of the surface of the body. They are simple tubular glands with convoluted secreting portions. The latter may lie in the subcutaneous tissue or in the deeper portion of the corium and are lined with cuboidal or columnar epithelium. The cytoplasm contains secretory granules or droplets. The ducts of the sweat glands are lined with a double layer of cells. The innermost layer is composed of myoepithelioid elements or cells which contain numerous longitudinal fibrils.

It is believed that these cells, by contracting, are responsible for the discharge of the secretion. The secretion is carried to the lower border of the epidermis, where it passes into a coiled channel through the tissues to emerge on the surface by way of a minute pore.

Sebaceous glands

Sebaceous glands are almost always associated with hair follicles, opening through ducts into the spaces between the follicles and the hair shafts. Structurally they are different from any other glands we have described hitherto. Their secreting portions are not composed of a single layer of cells grouped around a lumen but are rounded masses of cells. At the periphery of each mass the cells are cuboidal; in the center they are polygonal. The central cells are filled with vacuoles, so that their appearance is somewhat like that of developing adipose tissue cells. The secretion of the sebaceous glands is accompanied by the breaking down of the central cells, and their remains are poured out with the oily accumulation into the hair follicle. The cells thus destroyed are replaced from the peripheral layer.

NAILS

The nails are modifications of the epidermis. They include the following parts (Fig. 87):

1. The body with its free edge is composed of several layers of clear, flattened cells which differ from the stratum corium of the skin in that they are harder and also possess shrunken nuclei. The proximal part of the nail body lying under the fold of skin is called the root.

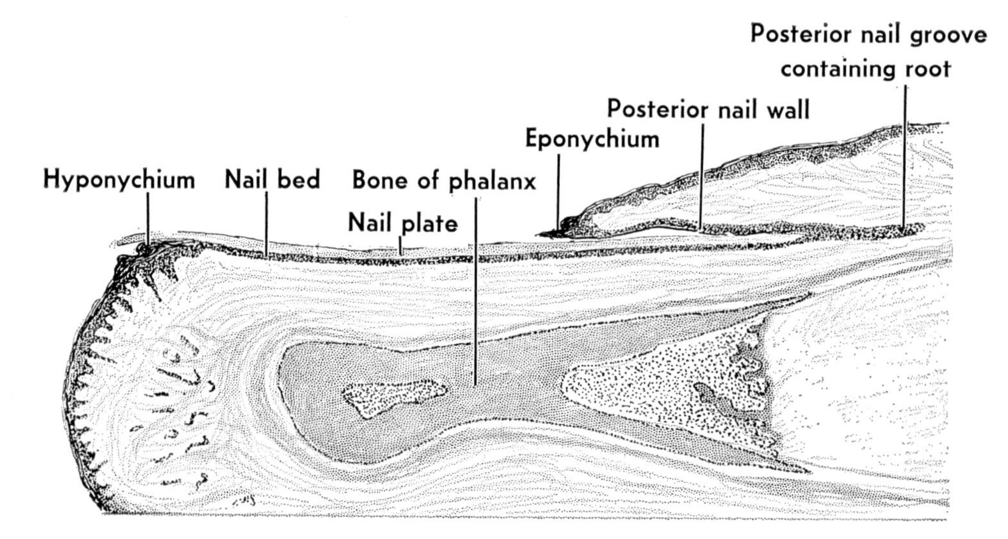

Fig. 87. Finger of newborn child.

2. The nail wall is the fold around the proximal and lateral borders of the nail, marked off from the latter by the nail groove. The wall consists of skin which has all the layers of other parts of the skin except, sometimes, the stratum lucidum. The stratum corneum of the wall at the proximal part of the fold extends out over the body of the nail (eponychium).

3. The nail bed is the skin under the body of the nail. It lacks the stratum corneum and stratum lucidum, and consists of the stratum germinativum only. Under the proximal part of the nail, in the region called the lunula, the germinativum thickens. It is from this region, the matrix, that growth of the nail takes place, the superficial cells of the matrix being transformed into nail cells. The corium of the nail bed has its connective tissue fibers arranged in two groups: (a) a group running in the long axis of the nail and (b) a group running vertically to the periosteum of the underlying bone. The dermal papillae of the nail bed form ridges which run in the long axis of the nail.

CHAPTER XIV

Oral cavity

LIPS

The lips are muscular organs covered on the outside by skin and on the inside by the mucous membrane of the mouth. The muscles of the lips are striated and consist of the orbicularis oris and the mimetic. The lip is usually sectioned vertically in preparation for microscopic study and when so cut presents as a sort of core the cross sections of the orbicularis oris, with a relatively small number of strands of the mimetic muscle cut longitudinally (Fig. 88).

The skin covering the outside of the lip is like that of the greater part of the body. It consists of stratified squamous epithelium which is cornified at the surface and rests upon a layer of connective tissue. In the latter are sweat glands, sebaceous glands, and the bases of hair follicles. In the region transitional between skin and oral mucosa, hair follicles and glands disappear and the epithelium is somewhat modified. Its basal layer follows a very irregular course so that there are tall projections of the underlying connective tissue extending toward the surface of the lip. These cells are not pigmented but are well supplied wtih blood vessels, giving this part of the lip a brighter color than that of the surrounding skin.

On the oral surface the epithelium changes again. The height of the connective tissue papillae gradually diminishes, as does the cornification of the surface, and at the base of the lip on the inside the mucous membrane is like that lining other soft parts of the oral cavity. In this region there are seromucous glands lying in the connective tissue between the epithelium and the muscle.

LINING OF THE ORAL CAVITY

The epithelium lining the oral cavity is of the stratified squamous variety. It rests on a tunica propria of reticular or fine areolar tissue, which blends in most parts of the cavity with a submucosal layer of areolar tissue. Beneath the submucosa lie tissues which vary in different parts of the mouth. In the cheeks and lips, for example, the mucosa and submucosa lie

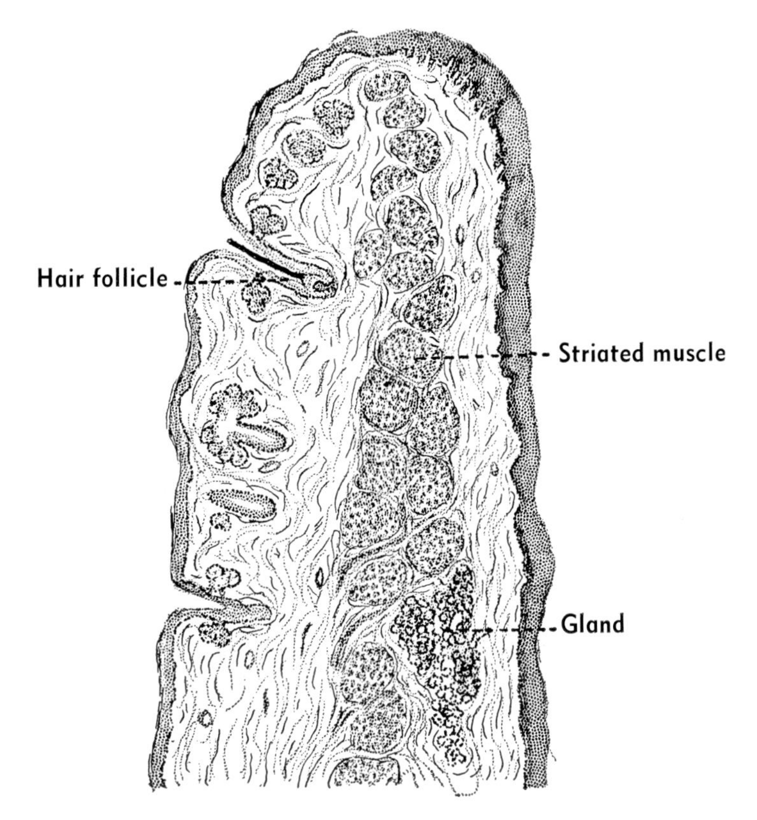

Fig. 88. Vertical section through lip of monkey.

against muscle, making a soft and somewhat elastic wall of the oral cavity. In the hard palate and the gingivae, on the other hand, the layers in question lie directly against bone. Modifications of the mucous membrane are correlated with these differences in the tissue it covers.

Lips and cheeks

The inner surface of the lip is a good example of conditions in parts of the mouth which are bounded by muscle. The epithelium is not cornified. It has a surface layer of flattened cells which slough off in patches. Connective tissue papillae are low; the tunica propria blends without demarcation with the submucosa. The latter is fairly thick and in some regions contains glands, the ducts of which penetrate the mucosa and open into the oral cavity.

Gingivae and hard palate

Where the mucosa and submucosa lie over bony tissue, as in the gingivae and hard palate, modifications of arrangement are to be observed. In the gingival region the connective tissue papillae of the tunica propria are

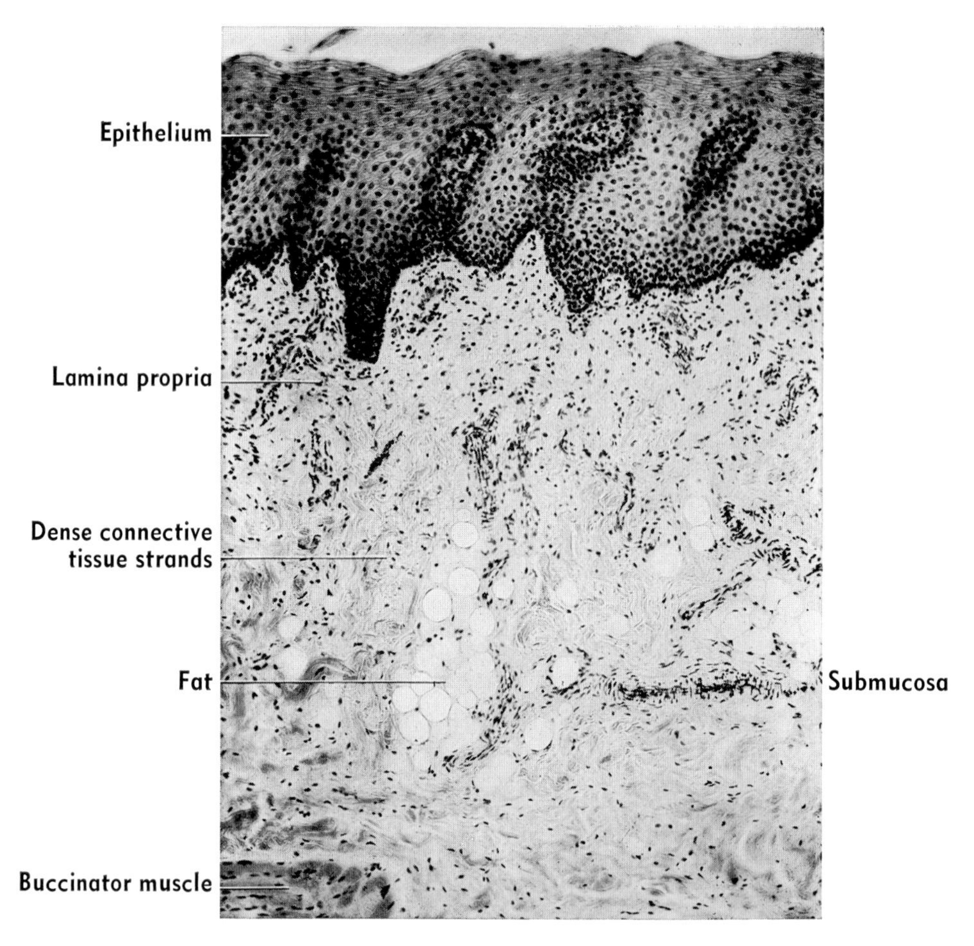

Fig. 89. Section through mucous membrane of cheek. Note the strands of dense connective tissue attaching the mucous membrane to the buccinator muscle. (From Orban, editor: Oral Histology and Embryology, St. Louis, 1957, The C. V. Mosby Co.)

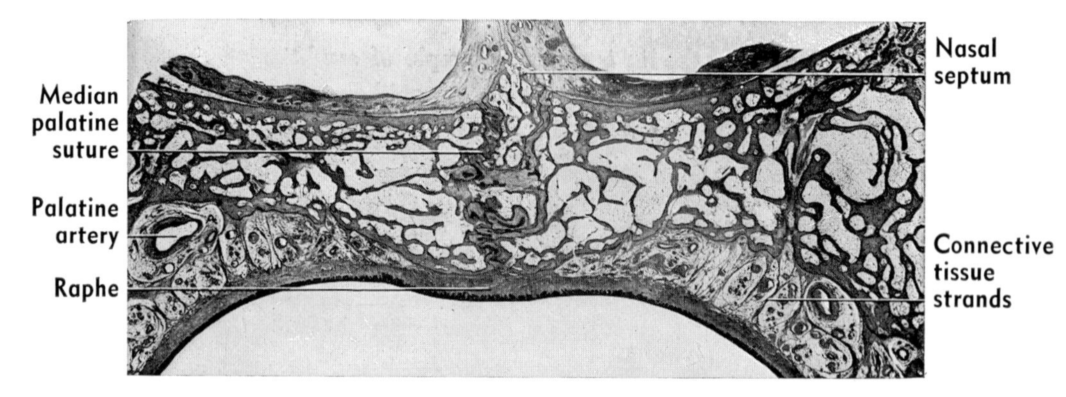

Fig. 90. Transverse section through hard palate. Palatine raphe; fibrous strands connecting mucosa and periosteum; palatine vessels. (From Pendleton.)

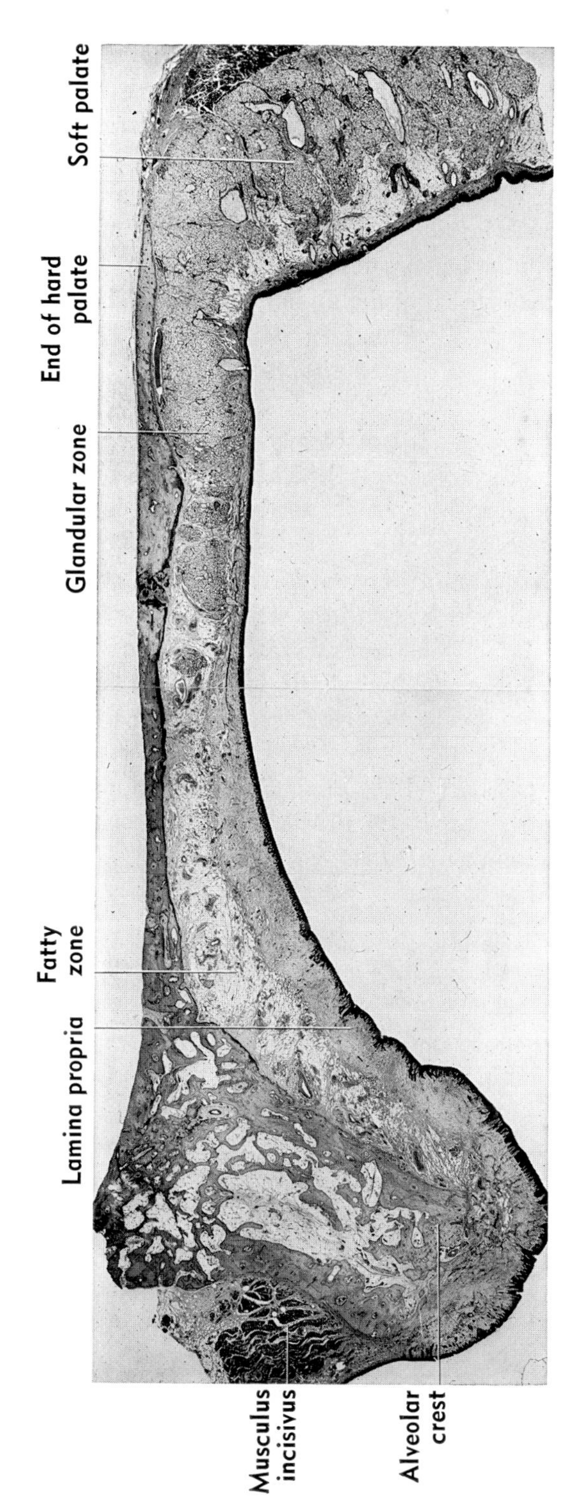

Fig. 91. Longitudinal section through hard and soft palate lateral to midline. Fatty and glandular zones of hard palate. (From Orban, editor: Oral Histology and Embryology, St. Louis, 1957, The C. V. Mosby Co.)

long and slender and close together. The submucosa blends with the periosteum of the underlying bone, and in the region immediately surrounding each tooth fibers are present which are specialized as part of the apparatus by which the tooth is held in its socket. There are no glands in this portion of the oral mucosa.

In the hard palate the papillae of the tunica propria are well developed, and there is a layer of elastic fibers which forms a line of demarcation between the mucosa and submucosa. The latter coat blends here, as in the gingivae, with the periosteum of the underlying bone. There are glands in the submucosa of the palatal region.

TEETH

The human dentition consists of twenty deciduous and thirty-two permanent teeth. The teeth vary among themselves as to size, shape, and number of cusps and roots; each particular tooth, however, has its own unique morphological characteristics.

The teeth are divided into two parts: (1) the crown, covered by enamel, is the part of the tooth which is ordinarily visible and extends beyond the margin of the gingivae; (2) the root is that part of the tooth which lies deep to the gingivae and is implanted within the socket. The term cervix or neck is sometimes used to designate a slight constriction at the junction of the crown and root.

The tooth consists of enamel, dentin, and cementum, which are calcified tissues. In addition, each tooth has a vascular connective tissue component, the pulp, located within the pulp cavity.

Early development

The teeth are derived from two embryonic tissues: (1) ectoderm, which gives rise to the enamel, and (2) mesoderm, which gives rise to the dentin, cementum, and pulp and also the supporting tissues.

The labiodental lamina appears in the human embryo at approximately the sixth week of the gestation period. This lamina is derived from the oral epithelium. It consists of a band of cells which proliferates from the epithelium and extends into the underlying mesenchyme. Taken as a whole, the lamina is U-shaped, following the shape of the jaw and foreshadowing the shape of the dental arch. There is one labiodental lamina in each jaw.

Soon after the labiodental lamina is differentiated one can observe that it is made up of two parts: one part consists of the original lamina, the other of an outgrowth which is inclined away from the tongue and is known as the labiogingival lamina. Later this lamina hollows out from the oral surface. The tissue located labially gives rise to the inside of the lip, and the tissue located lingually gives rise to the epithelium of the gums; the cavity between the two becomes the vestibule (Fig. 92).

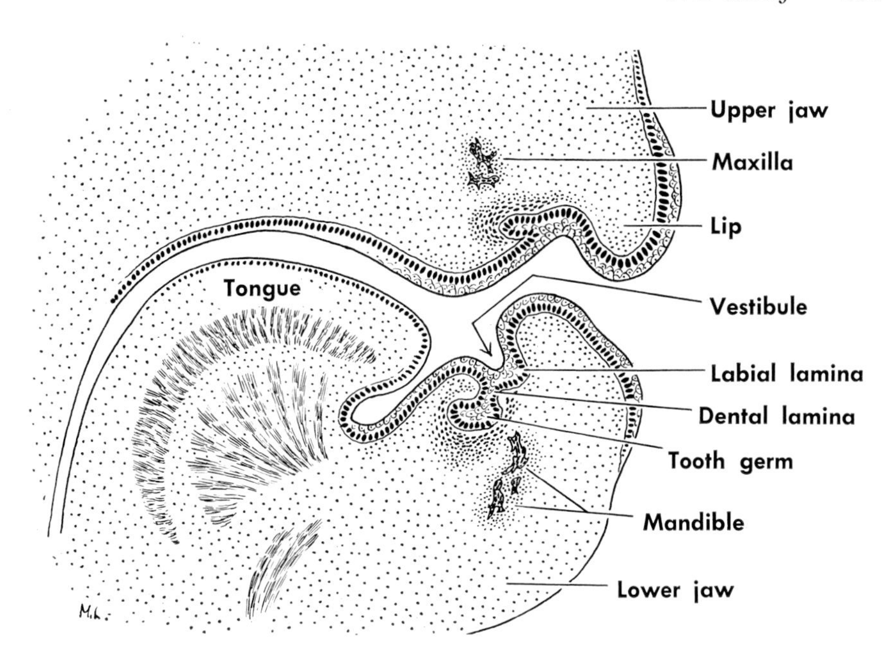

Fig. 92. Sagittal section through jaws of a human embryo of approximately eight weeks. Note relation of vestibule, lips, dental lamina, and tooth germ.

Development of the enamel organ

In each of the two dental laminae localized proliferations of tissue occur in the region where the future teeth are to form. There are ten of these outgrowths in each jaw; they are known as tooth buds or germs. These buds lie some distance removed from the oral epithelium and are connected with it by a narrow strand of the dental lamina. The tooth buds are at first rounded and solid. They gradually become invaginated on their distal surface by the invasion of the subjacent mesenchyme. The mesenchyme continues to proliferate and eventually this leads to a rearrangement of the epithelial part of the tooth germ from a solid organ to one which is hollow and goblet shaped. While the change in the external configuration takes place a differentiation of the tissues in this structure now known as the enamel organ also occurs. The rearrangement and differentiation result in the establishment of four distinct parts of the enamel organ: the outer enamel epithelium, the stellate reticulum, the stratum intermedium, and the inner enamel epithelium (Fig. 93).

In this stage of development in the human being (about ten weeks) the portion of the dental lamina connecting the enamel organ and the oral epithelium becomes reduced in size and begins to disintegrate. Its distal portion, however, now appears as a small projection on the lingual aspect of the enamel organ and later develops into the anlage for the permanent tooth. Enamel organs of permanent teeth which do not have deciduous pred-

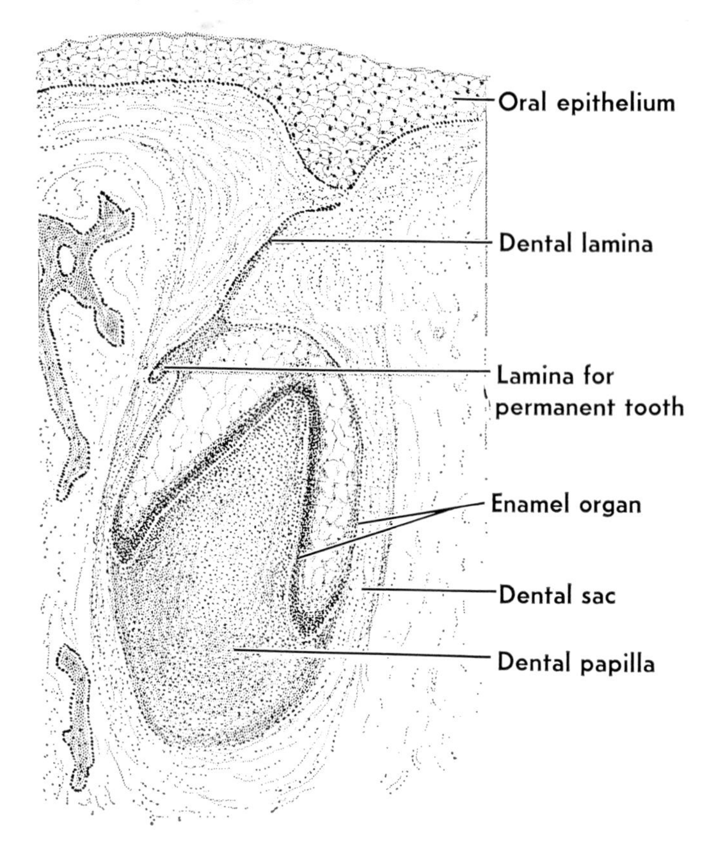

Fig. 93. Enamel organ and dental papilla of pig embryo before formation of dentin.

ecessors are derived from the original dental lamina in the same manner as the deciduous enamel organs—but at a later time.

Enamel formation. In the fifth to sixth month of intrauterine life, shortly after dentin has begun to form on the crown of the developing tooth, enamel formation begins. Before this occurs the several layers of cells which make up the enamel organ come together to form the combined enamel epithelium which is closely applied to the tip of the crown. The cells which compose the innermost layer, the inner enamel epithelium, have by this time differentiated into tall columnar cells with prominent nuclei which are located peripheral to the surface that is in contact with the dentin. These cells, known as ameloblasts, elaborate a rather wide protoplasmic process from the free surface of the cell, Tomes' enamel process, which comes in contact with the dentin. This is the future dentino-enamel junction. In the process of enamel formation this tissue is first laid down at the periphery of dentin and, as more enamel is deposited, the ameloblasts move outward—in a direction opposite to that which the odontoblasts move in dentin formation.

Tomes' processes gradually become impregnated with mineral salts; this

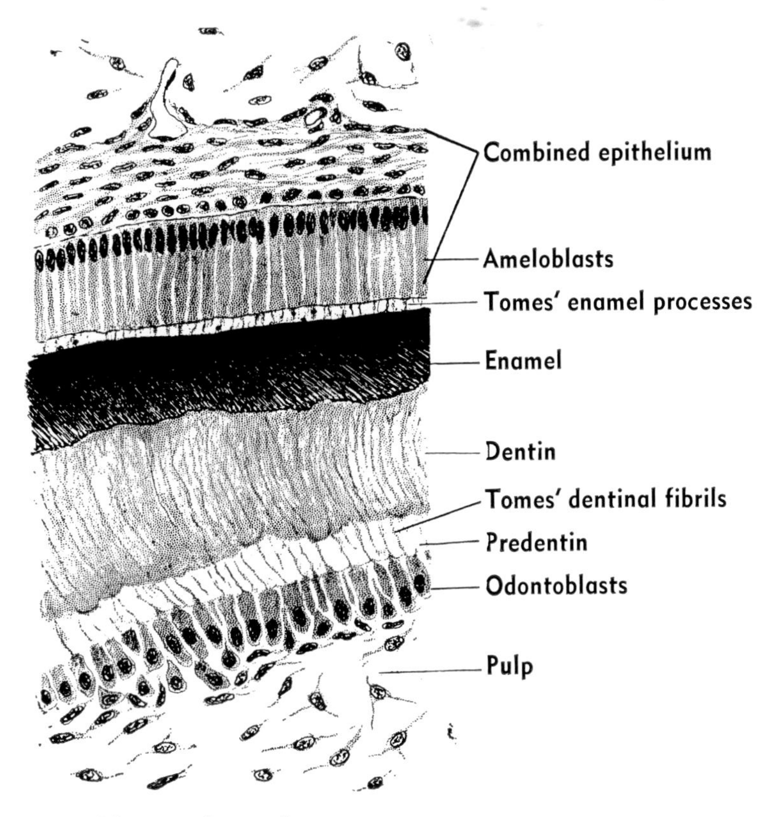

Fig. 94. Formation of dentin and enamel.

eventually leads to the production of the fully calcified enamel rod. Between the rods there are fine interstices which also contain calcified material. These interprismatic areas are, however, not as highly calcified as the rods in mature enamel. The process of enamel formation continues until the crown is completely formed. By the time the tooth erupts the ameloblasts and the other enamel epithelia in the coronal region degenerate, leaving only the enamel cuticle covering the crown.

Mature enamel. Enamel is the hardest tissue in the body.* It is calcified to the extent of approximately 98 per cent. It also contains small amounts of keratin and moisture. Enamel covers the crown of the tooth and is whitish in color. It is in relation with dentin, cementum, and the gingiva.

Enamel consists of highly calcified rods or prisms which are separated

*In the study of mature teeth we face a problem in regard to the preparation of tissues suitable for microscopic study similar to that encountered in the technical procedures required to prepare sections of bone. It will be recalled that the hardness of bone makes it impossible to prepare sections in the usual manner. Similarly, in the preparation of sections of mature teeth, two types of sections are prepared: (1) ground sections and (2) decalcified sections. In the study of mature enamel, however, we must limit our studies to but one type, the ground section. This is necessary because in decalcifying a tooth to the extent necessary to cut with a knife on a microtome all of the enamel is dissolved.

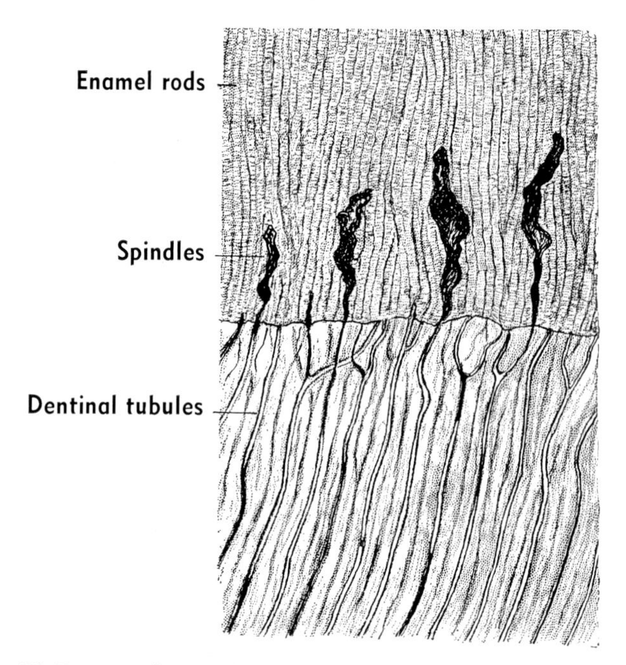

Fig. 95. Dentin and enamel from a ground section of a mature human tooth.

by minute amounts of interprismatic substance (Fig. 95). The enamel rods extend from the periphery of the dentin to the free surface of the crown. Their direction in general is radial in the region of the tip or the cusp; toward the cervix of the crown they sometimes form a slight angle with reference to the dentinal tubules. In certain parts of the crown the rods frequently intertwine. When viewed in longitudinal section this enamel appears gnarled. The shape of the enamel rod in cross section varies. It is sometimes hexagonal. Frequently, however, one side may be concave or convex.

Imbrication lines, known as the striae of Retzius, are frequently observed in sections of enamel. These striae take origin at the dentino-enamel junction and extend to the free surface of the crown in an arc paralleling the surface of the dentin. In transverse sections of the crown the striae appear concentrically arranged.

Organic material in the form of keratin appears in enamel of most teeth as strands or tufts which originate at the dentino-enamel junction. This organic component is most readily observed in transverse sections of the crown.

Development of dentin. Dentin is laid down in the developing deciduous tooth just before the appearance of enamel.

The first step in the development of this tissue consists of the formation of a reticular membrane which occupies a region just below the inner enamel epithelium. This tissue and other elements incorporated into dentin are derived from the mesenchyme which makes up the primitive pulp. The reticular fibers come to be arranged radially, first at the tip of the crown and later toward the apex of the developing tooth.

These radially arranged reticular fibers undergo two important changes during the development of dentin: (1) they come to lie within the calcified tissue more or less parallel to the contour lines of the tooth; (2) they change from reticular to collagenous fibers.

Dentin is first differentiated on the tip of the crown, then it gradually envelops the entire pulp cavity. When dentin is first formed certain cells which align themselves along the periphery of the pulp cavity gradually differentiate into special columnar cells known as odontoblasts. The odontoblasts have a dark-staining, rounded basal nucleus and relatively clear cytoplasm which stains intensely with eosin. A slender filamentous process known as Tomes' dentinal fibril, which comes to occupy a space in the dentin, is elaborated at the free surface of the cell. The basal surface of these cells frequently ends in a blunt tapering projection. In the tip of the crown the layer of odontoblasts is several cells deep. Approaching the apex the cells thin out until eventually they are arranged in a single epithelioid layer. It is in such an area that they may be most advantageously studied in sections of the developing tooth (Fig. 94).

The first dentin which can be observed in hematoxylin and eosin preparations appears as a relatively narrow zone of tissue peripheral to the pulp cavity. It takes the eosin stain and one may observe Tomes' dentinal fibrils occupying a radial position within this tissue. In this, the uncalcified state, it is known as predentin.

After the initial zone of predentin has been established examination of a slightly later stage in tooth development reveals that a new zone of predentin has formed on the pulpal side of the first increment. During this process the odontoblasts retreat pulpward, retaining meanwhile their connection with the dentin by means of the dentinal fibrils which lie embedded in the dentin.

While the second zone of predentin forms, the initial, or peripheral, zone undergoes partial calcification. In this process small droplets of bluish staining material appear which come together to form calcoglobules. This gives a fairly characteristic globular appearance to calcifying dentin. In the later stages of development the globules usually coalesce to form a tissue which is fairly uniform in appearance.

The dentinal fibrils meanwhile do not calcify. They occupy spaces within the calcified tissue which are known as dentinal tubules.

In comparing the development of enamel with that of dentin it should be emphasized that enamel is a solid, nontubular tissue which grows peripherally with reference to the dentin. Unlike dentin, which retains vital connections by means of Tomes' dentinal processes, enamel losses all contact with vital tissues when the tooth erupts. This has an important bearing on the metabolism of these tissues in the erupted tooth.

Mature dentin. Mature dentin is a translucent, compressible tissue consisting of a calcified component (apatite) and an organic component which is chiefly collagen. It also contains moisture. Examination of a ground section of this tissue reveals a relatively homogeneous translucent calcified tissue (Fig. 95). The collagenous fibers which are embedded within this calcified tissue are not visible except in specially prepared sections. Dentin is traversed by numerous tubules which extend from the pulp to the periphery of the dentin. In the living state these tubules contain Tomes' dentinal fibrils and dental lymph. The tubules are arranged in the form of the letter S in the crown. In the root they are relatively straight. Before they terminate the tubules branch dichotomously into from two to four branches. As the tubules traverse the dentin they also give off many lateral side branches known as tubiculi; some of these latter connect with tubiculi of adjacent tubules. The tubiculi are best shown in ground sections stained with silver nitrate. In decalcified sections stained with hematoxylin and eosin a dark zone surrounds the dentinal tubules. This is known as Neumann's sheath.

Variations. On the periphery of the root one may observe in ground sections of a tooth an imperfectly calcified zone of dentin which, because of its characteristic appearance, is known as Tomes' granular layer. Imbrication lines, also known as the lines of Owen, are also frequently observed in dentin. They are rather wide bands of dentin which follow the contour of the tooth and have a less dense appearance in section. They probably indicate disturbances in metabolism during the formation of dentin.

More extensive variations in the appearance of dentin may also be observed in many teeth which have developed under conditions of faulty mineral metabolism. These areas in the dentin are readily seen in ground sections of teeth and are most commonly observed in the crown just below the dentino-enamel junction. This tissue is known as interglobular dentin and represents areas practically devoid of calcified material. The scallop-edged areas appear black in ground section (reference to the method of calcification will make this more understandable).

Abrasion of tooth surfaces and caries also produce variations in the histological appearance of dentin. In the former situation the dentin in contact with an abraded area usually becomes hypercalcified or sclerosed, and in both of these situations an irregular variety of the tissue known as secondary dentin may be deposited on the margin of the pulp cavity in an apparent attempt to protect the pulp tissues.

Cementum

Cementum is a calcified tissue which forms a thin shell around the periphery of the root. In origin, appearance, and composition it closely resembles bone. It is first formed in the cervical part of the tooth; gradually it encloses the entire root.

There are two varieties of cementum: (1) primary, or cell free, which appears hyaline in ground sections and usually occurs on the coronal part of the root; (2) secondary, or cellular cementum, which is deposited later than primary cementum and occupies a position on the periphery of the apical third of the root. In ground sections of the tooth one observes a hyaline calcified tissue in which scattered cells, cementoblasts, occupy a space within lacunae—much as in sections of bone. The fibers of the peridental membrane which suspend the tooth in the socket are firmly anchored to the root of the tooth by means of cementum.

Pulp

Pulp is essentially a connective tissue organ. In ordinary sections the pulp in the young tooth is extremely cellular. The appearance of the pulp cells is similar to that of fibroblasts. Histiocytes have also been described as being present in the pulp. As the tooth increases in age the character of the pulp changes: the relative number of cells decreases and the fibers increase.

Odontoblasts, previously referred to, occupy a position on the periphery of the pulp. These cells constantly retreat pulpward as dentin is slowly deposited throughout the life of the tooth. In the mature tooth the region just below the odontoblasts has fewer cells than other parts of the pulp and is known as the cell-poor zone of Weil.

The pulp tissue contains an abundant nerve and vascular supply.

Gingiva

The gingiva is the modified part of the oral mucous membrane which covers the surface of the alveolus (Fig. 96). It is attached to the tooth at the level at which the tooth is inserted into the oral cavity. It consists of two parts: (1) dense connective tissue, the lamina propria, and (2) a covering of stratified squamous epithelium.

The tissues which make up the gingivae are normally attached to the alveolus and to the tooth surfaces. The undersurface of the epithelium is frequently thrown into folds or pegs. The outer surface usually shows a slight degree of cornification. The chief function of this tissue is protective. The following parts of the gingivae are usually recognizable in sections: (1) the outer border of the gingiva, known as the gingival margin; (2) the gingival crevice, a space of variable size between the tooth surface and the gingiva; (3) the epithelial attachment, a strip of stratified squamous epithelium which takes origin at the approximate level of the cemento-enamel junction. It is attached to the tooth at this level and continues up to the free

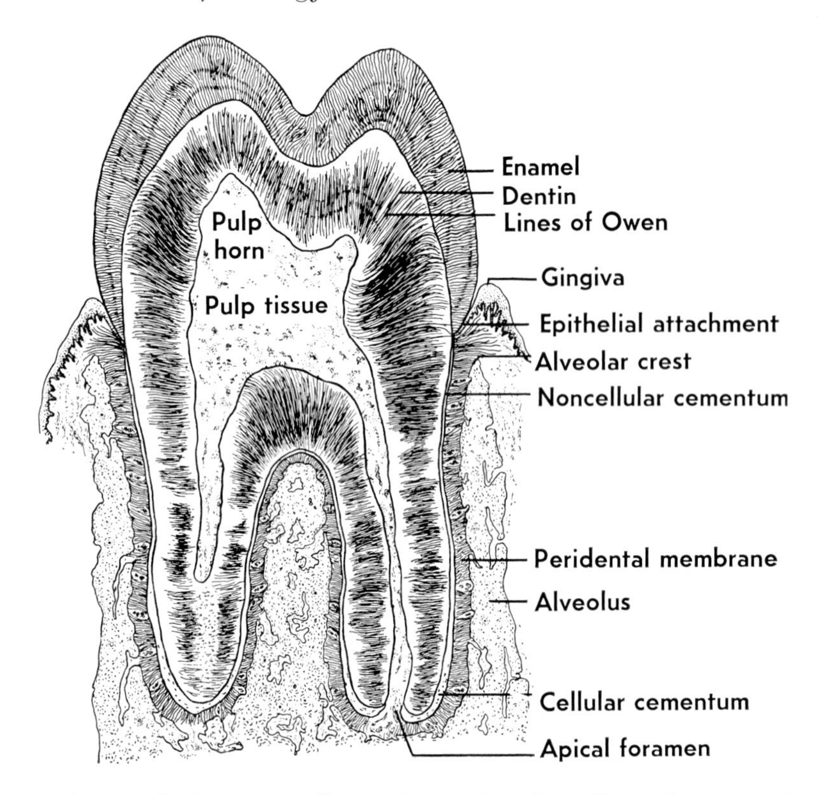

Fig. 96. Section of a human maxillary molar cut buccolingually to show general relationships of tooth and surrounding tissues.

margin of the gingiva. For some considerable distance it is in intimate contact with the cervical part of the crown. With advancing age this tissue migrates rootward.

Peridental membrane

Peridental membrane is a term used to designate a group of collagenous fibers which suspend the tooth in the socket and support the gingivae. The fibers occupy a space between the bony socket or alveolus on the one hand and the periphery of the root on the other. Above the level of the alveolus the fibers run up to the gingiva. They also connect the cervical parts of adjacent teeth.

The fibers concerned with the suspension of the tooth and support of the gingivae are known as principal fibers. They are relatively short fibers which, in the region of the root, are arranged horizontally or obliquely with reference to the long axis of the tooth.

Other fibers known as interstitial fibers occur in the peridental space as isolated islands of connective tissue in which one may observe in section the vessels and nerves which supply this tissue. Clusters of dark-staining cells, the epithelial rests, may frequently be seen in the peridental membrane. They are remnants of the enamel epithelium.

Alveolus

The alveolus or socket is the bony crypt in which the tooth is suspended (Fig. 96). The alveolus proper, or cribriform plate, consists of a thin lamina of bone which surrounds the root just peripheral to the peridental membrane. This plate is made up of compact bone. The distal ends of the fibers of the peridental membrane are firmly cemented into this tissue. Between the compact bone making up the cribriform plate and the external parts of the jaw there are numerous trabeculae of supporting bone which are advantageously arranged to take up the stresses which the teeth transmit to the bone surrounding them.

TONGUE

The tongue is primarily a muscular organ. It is covered with a mucous membrane, parts of which are modified to conform to its function as an organ of mastication and of taste.

The muscles of the tongue are in three main groups: longitudinal, transverse, and sagittal fibers, arranged in interlacing groups and embedded in areolar and adipose tissue.

The mucosa covering the dorsal surface of the tognue is modified to form a great number of elevations or papillae. It should be noted that these papillae are different from the projections of connective tissue of the epithelium which have been mentioned in descriptions of other parts of the oral mucosae. The papilla of the tongue is an elevation of both connective tissue and epithelium. Within each of them there may be also projections of the tunica propria into the epithelium, which are termed secondary papillae. The distribution and characteristic forms of the papillae of the tongue are filiform, fungiform, foliate, and vallate.

Filiform papillae

Filiform papillae are the most numerous of the papillae and are distributed over the entire dorsal surface of the tongue. Each consists of a conical elevation of the tunica propria and stratified squamous epithelium. The whole papilla is inclined in an anteroposterior direction. Its surface epithelium is cornified, the cornification extending in strands, which gives this type of papilla its name (threadlike) (Fig. 98).

Fungiform papillae

Fungiform papillae are distributed unevenly among the filiform papillae on the dorsal surface of the tongue, being most numerous near the margin

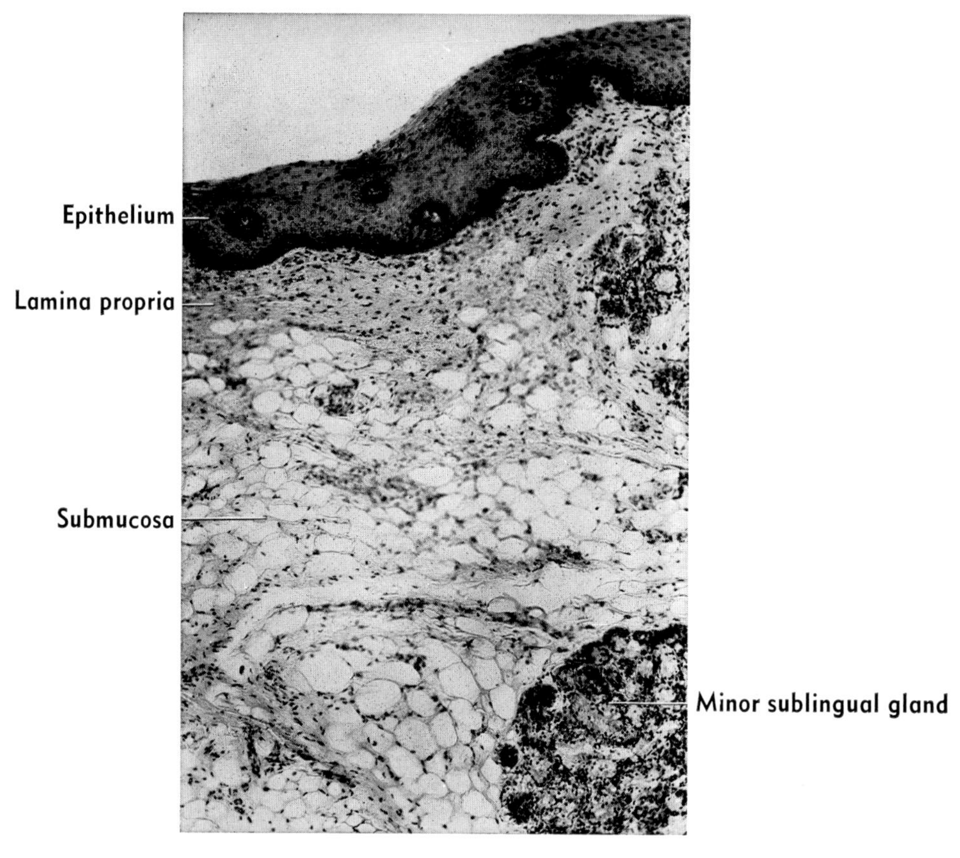

Fig. 97. Mucous membrane from floor of mouth. (From Orban, editor: Oral Histology and Embryology, St. Louis, 1957, The C. V. Mosby Co.)

of the organ but never as numerous as the filiform variety. They are club shaped, with flattened free surfaces, and have a diameter somewhat greater than that of the basal portion of a filiform papilla. The epithelium covering them shows little, if any, cornification and is relatively thin. This, combined with the fact that they have a rich blood supply, gives them a red color in the living state. Their secondary papillae are a characteristic feature of these structures (Fig. 98). Taste buds are sometimes visible on the free surfaces of fungiform papillae but are small and not always noticeable.

Foliate papillae

Foliate papillae are well developed on the tongues of certain rodents but are rudimentary in man. When fully developed they have some features in common with fungiform papillae, being club shaped with flat tops. The types are readily distinguishable, however, by the following facts: (1) the foliate papillae occur in groups along the lateral margins

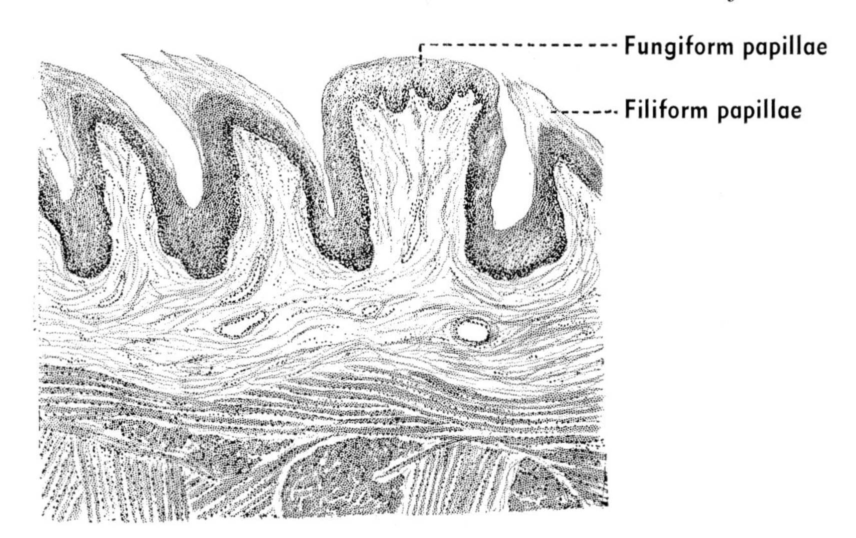

Fig. 98. Dorsal surface of tongue of dog.

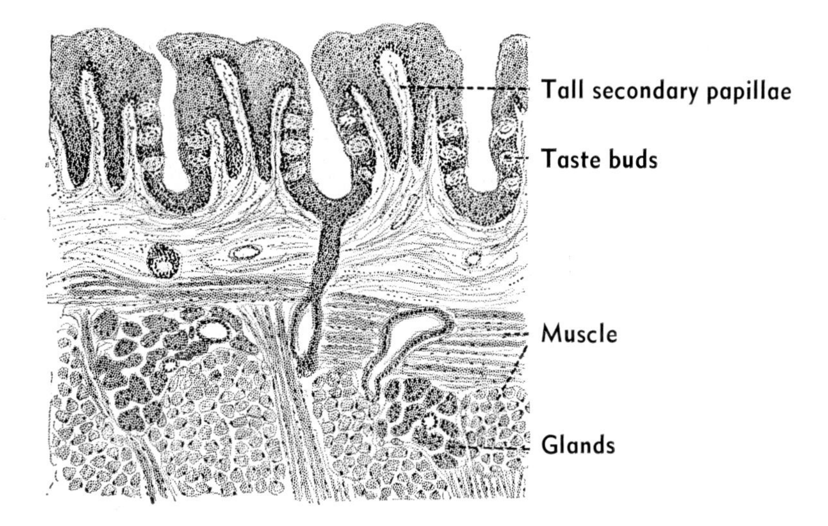

Fig. 99. Foliate papillae from tongue of rabbit.

of the tongue and are not intermingled with filiform papillae; (2) they have numerous prominent taste buds set close together along their sides; and (3) they are characterized by the presence of the secondary connective tissue papillae which occupy approximately three-fourths of the depth of the primary papilla. Lingual glands occur in the same part of the tongue as do the foliate papilla (Fig. 99).

Vallate (circumvallate) papillae

Vallate (circumvallate) papillae are the largest papillae of the tongue and the least numerous. There are only from twenty to thirty of them,

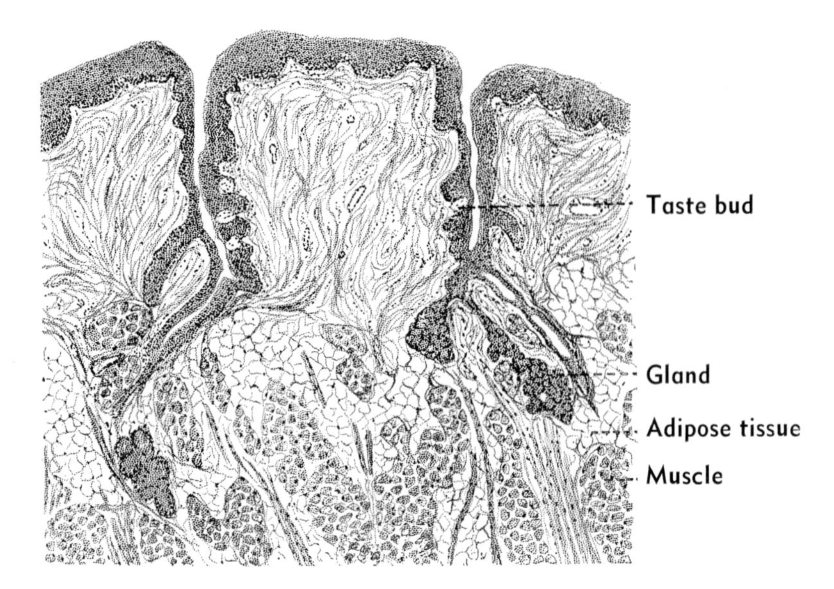

Fig. 100. Vallate papilla.

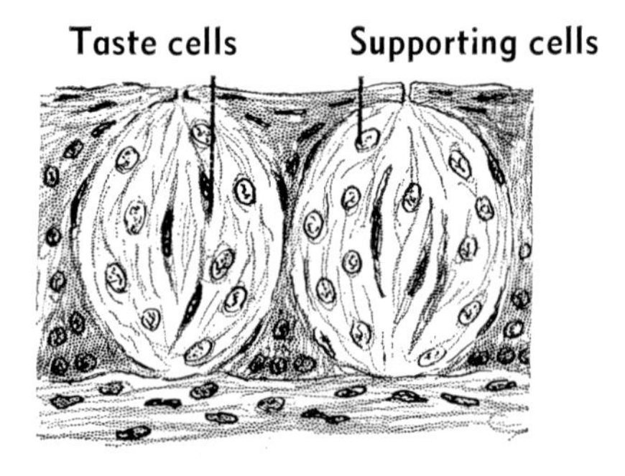

Fig. 101. Taste buds from tongue of rabbit. (Hematoxylin and eosin stain.)

arranged along the sulcus terminalis, and they are so large that they are macroscopically visible. Each projects but a short distance above the surface of the tongue but is, as the name implies, surrounded by a deep groove (Fig. 100). Their secondary papillae are short and usually occur only on the surface. The outstanding characteristics, aside from their size and positions, are: (1) the walls of the grooves surrounding them are beset with large taste buds, and (2) the grooves serve as the point of exit for the ducts of conspicuous serous glands, which are present in this part of the tongue (Ebner's glands).

The taste buds are composed of two kinds of cells: the specialized taste cells and the supporting cells. In ordinary sections the two kinds may be distinguished by their nuclei, those of the taste cells being dark and spindle shaped and those of the supporting cells pale and round or oval

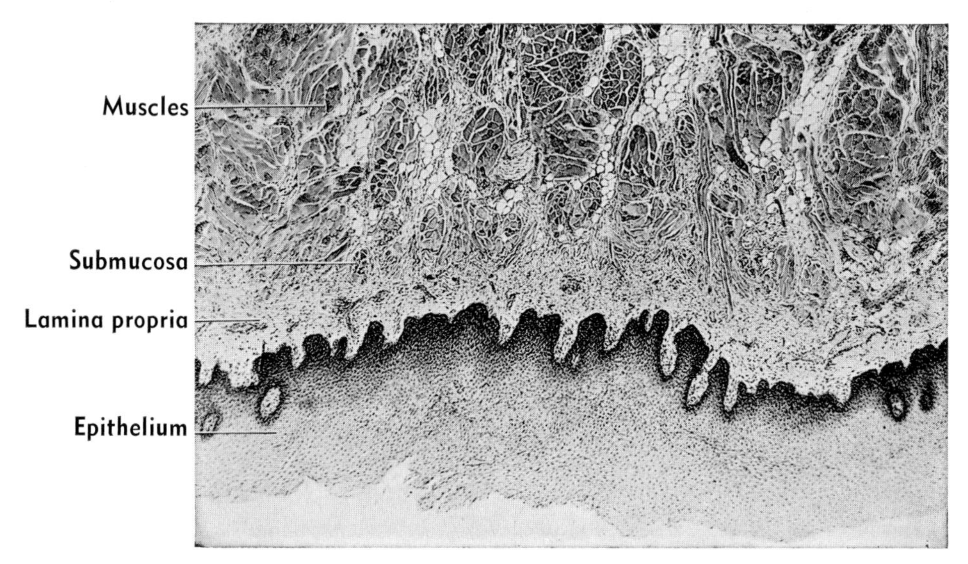

Fig. 102. Mucous membrane on inferior surface of tongue. (From Orban, editor: Oral Histology and Embryology, St. Louis, 1957, The C. V. Mosby Co.)

shaped. The taste bud as a whole is a flask-shaped structure lying in the epithelium and opening onto the surface through a minute circular pore (Fig. 101). In specimens treated with silver nitrate, nerve fibers may be traced into the center of the buds.

The ventral surface of the tongue is covered by mucous membrane not unlike that lining the lips and cheeks. In all parts of the organ the interlacing bands of striated muscle are a characteristic feature. In regions where glands occur their secreting portions lie in the connective tissue which forms a stroma around the muscles, producing an arrangement of glandular and muscular tissue not often seen in other organs. It may be said that the tongue has no submucosa, this layer being replaced by a mixture of connective tissue, muscle, and glands.

GLANDS OF THE ORAL CAVITY

Saliva, the fluid in the oral cavity, is secreted principally by three large glands, the parotid, the submaxillary, and the sublingual, which lie outside the lining of the cavity and communicate with it by means of large ducts. Contributions to the saliva are made, also, by numerous smaller glands which are situated in the submucosa of some parts of the wall of the oral cavity and among the muscles of the tongue. They are of three kinds, serous, mucous, and seromucous, and are located as follows: (1) The serous glands are located in the tongue, in the region of the vallate papillae (Ebner's). (2) The mucous glands are located on the anterior surface of the soft palate (palatine), on the hard palate, on the borders near the foliate papillae (lingual) of the tongue, and on the root of the tongue. (3) The seromucous glands are located on the anterior portion (anterior lingual) of the tongue and on the lips (labial).

Posterior to the sulcus terminalis there are no papillae on the dorsal surface of the tongue. It is covered by stratified squamous epithelium like that lining the remainder of the cavity at this point. The tunica propria consists of reticular tissue and contains condensations of lymphoid tissue and the palatine and lingual tonsils described in Chapter IX. There are mucous glands in the submucosa of the fauces.

PHARYNX

The oral cavity opens through the *fauces* into the oropharynx. This region is only partly separated from the upper respiratory region or *nasopharynx* by the soft palate and the uvula. The latter abutts on the *pharyngeal tonsils* (adenoids). At the level of the hyoid bone the oropharynx merges into the *laryngeal pharynx*, which in turn leads to the epiglottis of the respiratory system and the esophagus of the digestive system.

The pharynx is thus the meeting place for the nasal passages, oral cavity, larynx, and esophagus. Histologically the pharynx takes on the mixed characteristics of all these structures.

The nasopharynx has a lining characteristic of the respiratory tract, namely, a pseudostratified epithelium and a tunica propria which is separated from the submucosa by an elastic membrane. This region will be described in the chapter on the respiratory system.

The oropharynx and laryngopharynx are intermediate in composition, as they are in position between the oral cavity and the esophagus. They are lined with nonkeratinized stratified squamous epithelium and have a lamina propria containing numerous elastic fibers, some of which form an incomplete membrane at the border of the mucosa. Branches of this elastic lamina also extend between groups of muscle bundles.

In the superior lateral regions of the pharynx the submucosa may be of considerable extent and contain the secreting portions of mucous glands. In some parts of the pharynx, however, the elastic membrane of the mucosa rests immediately on the muscular layer, in which situation the glands occupy a position between the strands of muscle, similar to the pattern found in the tongue. The arrangement described has given rise to the statement that the pharynx has no submucosa. It is obvious, however, that in a transitional region such as the pharynx different conditions obtain at different levels of the organ. Sections of the laryngopharynx are in fact difficult to distinguish from sections of the upper part of the esophagus, especially since the elastic lamina is thoroughly dispersed in this region.

The muscular layer of the pharyngeal wall consists of bundles of striated muscle obliquely arranged to form a constrictor. The bundles interlace and form irregular layers.

CHAPTER XV

Digestive tract

The digestive tract is a hollow tube running from the oral cavity to the anus, modified in its various parts but consisting throughout of four coats or layers: mucosa, submucosa, muscularis, and adventitia or serosa.

Mucosa. The mucosa is made up of (1) an epithelial lining which borders on the lumen of the tract and rests upon (2) a tunica propria of reticular or fine areolar tissue. The tunica propria may contain glands, scattered fibers of smooth muscle, and lymph nodules. The nodules are often quite large, extending below the mucosa into the adjacent coat of the tract. Fine capillaries and lymphatics are present in the tunica propria. In the greater part of the digestive tube the mucosa includes a third layer (3) the muscularis mucosae, which is a thin coat of smooth muscle fibers.

Submucosa. The second coat of the wall is the submucosa. This is composed of areolar tissue which contains a plexus of small blood vessels known as Heller's plexus. It also includes numerous lymphatics and a plexus of nerves (Meissner's plexus). In the esophagus and the duodenum the submucosa contains the end pieces of mucous glands. In other parts of the tube lymphoid tissue extends from the mucosa into the submucosa.

Muscularis. The muscularis is composed of two layers of muscle. The fibers of the inner coat are arranged circularly about the tube, whereas those of the outer coat lie in its long axis. This arrangement is followed throughout the tract, but in the stomach there is a third oblique layer, next to the submucosa. Thickenings of the circular layer form sphincters at various points of the tract. In the upper end of the esophagus and the lower end of the rectum the muscle is striated; elsewhere it is smooth. The two layers of muscle are separated by a thin layer of connective tissue in which may be seen the myenteric (Auerbach's) plexus of nerves.

Adventitia or serosa. The adventitia or serosa, the fourth layer of the tract, is composed of loose areolar tissue frequently containing adipose tissue. Where the tract borders on the body cavity the areolar

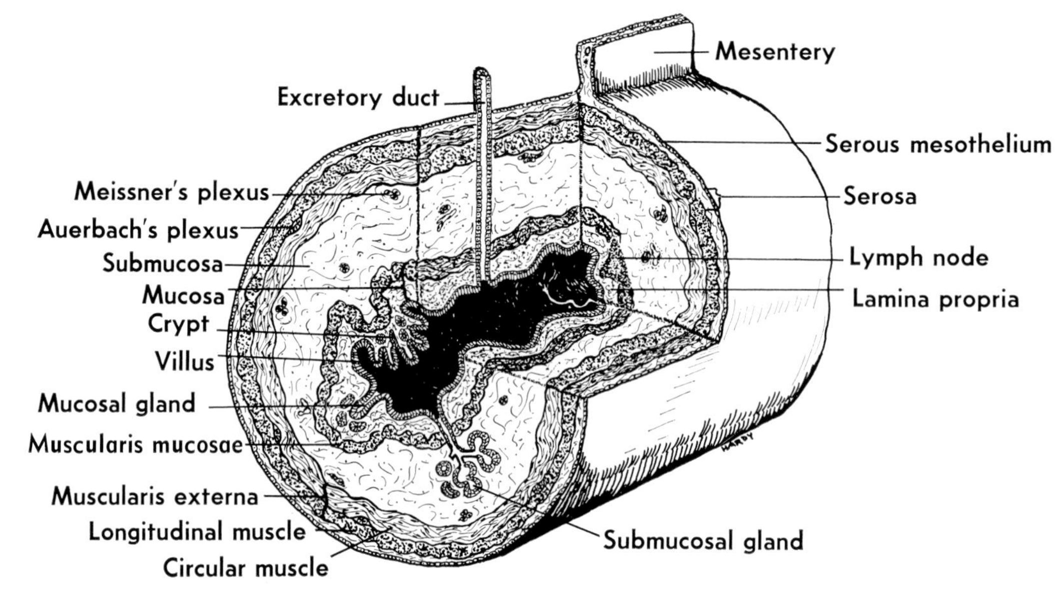

Fig. 103. Stereogram of general plan of gastrointestinal tract.

tissue is covered by the mesothelium and is called the serosa. Elsewhere it blends with the surrounding fascia and is called the adventitia.

The coats of the digestive tract are summarized as follows.

1. Mucosa
   (a) Epithelium
   (b) Tunica propria, containing
      *Glands**
      Lymphoid tissue
      Scattered muscle fibers
      Capillaries and small lymphatics
      Muscularis mucosae
2. Submucosa
   (a) Areolar tissue, containing
      Glands
      Lymphoid tissue
      Heller's plexus of blood vessels
      Meissner's plexus of nerves
      Lymphatics
3. Muscularis
   (a) *Oblique layer*
   (b) Circular layer
   (c) Connective tissue containing Auerbach's plexus of nerves
   (d) Longitudinal layer
4. Adventitia or serosa
   (a) Areolar tissue, containing
      Adipose tissue
      Blood vessels
      Mesothelial covering

*Italics indicate the structures present in some but not all divisions of the digestive tract.

ESOPHAGUS

Mucosa. This region of the mucosa of the digestive tract is distinguished from the remainder by the fact that it is lined with stratified squamous epithelium which rests upon a fairly thick tunica propria (Fig. 104). In many mammals the epithelium is cornified at its surface. There are two narrow zones of glands in the mucosa of the esophagus, one at its junction with the stomach, and the other at the level of the cricoid cartilage. These glands, called superficial glands, are shallow branching tubules secreting mucus into the lumen of the organ. The mucosa also contains small lymph nodules and scattered lymphoid tissue.

The muscularis mucosae is absent in the upper part of the esophagus, its place being taken by a rather indefinite elastic membrane which separates the mucosa from the submucosa. Smooth muscle first appears about one-fourth of the way down the tube in the form of scattered bundles longitudinally arranged. Farther down the tract these are consolidated in a complete layer. A unique feature of the muscularis mucosa of the esophagus is that it is thicker than in any other part of the digestive tract, also, the fibers run in only one direction.

Submucosa. The submucosa of the esophagus is generally described as a layer of areolar tissue containing throughout its length blood ves-

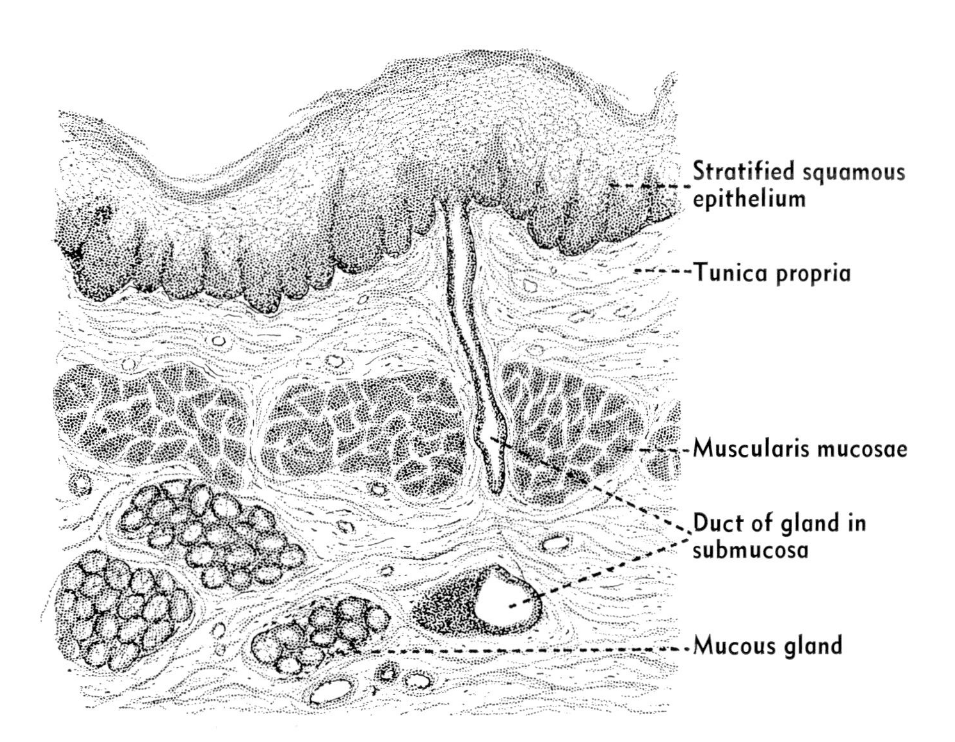

Fig. 104. Mucosa and submucosa of human esophagus.

sels, nerves, and the secreting portion of mucous glands, the ducts of which run through the mucosa to open onto the epithelial surface. As a matter of fact the glands are not constant in their distribution, and some animals (for example, the monkey) have only a few in this layer.

Muscularis. In the upper half of the esophagus the muscle is striated like that of the tongue. It is not, however, under the control of the will. In the lower half of the esophagus the muscle changes to the smooth variety; in the middle portion the two kinds may be found intermingled. The arrangement of the muscular coats of the esophagus is less regular than that of other parts of the digestive tract. Two coats are present, but both may have the fibers obliquely placed so that the typical orientation in any inner circular and outer longitudinal layer may not be apparent. This is particularly true in the esophagus of the dog.

The mucosa and submucosa of the esophagus are illustrated in Fig. 104. Particular attention is called to the wide lumina of the ducts which lead from the glands of the submucosa to the surface.

STOMACH

Mucosa. At the junction of the esophagus and stomach the lining epithelium changes abruptly from stratified squamous to simple columnar, the cells of which secrete mucus. The epithelium of the stomach, unlike that of the small intestine, does not have a cuticular border. The surface of the mucosa is thrown into folds (rugae), the height and number of which depend on the degree of distention of the organ. In addition to the rugae the surface of the mucosa is marked by closely set pits, which are lined with

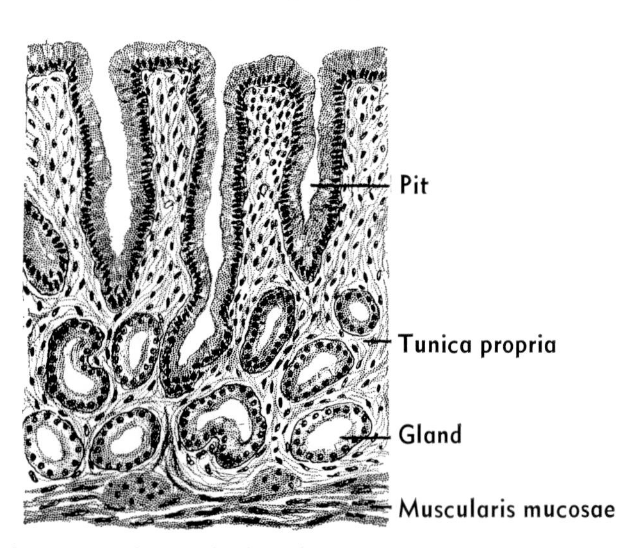

Fig. 105. Mucosa of cardiac region of stomach of monkey.

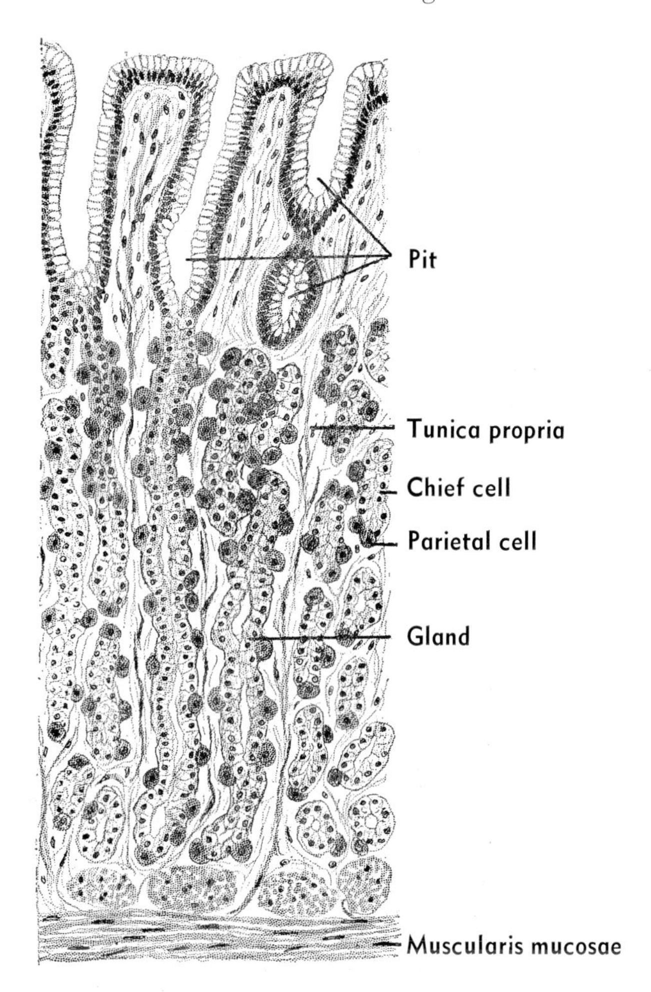

Fig. 106. Mucosa from fundus of stomach of monkey.

the same sort of epithelium. Beneath the epithelium there is a tunica propria of reticular or fine areolar tissue, and below the level of the pits this layer contains glands. The shape and proportionate depth of the pits and the characteristics of the glands are different in different parts of the stomach. At the junction of the esophagus and stomach the pits are shallow, and the glands, which are lined with a simple cuboidal epithelium, have wide lumina and secrete thin mucus (Fig. 105).

In the fundic region (Fig. 106) the mucosa is much deeper than in the zone immediately below the esophagus and it contains a greater number of glands. The tunica propria is reduced to a fine interglandular stroma in its deeper portion, and the pits extend only about one-fourth of the distance from the surface to the muscularis mucosae. The glands are called fundic glands or (since they are found in all parts of the organ except the cardiac and pyloric zones) they may be called gastric glands. Each is composed of three types of cells which may be recognized in hematoxylin and eosin preparations. The types are (1) mucous neck cells, (2) chief cells, and (3) parietal cells. The mucous neck cells are like the mucus-secreting cells occurring in the lining of the pit. They are situated in the part of the gland nearest the pit, scattered among cells of the second type. Chief cells are pale in color, their cytoplasm staining faintly with the nuclear dye. Parietal cells, on the other hand, take the cytoplasmic stain deeply, so that with a good hematoxylin and eosin stain the difference between the two kinds of cells is marked, the chief cells being pale and bluish and the parietal cells deep pink or red. The epithelium of the glands is of the simple columnar type, arranged about a lumen. The lumen is, however, so narrow that it is almost imperceptible, and the effect produced is that of a cord of cells. The parietal cells are most numerous at the neck of the gland. They do not border directly on the lumen of the gland but

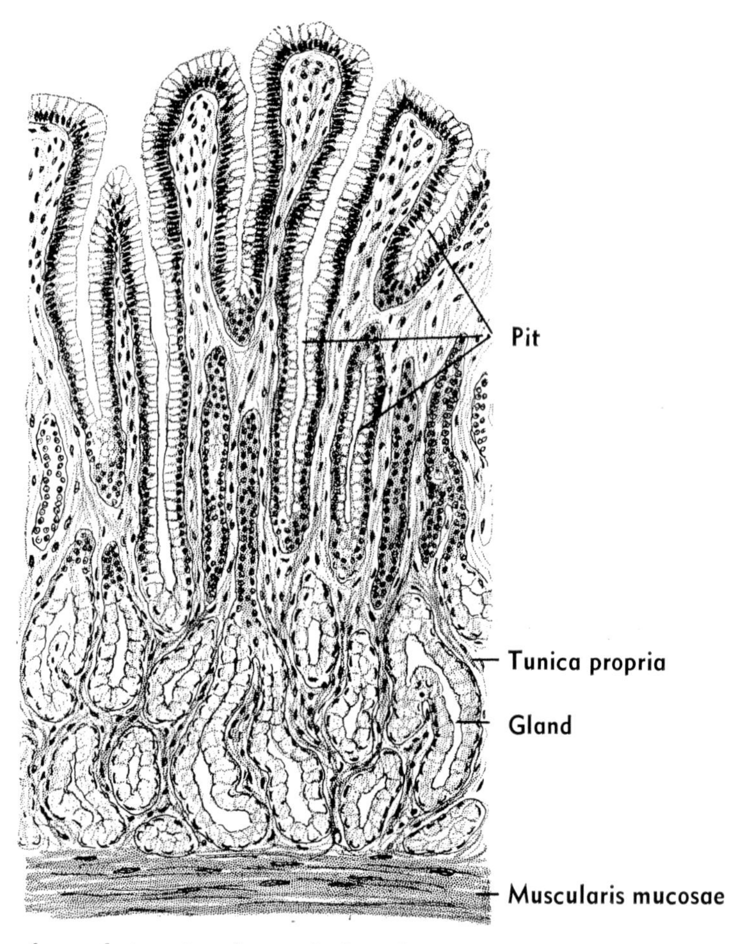

Fig. 107. Mucosa from pyloric region of stomach of monkey.

are crowded away from it by the chief cells. The parietal cells are oval shaped, with the narrow end directed inward and the outer end protruding beyond the bases of the adjacent chief cells. The chief cells contain zymogen granules, which suggest secretory activity, whereas the parietal cells contain the antecedent of hydrochloric acid. The secretions of both types of cells enter the cavity of the stomach through the pits, each of which serves as a duct for several gastric glands.

In the pyloric region the pits are relatively deep, extending at least halfway to the muscularis mucosae. (Fig. 107). They are V shaped, tapering off into the glands which open into them. The glands in this portion of the stomach are composed of large mucus-secreting cells and have wide lumina. There are no parietal cells in the pyloric glands except in the transition zone, where they merge with glands of the gastric type.

The muscularis mucosae of all parts of the stomach is a complete layer of smooth muscle which includes both the circular and the longitudinal fibers.

Submucosa. The submucosa is composed of areolar tissue and does not contain glands in any part of the stomach. In a section of the junction of the esophagus and stomach some of the end pieces of deep mucous glands may extend into the submucosa of the stomach, but since their ducts open into the esophagus they should be considered as part of the wall of the latter organ. Small arteries, veins, and lymphatics may easily be seen in the submucosa. Meissner's plexus of nerves and ganglia is less conspicuous.

Muscularis. In the stomach the muscular coat consists of two complete layers (inner circular and outer longitudinal) with an incomplete layer of obliquely arranged fibers between the circular layer and the submucosa. The circular layer is by far the thickest of the three coats. The arrangement of fibers is somewhat irregular, and there may be some difficulty in distinguishing the three coats of the muscularis in a microscopic section of this region. Auerbach's plexus is present between the circular and longitudinal fibers.

Serosa. The greater part of the stomach is covered with a layer of mesothelium outside the loose connective tissue which invests the muscle layers. This is, however, usually destroyed in the preparation of the piece of tissue for sectioning, so that all that is seen of the serosa is a coating of areolar tissue containing blood vessels, adipose tissue, and occasional nerve trunks.

SMALL INTESTINE

The small intestine extends from the pyloric part of the stomach to the large intestine. Its inner surface may be seen, on gross examination, to

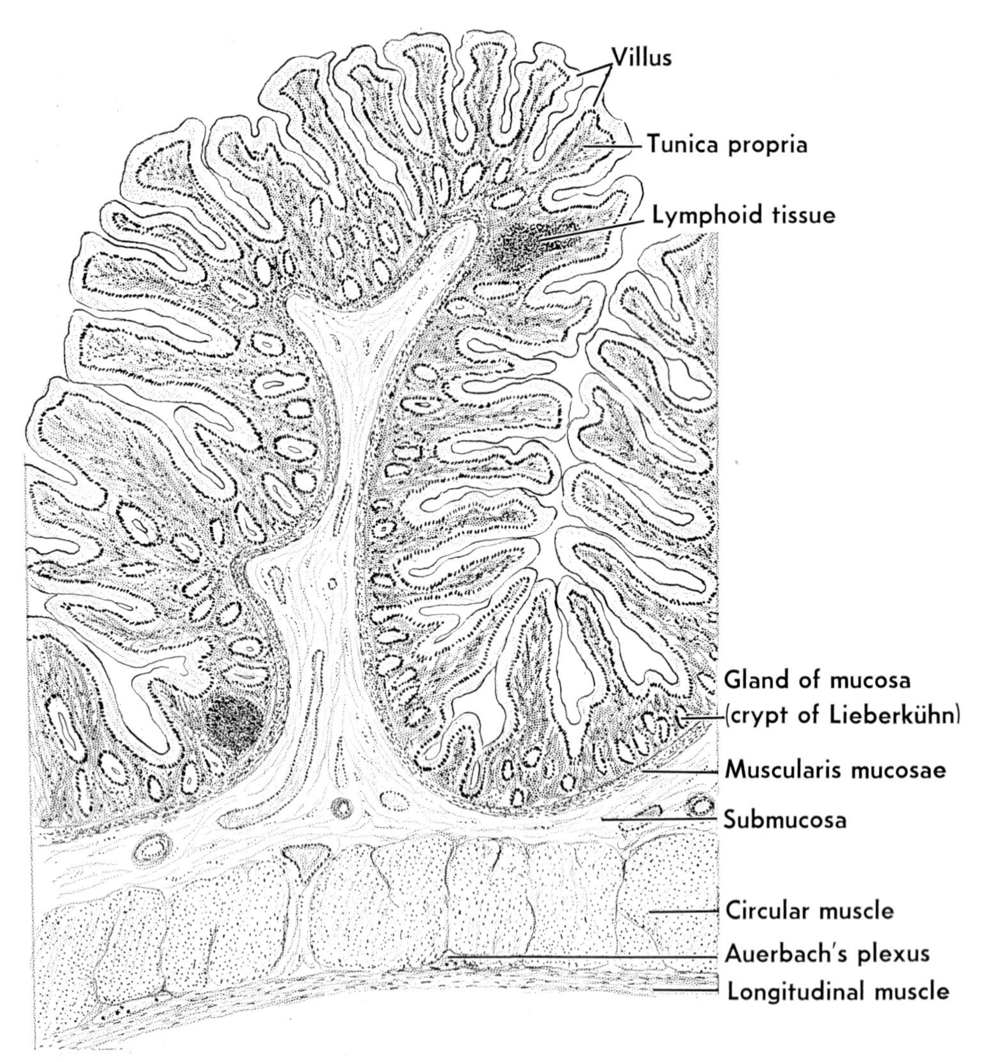

Fig. 108. Longitudinal section of jejunum of monkey, showing a plica circularis.

be marked by the presence of ridges which are circularly disposed and which extend into the lumen throughout this part of the tract. These ridges are the plicae circulares. Each consists of a projection of the connective tissue of the submucosa covered by the mucosa. The plicae circulares provide a greater surface for the absorption of food. The mucosal surface is still further increased by the presence of minute finger-like projections of epithelium and tunica propria which cover the surface of each plica. These are the villi which are hardly visible to the naked eye (Fig. 108).

Mucosa.

Villi. Under the microscope each villus is seen to consist of a projection of the tunica propria covered by simple columnar epithelium.

The tunica propria is reticular tissue and contains capillaries, lymphatics, and scattered muscle fibers. In an injected specimen it is apparent that the vessels have a definite plan of distribution. There is in each villus a central lymphatic called a lacteal (Figs. 109 and 110), into which nutriment from the tract is absorbed. An arteriole enters the villus at one side and breaks up into capillaries at the distal end. Blood is collected from the capillaries by a venule which passes out along the side opposite that occupied by the arteriole. Villi occur in all parts of the small intestine and are its most characteristic feature. In the duodenum they are leaf-shaped; in the jejunum, tall and somewhat enlarged or forked at their distal ends. The ileum has shorter, club-shaped villi. Other parts of the tract have projections which at first sight might be mistaken for villi. In the stomach, for instance, the tissue between two pits has somewhat the same form as a villus and consists of a mass of reticular tissue covered by columnar epithelium. Closer examination reveals, however,

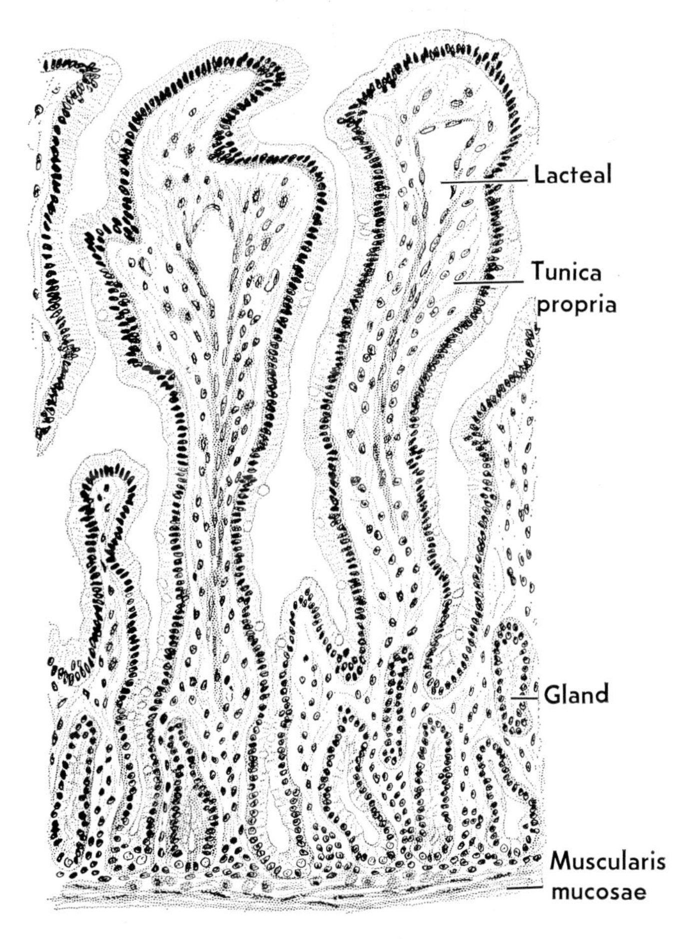

Fig. 109. Mucosa of jejunum of monkey, showing villi and crypts of Lieberkühn.

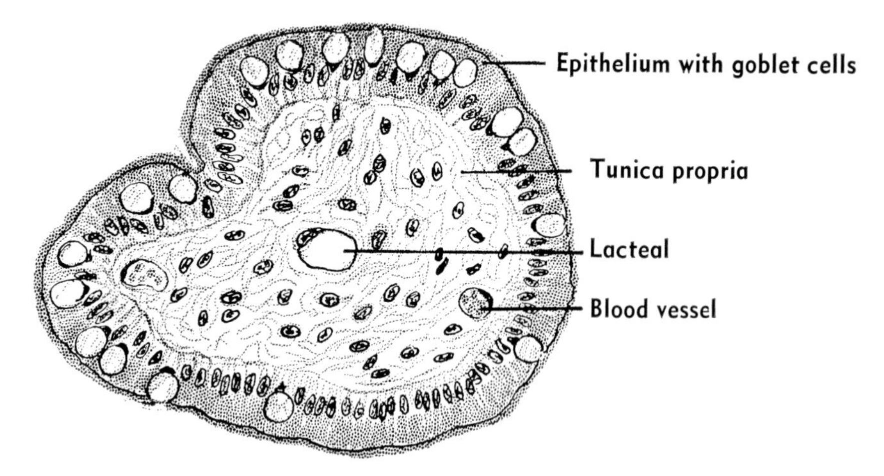

Fig. 110. Transverse section of a villus.

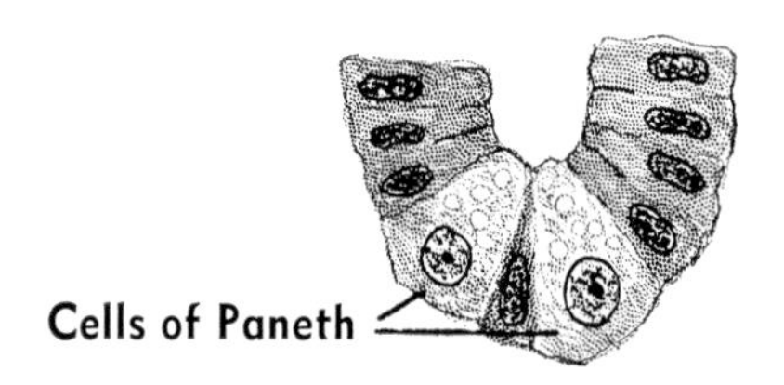

Fig. 111. Epithelium at base of a crypt of Lieberkühn.

that the organization of vessels which is characteristic of a villus is lacking in the stomach.

Glands. Between the bases of the villi glands extend into the lower part of the mucosa (Fig. 109). These are the intestinal glands (crypts of Lieberkühn). At the base of each gland is a group of cells, the cells of Paneth, which are somewhat larger than the surrounding cells and have paler nuclei (Fig. 111). Their cytoplasm is sometimes darker, sometimes lighter than that of the surrounding cells. They are believed to form a digestive enzyme. Cells similar to the Paneth cells have been found in other parts of the digestive tract, but it is in the small intestine that they are most numerous and therefore most easily found.

The rest of the crypt is lined with columnar epithelium somewhat resembling that which covers the villi. Its cells are, however, not quite as tall, and fewer of them are goblet cells. Special stains bring out the fact that some of the lining cells have an affinity for silver stains, but this type (argentaffine cells) is not distinguishable when stained with hematoxylin and eosin. Like the cells of Paneth, argentaffine cells occur in other parts of the gut as well as in the small intestine.

Lymphoid tissue. Lymphoid tissue is widely distributed throughout the mucosa of the small intestine. In the ileum the nodules are gathered into groups (Peyer's patches) and fill not only the mucosa but also the submucosa. These groups of nodules will be further described later in this discussion.

Muscularis mucosae. The muscularis mucosae consists of two thin layers of smooth muscle, an inner circular and an outer longitudinal layer. It thus repeats in miniature the arrangement of the muscularis coat.

Submucosa. The submucosa of the intestinal wall is different in the three divisions of the small intestine. Its basis is the same throughout, a layer of areolar tissue containing the vessels and nerves of Heller's and Meissner's plexuses, respectively. In the duodenum the layer contains, in addition, groups of mucous glands. These are duodenal glands of Brunner (Fig. 112). Their secretion, which is mucus like that formed in the cardiac glands of the stomach, enters the duodenum through ducts which open on the surface between the crypts of Lieberkühn or into the crypts themselves. In the ileum there are groups of lymph nodules which occupy both mucosa and submucosa (Fig. 113). Each group consists of from ten to sixty nodules with germinal centers, and the groups are so large that they are visible to the naked eye. They not only fill the submucosa

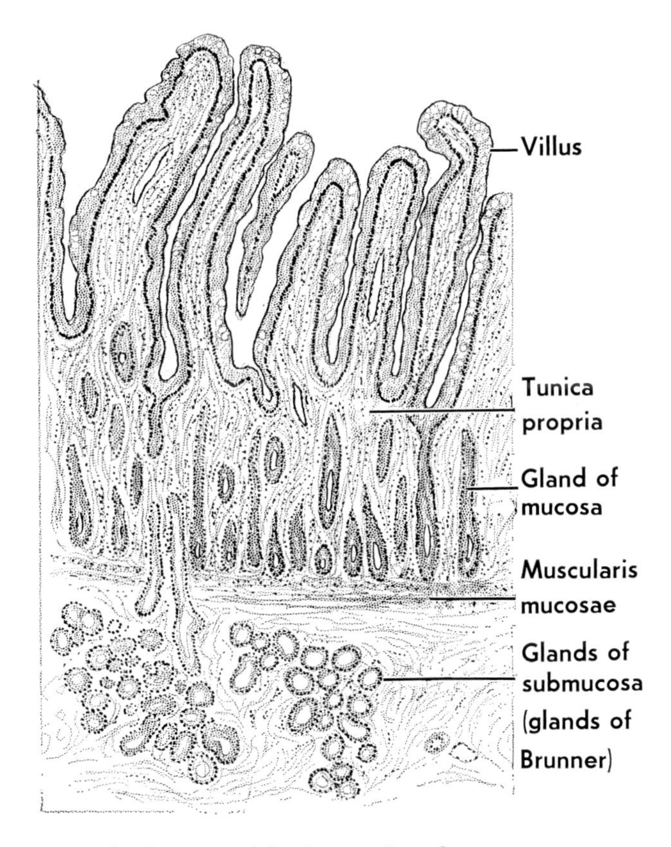

Fig. 112. Mucosa and submucosa of duodenum of monkey.

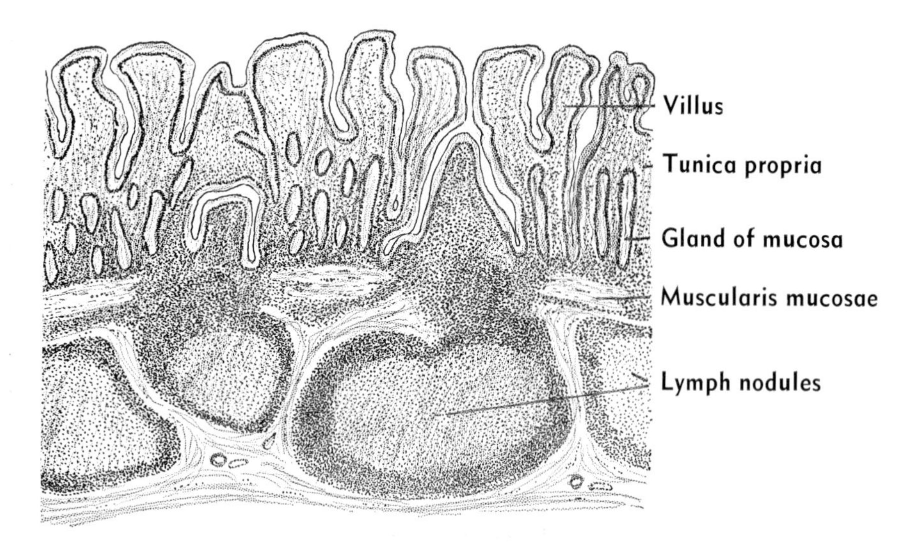

Fig. 113. Mucosa and submucosa of ileum showing Peyer's patches.

and the mucosa, but extend a little into the lumen of the intestine, obliterating the villi. They are called Peyer's patches or the aggregate lymph nodules of the intestine. There may be similar aggregates in the lower part of the jejunum, but the majority of the sections from this part of the tract have only a small amount of lymphoid tissue in them. Glands are never found in the submucosa of the jejunum. It is characterized by its exceptionally high branching plicae circulares and its long villi.

Muscularis. The muscularis of the small intestine consists, throughout its length, of an inner circular and an outer longitudinal layer of smooth muscle. Between these, as in other parts of the tract, lies Auerbach's plexus of nerves.

Serosa. As in the stomach, the serosa is a layer of connective tissue covered by mesothelium.

LARGE INTESTINE

In this division of the digestive tract the plicae circulares are replaced by the semilunar folds which include not only the mucosa and submucosa but also the inner layer of the muscularis and are grossly visible on the outside as well as on the inside of the gut. As the name implies, they are crescentic in shape, each one extending about one-third of the way around the wall of the large intestine. Following is a description of the characteristics of the four coats of this region.

Mucosa (Fig. 114). Water is absorbed from the large intestine, and its lining is well supplied with mucus-secreting cells. It has no villi. In the embryo villi are present in the large intestine, but they disappear during late fetal life. The epithelium is simple columnar with conspicuous goblet cells. The tunica propria contains many glands. These are simple tubular glands, closely set, lined with epithelium like that which covers the surface of the mucosa. They have very few cells of Paneth in them. The tunica propria contains blood and lymph capillaries, but these are not organized in definite units like those of the small intestine. Solitary lymph nodules are present and are often so large that they break through into the submucosa. The muscularis mucosae is composed of an inner circular and an outer longitudinal layer (Fig. 115), as in the small intestine.

Submucosa. The submucosa of the colon has no glands in it. Besides the areolar tissue with vessels and nerves it contains only the solitary lymph nodules mentioned.

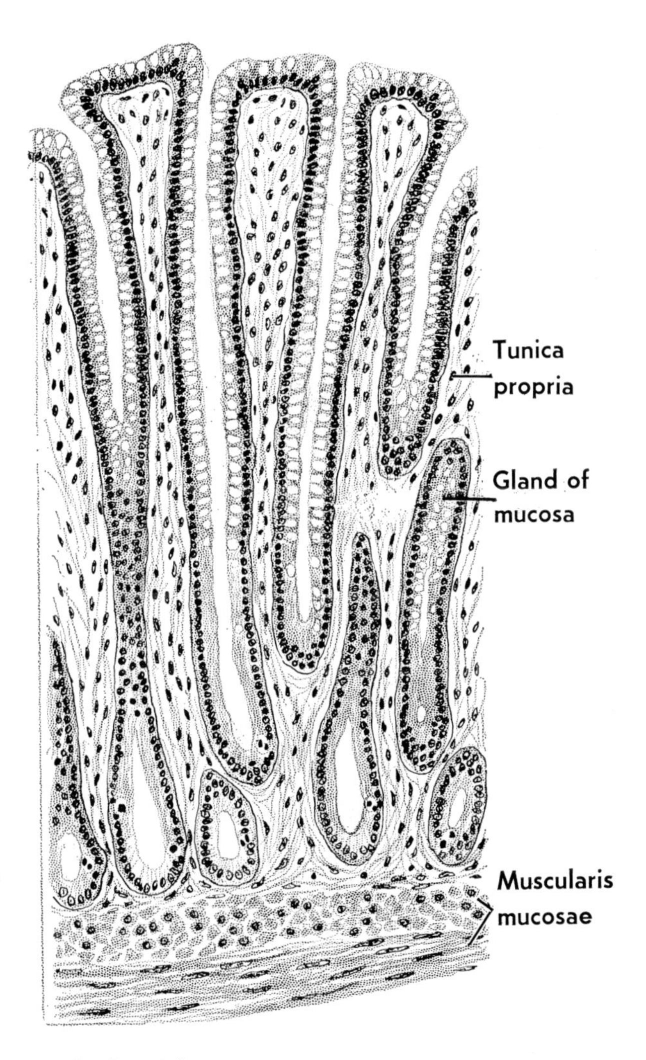

Fig. 114. Mucosa of colon of dog.

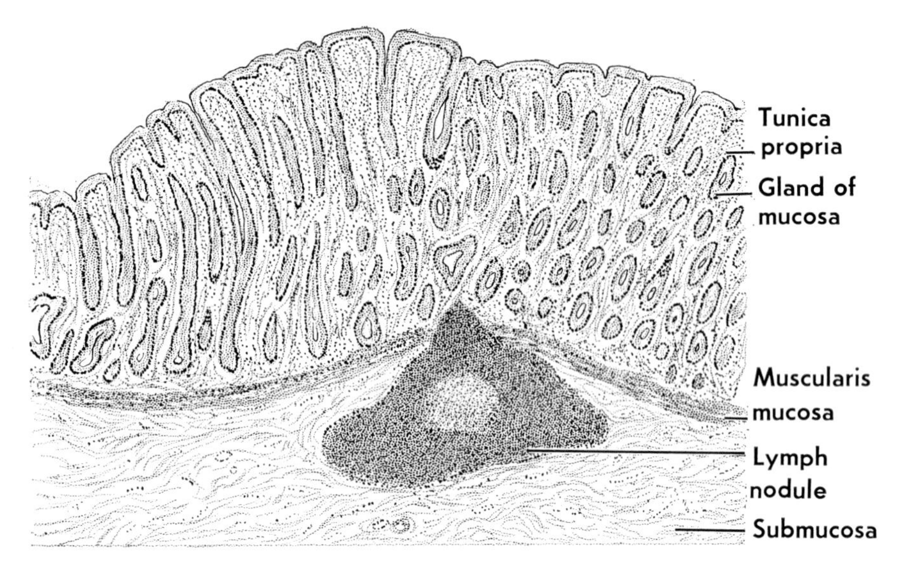

Fig. 115. Mucosa and submucosa of colon of dog, showing a solitary lymph nodule.

Muscularis. The inner circular layer of the muscularis is continuous around the wall and is thrown into folds with the mucosa and submucosa. The longitudinal layer is in the form of three bands which run through the length of the large intestine. These are called the taeniae coli. When dissected away from the rest of the wall they are found to be considerably shorter than the wall, and this difference in length produces the semilunar fold in the longer parts. The effect of the taeniae is like that of a drawstring run through a piece of cloth.

Serosa. The serosa contains large deposits of adipose tissues which protrude on the outer surface of the tube and are macroscopically visible as the appendices epiploicae.

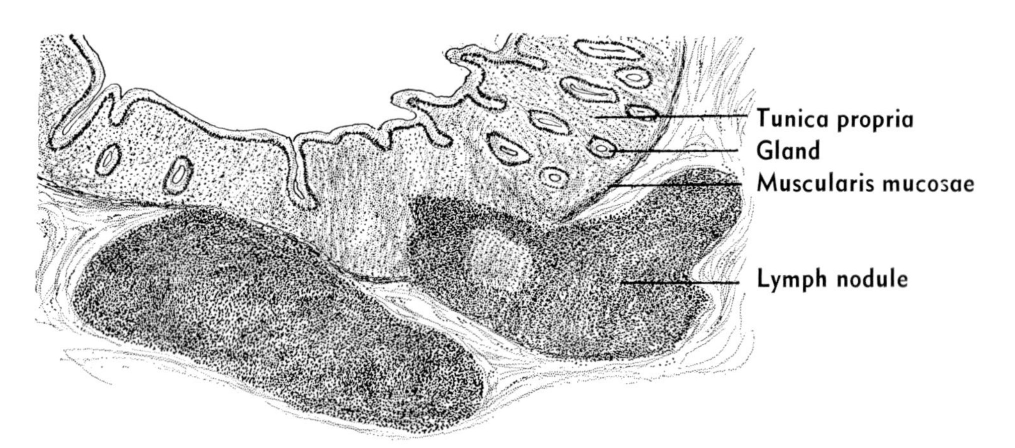

Fig. 116. Mucosa and submucosa of human appendix.

VERMIFORM APPENDIX

The wall of the vermiform appendix resembles that of the colon (Fig. 116).

Mucosa. The epithelium of the mucosa is simple columnar, with goblet cells, forming glands like those of the colon. The tunica propria contains a great deal of lymphoid tissue. Often the nodules are confluent and the number of glands greatly reduced. The muscularis mucosae is interrupted by the lymph nodules, so that in places only a few strands of it are present.

From the description given it will be seen that the appendix is composed of the same elements as those which form the colonic mucosa. In

Table 3. Peculiarities in parts of digestive tract

	Mucosa	*Submucosa*	*Muscularis*
Esophagus	Stratified squamous epithelium Glands confined to two narrow zones Muscularis mucosae lacking in upper part	Mucous glands	Striated in upper part
Stomach	Pits in surface Glands closely packed and long; made up of chief and parietal cells		Oblique layer of muscle inside circular layer
Duodenum	Villi; leaflike	Mucous glands; plicae are low	
Jejunum	Villi; tall	Tall branching plicae	
Ileum	Villi; club-shaped	Large groups of lymphoid nodules	
Colon	No pits or villi Many goblet cells in epithelium		Longitudinal muscle arranged in three bands
Appendix	No pits or villi; much lymphoid tissue	Much lymphoid tissue	
Rectum	Partly like colon; partly stratified squamous		
Anus	Stratified squamous; three-layer muscularis mucosae		Circular muscle forms two sphincters

the appendix, however, the glands are less numerous, and there is a greater amount of lymphoid tissue.

Submucosa. The submucosa is composed of areolar tissue with vessels, nerves, and lymphoid tissue.

Muscularis. The muscularis is composed of two complete layers, as in other parts of the tract.

Serosa. The serosa presents no exceptional features.

The pecularities of the different parts of the digestive tract which may be used as diagnostic features in identifying sections are presented in Table 3.

RECTUM AND ANUS

The upper part of the rectum resembles the colon. Its glands are of the same type as those of the colon but are somewhat longer. The longitudinal muscle of the taeniae coli spreads out in the rectum to form a continuous coat like that in other parts of the digestive tract.

In the lower part of the rectum and the upper part of the anal canal the lining is thrown into longitudinal folds called rectal columns. In

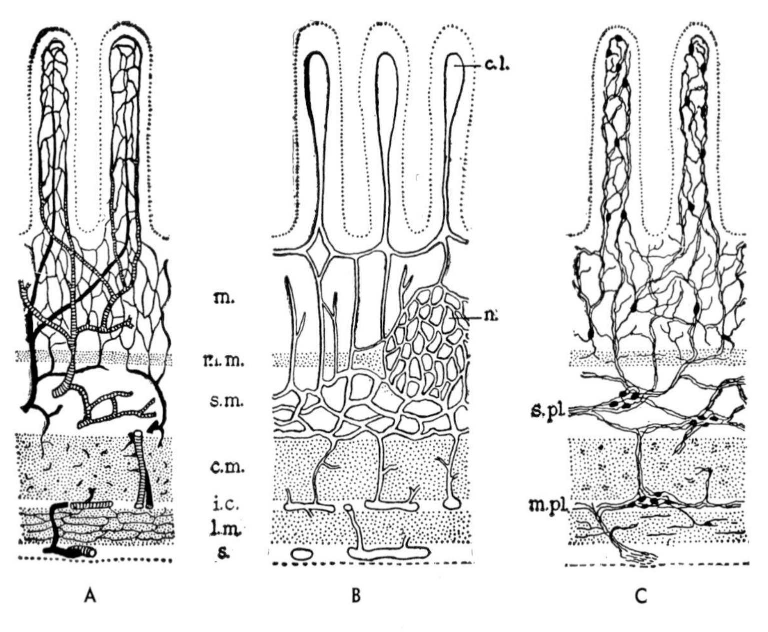

Fig. 117. **A**, Diagram of blood vessels of small intestine; the arteries appear as coarse black lines, the capillaries as fine ones, and the veins are shaded (after Mall). **B**, Diagram of lymphatic vessels (after Mall). **C**, Diagram of nerves based upon Golgi preparations (after Cajal). The layers of the intestine: **m**, mucosa; **mm**, muscularis mucosae; **sm**, submucosa; **cm**, circular muscle; **ic**, intermuscular connective tissue; **lm**, longitudinal muscle; **s**, serosa; **cl**, central lymphatic; **n**, nodule; **spl**, submucous plexus; **mpl**, myenteric plexus. (From Bremer and Weatherford: Text-Book of Histology, Philadelphia, 1948, The Blakiston Co.)

this region the epithelium changes from simple columnar to stratified columnar and then to stratified squamous, and the glands disappear. In the anus the surface of the epithelium becomes cornified, and there are glands at this point (circumanal glands) which resemble sweat glands. The muscularis mucosae of the anal portion may be three-layered, the layers being longitudinal, circular, and longitudinal. The submucosa contains nerves and lamellar corpuscles. The circular layer of the muscularis coat is thickened around the anus to form two sphincters; the upper one of these is composed of smooth muscle, whereas the fibers of the lower are striated.

BLOOD SUPPLY OF STOMACH AND INTESTINES

The arteries which supply the gut pass through the mesentery to reach the serosa where they branch into smaller vessels. The latter continue through the two coats of the muscularis to the submucosa where they form an extensive plexus (Heller's plexus). From the plexus of the submucosa blood passes to the mucosa and to the muscular coat of the gut. (Fig. 117.)

NERVE SUPPLY OF STOMACH AND INTESTINES

The nerve supply of the stomach and intestines consists chiefly of nonmedullated and medullated (preganglionic) fibers of the autonomic system. When the nerves reach the connective tissue between the two layers of the muscularis coat they are associated with ganglion cells to form the plexus of Auerbach. From the plexus fibers pass to the submucosa where they form another plexus, Meissner's plexus.

CHAPTER XVI

Glands associated with the digestive tract

In addition to the glands situated in the wall of the digestive tract there are large masses of glandular tissue which lie outside the limits of the tube and pour their secretion into it through ducts. These are the salivary glands, the ducts of which open into the oral cavity, and the pancreas and liver, secretions of which go to the intestine. The pancreas resembles the salivary glands and is most conveniently studied in connection with them.

SALIVARY GLANDS

The saliva is formed by a number of collections of serous and mucous cells, some of which were discussed in Chapter XV. In this discussion the large salivary glands which lie outside the walls of the oral cavity are to be considered. They are the parotids, the submaxillaries, and the sublinguals. They are compound alveolar or tubuloalveolar glands composed of varying proportions of serous and mucous cells.

Parotid gland

As will be seen from Figs. 118 and 119, the parotid has excretory, secretory, and intercallated ducts which lead out from serous alveoli. The arrangement of these elements in sequence is not as clear in sections as it is in Fig. 118. A number of alveoli with intercalary and secretory ducts are crowded together to form a lobule. A fine connective tissue stroma, often containing fat cells, surrounds the alveoli, and a heavier sheath of the same tissue separates adjacent lobules. A group of lobules forms a lobe, which is in turn covered with a connective tissue sheath which mingles at the outer borders of the gland with the surrounding fascia. Within the lobule the alveoli and ducts are cut in various directions, and their connections are not always clear. One may, however, find a group of alveoli through which the plane of section has passed vertically, and in such a case the arrangement is visible.

Several alveoli open together into a fine duct called the intercalary duct. This tubule is composed of flattened cells. Several intercalary ducts open into a tubule lined with cuboidal epithelium, the secretory (striated) duct. The cells lining this branch of the duct system show, under special treatment, striations in the basal part of the cytoplasm which are supposed to be indicative of secretory activity. These ducts open in turn into excretory ducts which are lined with tall columnar epithelium. As one traces these ducts toward the opening into the oral cavity, the epithelium is seen to change first to pseudostratified and then to stratified squamous.

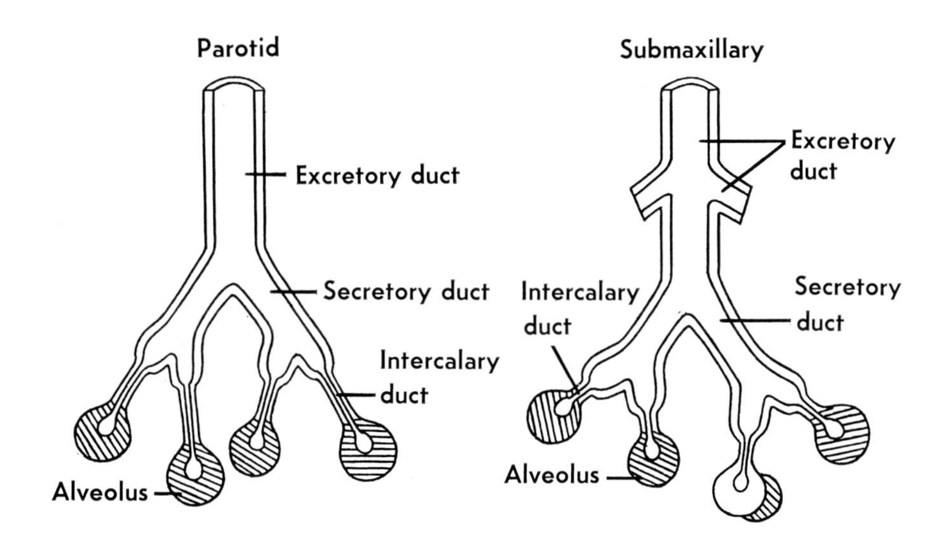

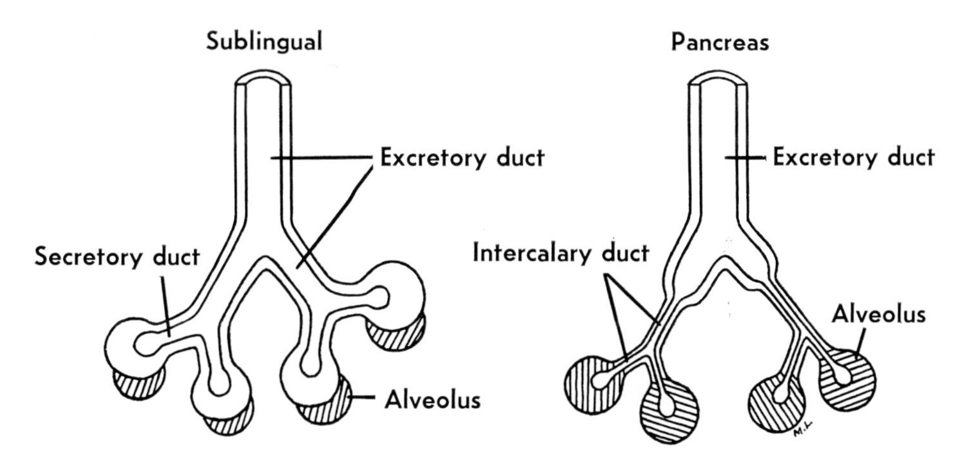

Fig. 118. Diagram to show composition of secreting portions and duct systems of salivary glands and pancreas. Alveoli and crescents which are shaded are serous cells; those unshaded are mucous cells.

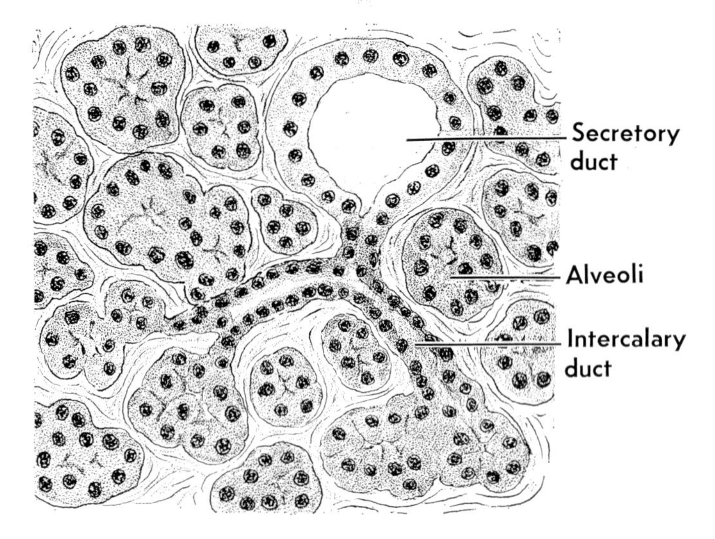

Fig. 119. Section of parotid gland of dog.

The end pieces or alveoli are composed entirely of serous cells which are wedge shaped and grouped about a small lumen. The cytoplasm is granular and the nuclei round, as in all serous cells. Immediately outside the alveoli is a basement membrane which contains stellate cells. These are, however, difficult to see in ordinary slides.

Submaxillary glands

As in the parotid gland, there are excretory, secretory, and intercalary ducts in the submaxillary gland (Fig. 118), but the last named are short and difficult to find. The alveoli are of two kinds. Many are pure serous,

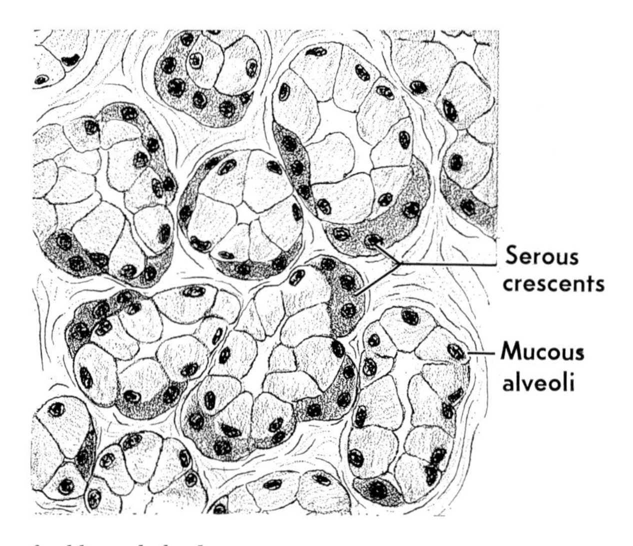

Fig. 120. Section of sublingual gland.

like those of the parotid; others are mixed serous and mucous. The mucous cells of a mixed alveolus are grouped around the lumen and are distinguished from the serous cells by their paler cytoplasm and their basal, flattened nuclei (Fig. 120). The serous cells are arranged in the form of a cap outside the mucous cells. They do not border on the lumen of the alveolus but pour their secretion into it through minute channels between the mucous cells. Such groups of serous cells are often crescent shaped in sections and are called demilunes of Heidenhain. In the submaxillary gland, which has many purely serous alveoli, the demilunes of the mixed alveoli are small.

Sublingual glands

The duct system of the sublingual gland differs from that of the other salivary glands in that it lacks intercalary ducts (Fig. 118). The alveoli open directly into short secretory channels. All the alveoli are of the mixed type, consisting of mucous cells bordering on the lumen and large serous crescents.

The salivary glands have a relatively rich blood supply consisting of arteries, veins, and lymphatics which run in the connective tissue septa along with the ducts. The arteries branch into capillary networks where they eventually surround the alveoli.

Nerve supply. The innervation of the salivary glands is complicated, involving fibers of the sympathetic and parasympathetic systems.

PANCREAS

The pancreas is really a union of two organs having entirely different functions. These are the pancreatic tissue proper and the islands of Langerhans. The former tissue makes up a gland of external secretion; the latter are endocrine in function.

The pancreas has long intercalary ducts which lead directly into excretory ducts without the intervention of a secretory portion (Fig. 118). The alveoli are shorter and rounder than those of the parotid and are composed, like them, of serous cells (Fig. 121). With careful preparations some of the cells may show dark granules in the portion toward the lumen. These are zymogen granules, which are transformed into the secretion of the gland.

A peculiar feature of the pancreatic alveoli is the presence of centroalveolar cells. These are small cells with dark, oval nuclei which are situated in the lumen of the alveolus, often filling it completely. The centroalveolar cells may be recognized by their dark, oval nuclei as well as by their position. Their function is unknown. It has been suggested that they are derived from the cells of the intercalary duct which they resemble in form.

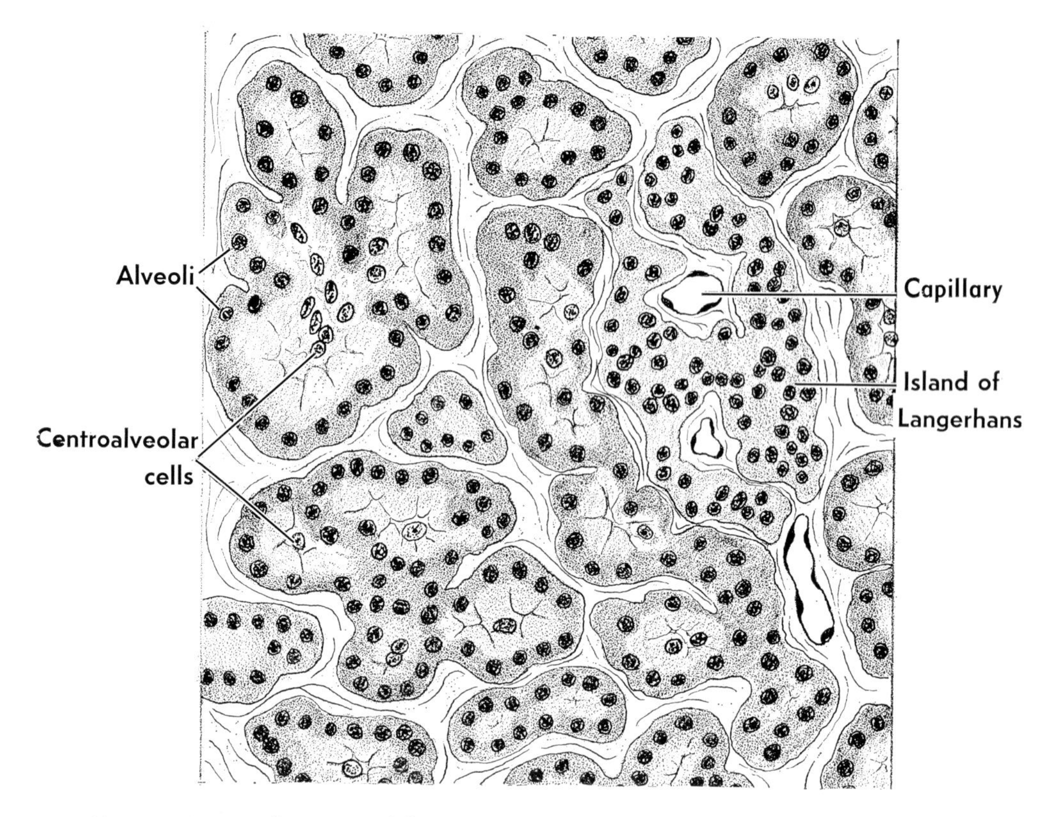

Fig. 121. Section of pancreas of dog.

The islands of Langerhans are collections of cells which arise as outgrowths from the walls of the ducts of the pancreas during embryonic life. Although they are thus connected developmentally with the ducts, they do not secrete into the tubules. They may become entirely detached from them or retain a connection through a cord of cells which has no lumen. They consist of coiled anastomosing cords of cells penetrated by a network of capillaries into which they secrete (Fig. 121). The cells are pale in color and polygonal in shape, containing vesicular nuclei. With special treatment three kinds of cells may be distinguished, according to some investigators, but they are not differentiated by the ordinary fixatives and stains.

If the entire pancreas is removed from an animal, diabetic symptoms occur which indicate a disturbance of the carbohydrate metabolism. If, however, the pancreatic duct is ligated, the alveoli degenerate but the islands of Langerhans are unharmed. In this case there is no disturbance of carbohydrate metabolism. It is thus clear that the two kinds of tissue have entirely different functions. The alveoli compose a gland of external secretion, forming an alkaline fluid containing enzymes used in digestion (trypsin, amylase, lipase). The islands are glands of internal secretion (endocrine glands). They secrete insulin which passes into the blood stream and controls the metabolism of sugars and starches.

Blood supply. The blood supply to the pancreas is derived chiefly from the superior and inferior pancreatico-duodenal arteries and also from divisions of the splenic artery. As in the case of the salivary glands, the arteries pass in the connective tissue septa to end in capillaries among the acini and islands of Langerhans. Corresponding veins return the blood to the superior mesenteric and portal veins.

Nerve supply. The nerves which supply the pancreas are derived from the splanchnic and the vagus.

Summary

It is sometimes difficult for the student to distinguish the four glands just described (parotid, submaxillary, sublingual, and the pancreas) and to aid him in doing so the following facts may be emphasized. Of the four, two contain no mucous cells. These are the parotid and the pancreas, which are alike in that the cells of their alveoli are all serous. They are differentiated by the presence of islands of Langerhans and centroalevolar cells in the pancreas. In differentiating between the submaxillary and sublingual, one should look for purely serous alveoli in the former. It must be remembered, however, that the large serous crescents of the sublingual may be so cut that their relation to the mucous alveoli is not seen and they appear to be separate alveoli. Such instances are, however, isolated, and if more than one-half the cells in a section are serous it is quite certain the section is from the submaxillary gland. Some specimens are difficult to identify, especially as the proportions of serous and mucous cells vary in different animals and even in different parts of the same gland.

LIVER

The liver develops embryologically as an outgrowth from the wall of the gut, lying in the pathway of the vitelline veins. It later intercepts the umbilical veins, and all four vessels are broken up by the glandular tissue into a multitude of small sinusoids. The liver tissue is divided into lobules, each of which is surrounded by a connective tissue sheath. These sheaths are continuous with the superficial covering of the whole liver, and the aggregate of connective tissue is known as Glisson's capsule.

Under the low power of the microscope a section of a piece of the liver of a pig appears as a group of lobules which are, roughly, six-sided (Fig. 122). Each is surrounded by connective tissue which, at certain of the angles of the lobules, forms a conspicuous island containing blood vessels and ducts. These islands are the portal canals. Along some of the straight sides of lobules, vessels may be seen which are the interlobular veins. The

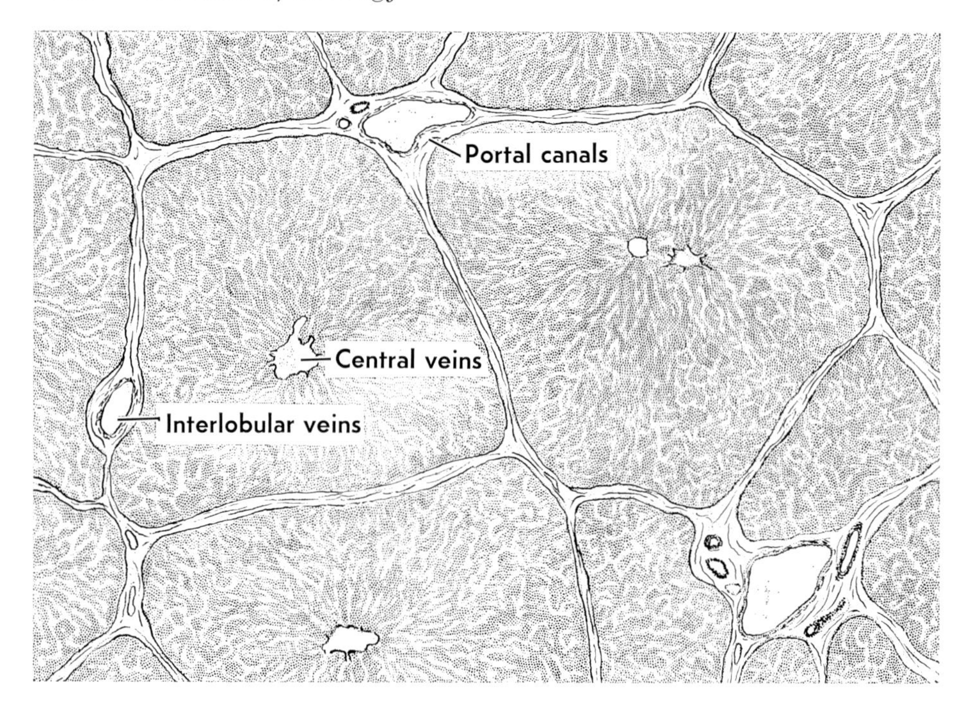

Fig. 122. Liver of pig, low magnification, showing relations of lobules to portal canals, central veins, and interlobular veins.

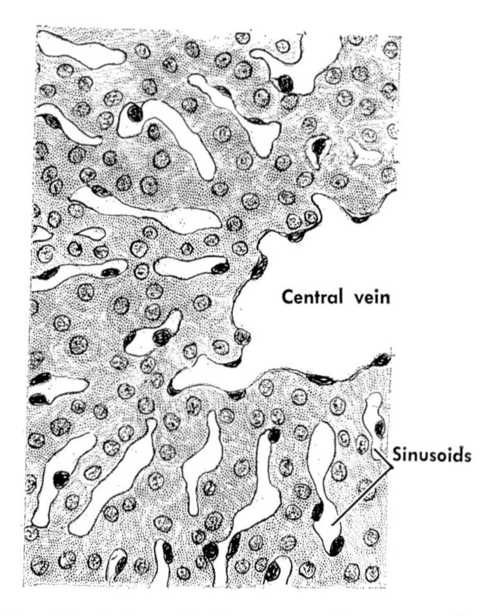

Fig. 123. Region of liver lobule immediately surrounding a central vein.

same arrangement of vessels is present in human liver, but the connective tissue capsules surrounding the lobules are much thinner and therefore less easy to see. The tissue of the lobule is made up of radiating cords of cells alternating with sinusoids. The sinusoids converge to a vessel in the center of the lobule (central vein). Under higher magnification the arrangement of cords and sinusoids is much clearer and following is a discussion of the details that may be seen.

Liver cells and sinusoids. The parenchyma of the liver is composed of large epithelial cells apparently arranged in solid cords two cells each in breadth (Fig. 123). Special technique is required to demonstrate the capillaries by which the bile, secreted by the liver cells, is carried to the larger ducts in the portal canals. Each cell has, in the side adjacent to its neighboring cell, a minute groove. Two grooves fitting together form a duct. The cells are polygonal and often binucleate. (Fig. 124). The cytoplasm is eosinophilic and contains granules, protein inclusions, or vacu-

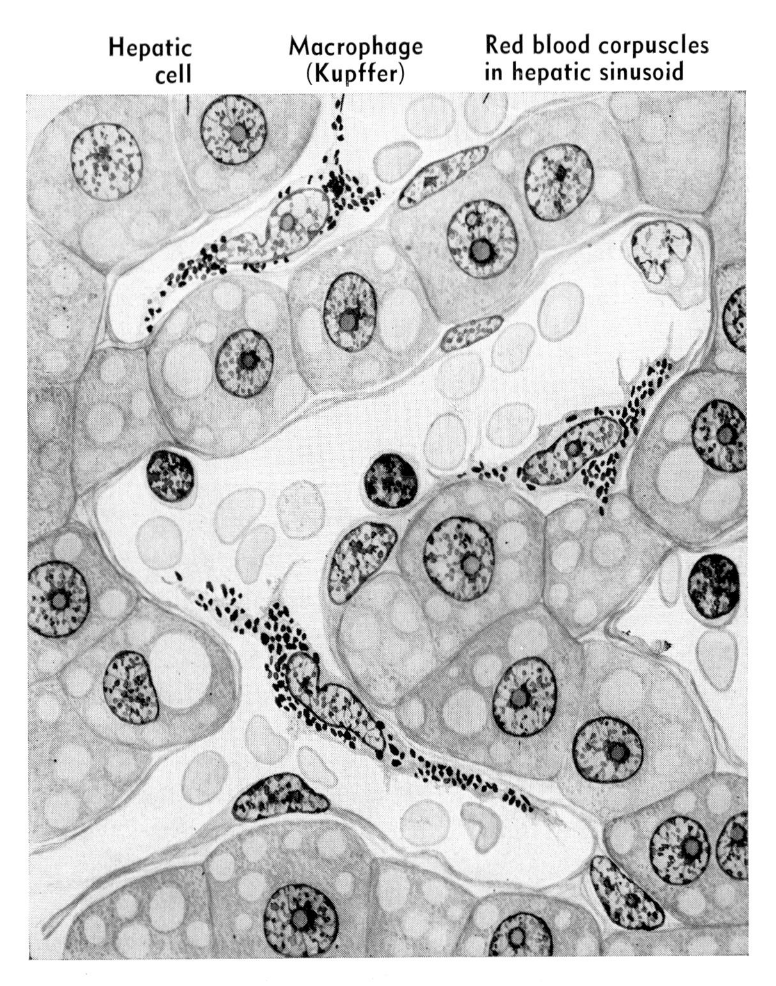

Fig. 124. Hepatic sinusoids, showing endothelial cells and macrophages lining them. (×1,200.) (From Nonidez and Windle: Textbook of Histology, New York, 1953, McGraw-Hill Book Co., Inc.)

oles, depending on the functional state of the cell at the time of fixation. The cords of cells anastomose freely, forming a spongy network which radiates from the central vein. The meshes of the network of secreting cells contain the sinusoids which are lined with an endothelium, part of which belongs to the reticuloendothelial system. In an ordinary preparation stained with hematoxylin and eosin the lining of these vessels appears to be composed of cells which lie flat along the sides of the liver cells. The nuclei of these endothelial cells are small and dark and their cytoplasm forms a thin film along the border of the sinusoid. Such cells are the undifferentiated lining cells. With special methods a second type of cell may be demonstrated, the stellate cell of Kupffer. When properly stained these cells appear to be in the blood stream anchored to the wall of the sinusoid by cytoplasmic processes. Their reaction to vital dyes is that characteristic of other reticuloendothelial cells.

Portal canal. The portal canal consists of an island of connective tissue which is approximately triangular in shape. It contains a branch of the hepatic artery, a branch of the portal vein, and the bile duct. Of these the vein is by far the largest. The bile duct is readily distinguished from the blood vessels by its lining of columnar epithelium (Fig. 125).

Circulation. The circulation of the liver is peculiar in that it is derived from two sources: (1) arterial blood from branches of the hepatic artery

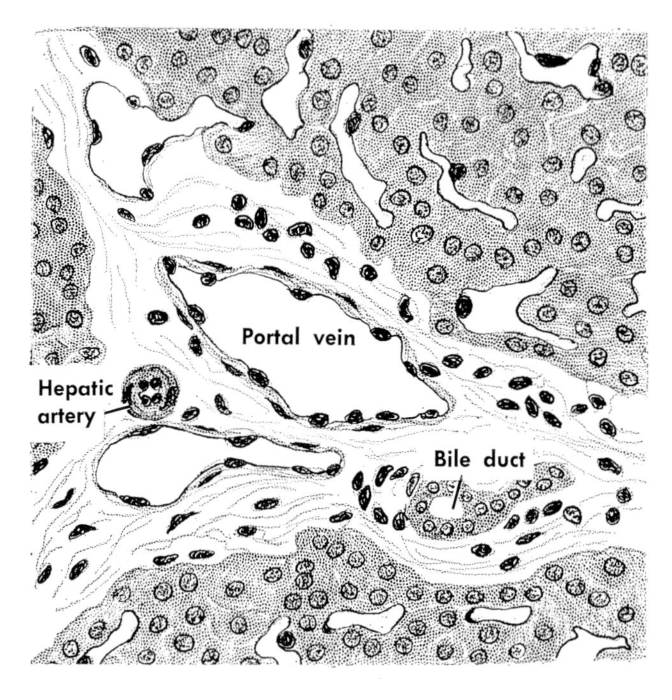

Fig. 125. Portal canal containing branch of portal vein. Notice in upper left-hand part of illustration a small vein opening into a sinusoid.

and (2) venous blood by way of the portal vein (Fig. 126). The hepatic artery is chiefly concerned with nourishment of the liver tissue.

The portal vein carrying venous blood from the intestine, together

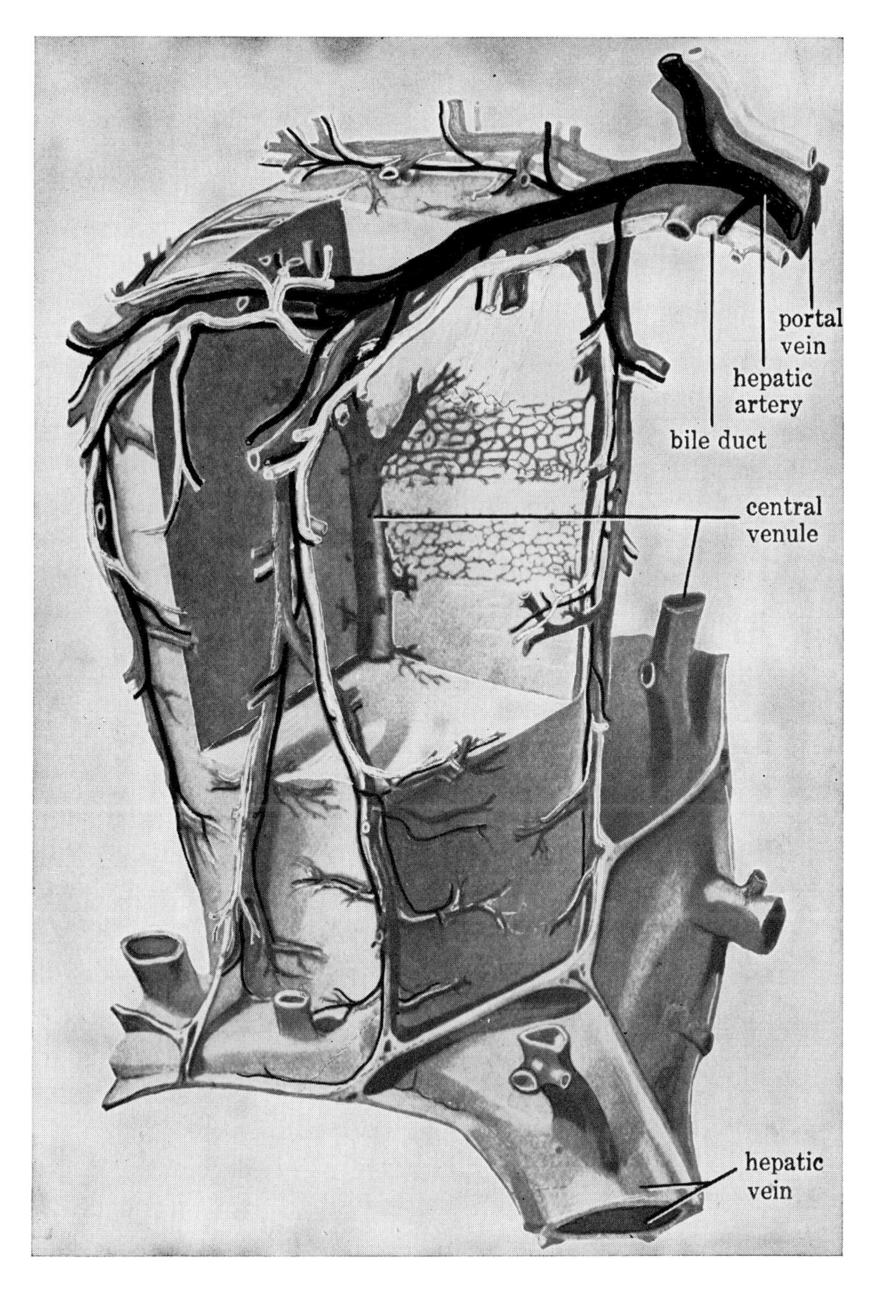

Fig. 126. Reconstruction of liver lobule of pig, showing relation of blood vessels and bile ducts to liver parenchyma. (Modified from Braus: Anatomie des Menschen, vol. 2, Berlin, 1924, Julius Springer; from Nonidez and Windle: Textbook of Histology, New York, 1953, McGraw-Hill Book Co., Inc.)

with branches of the hepatic artery, enters the liver at the aorta. These vessels divide and run through the connective tissue septa of the lobes as the interlobar vessels. The interlobar veins give off branches which run between the lobules and are known accordingly as interlobular veins. These vessels encircle the lobule, eventually penetrate it, and break up into fine capillaries, the hepatic sinusoids. The sinusoids empty into the central vein which is considered to be the first part of the efferent system of the hepatic vessels. The central vein passes down through the lobule collecting blood from many sinusoids and eventually unites with other central veins which lead into the sublobular vein. Blood from these veins is eventually collected by the hepatic vein and is finally carried to the vena cava.

It is this circulatory arrangment which enables the liver to perform one of its functions, namely, the storage of glycogen. The blood of the portal vein comes from the intestine and is laden with nutriment. Through the arrangment of sinusoids it easily reaches the liver cells which store glycogen obtained from the blood. The same arrangment serves to return the nourishment to the circlulation when it is needed.

Another function of the liver is the formation of bile for the digestion of food in the intestine. This substance is apparently secreted by the same cells which store the glycogen. The bile duct system consists of intrahepatic and extrahepatic portions. The interlobular ducts of the right and quadrate lobes form the right hepatic duct. Those of the left and caudate lobes form the left hepatic duct. The right and left ducts unite to form the common hepatic; this receives the cystic duct and then continues to the duodenum as the common bile duct.

In addition to the functions mentioned the liver also plays an im-

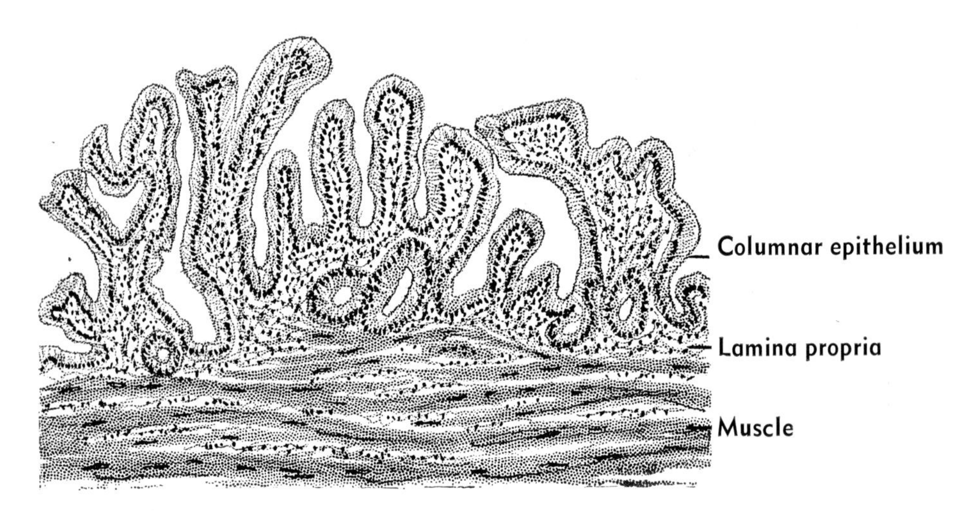

Fig. 127. Gallbladder of monkey.

portant role in intermediate carbohydrate metabolism as well as in the metabolism of amino acids and lipids. It produces numerous phagocytic cells and is known to be concerned with the elaboration or storage of certain hormones and enzymes. Finally, the liver is also involved in the mechanism of blood clotting by virtue of its ability to form or store fibrinogen and heparin.

Nerve supply. The nerves which supply the liver are chiefly nonmedullated fibers derived from the sympathetic system. They accompany the blood vessels and ducts, terminating in these structures and among the liver cells.

GALLBLADDER

The gallbladder is a hollow, pear-shaped organ closely adherent to the posterior surface of the liver. It consists of a blind end known as the fundus, a body, and a neck, which continues as the cystic duct.

The four layers common to other parts of the digestive tract are poorly developed and are more or less intermingled in the gallbladder (Fig. 127). It is lined with a columnar epithelium in which the cell walls are distinct. This epithelium rests on a connective tissue layer (lamina propria) which represents the tunica propria and submucosa of other parts of the tract. The connective tissue and epithelium are irregularly folded, forming numerous elevations and pockets. Often the latter are tangentially cut so that they appear as closed sacs which look like glandular follicles. There is, however, no secretion in the gallbladder except that of a small group of mucous glands near its neck.

Outside the connective tissue there is a layer of smooth muscle, which consists of intermingled groups of circular, longitudinal, and oblique fibers. The muscular coat is thin and has much connective tissue combined with the muscle fibers. There is a fairly thick serosa of loose connective tissue covered by the mesothelium.

Blood supply. The gallbladder is supplied by the cystic artery, and the venous blood is collected by veins which empty into the cystic branch of the portal vein. The gallbladder is richly supplied by lymphatics, and many plexuses occur in this organ.

Nerve supply. Branches of both the vagus and splanchnic nerves supply the gallbladder.

CHAPTER XVII

Respiratory tract

For the purpose of presentation, the respiratory tract is arbitrarily divided into an upper part, extending from the nose to the larynx, and a lower part, which includes the trachea and its branches within the lung. Strictly speaking, this division is not anatomically accurate.

The upper part of the respiratory system (Fig. 128) is composed of two nasal passages, the nasopharynx, oropharynx, laryngopharynx, and larynx. The lower part consists of the trachea, two primary bronchi which enter the lungs and branch repeatedly to form a system of bronchi, bronchioles, and finally alveolar sacs. The oral cavity and thoracic rib cage are secondarily included as part of the respiratory system, as is the diaphragm, the latter separating the thoracic and abdominal cavities.

Aside from its respiratory function (which involves the exchange of gases between the tissue fluids, plasma, and air spaces in the lung) the air in the respiratory system must be moistened, filtered, and warmed to permit proper functioning of the parts. The mucus supplied by goblet cells in pseudostratified epithelium and by the submucosal glands serves to entrap dust particles and bacteria and also to supply enzymes which lyse certain bacteria. The same secretion serves to moisten the air and also dissolves certain molecules which are perceived as odors with the aid of the olfactory organ in the nasal passages. The coordinated beating of cilia on cell surfaces serve to move the secretions from the nasal passages through the nasopharynx to the oropharynx, while similar activity of ciliated cells located in the bronchioles, bronchi, and trachea propels mucus to the epiglottis. From this locus the secretions are either expectorated or pass into the esophagus. An abundant supply of venous blood vessels in the submucosal tissues of the nasal passages warm the air. Several of the functions mentioned are facilitated by an abundant surface area in each nasal passage by virtue of (1) four accessory sinuses (frontal, ethmodial, sphenoidal, and maxillary, named for the bones which enclose them) and (2) the presence of three conchae containing the tortuously twisted turbinate bones. Certain phagocytic cells called "dust cells" are located in the lung tissues.

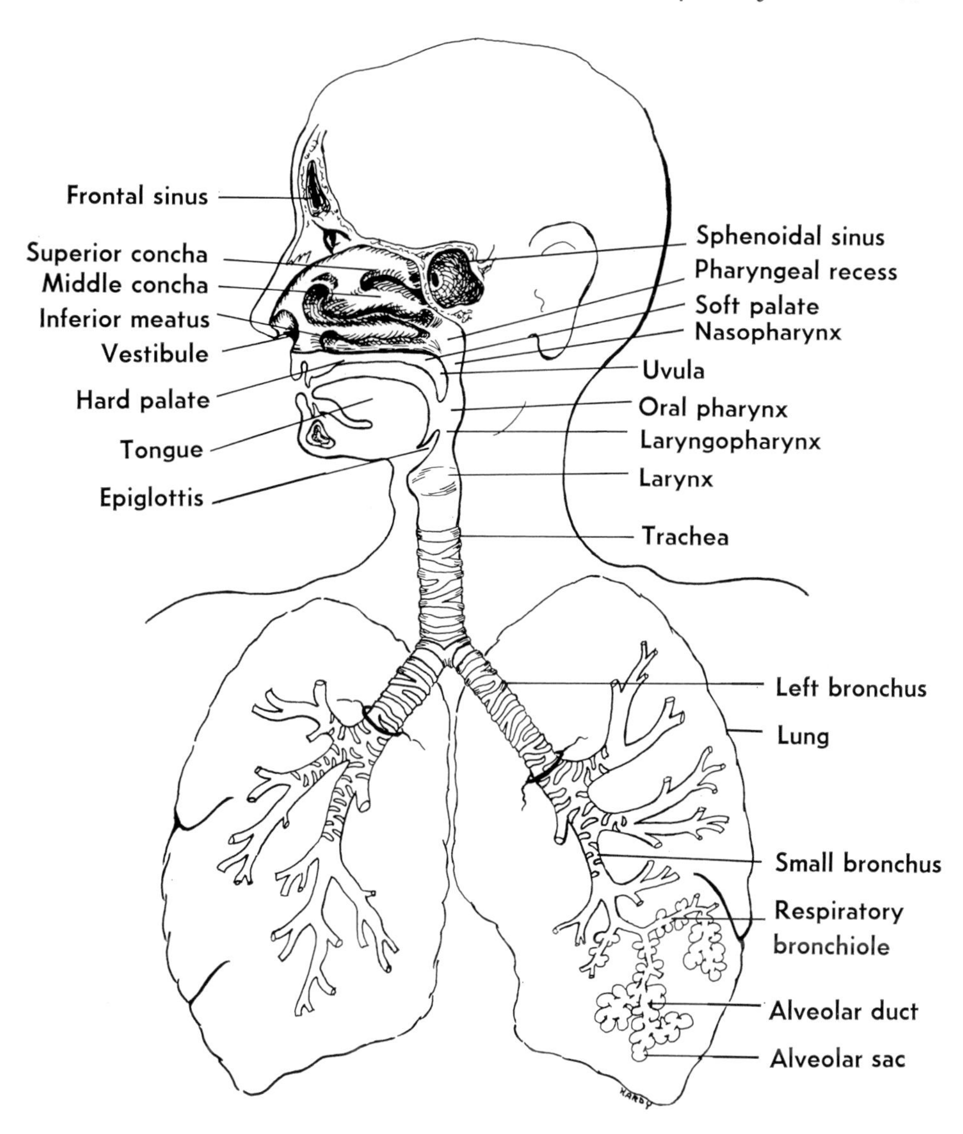

Fig. 128. Topographic representation of respiratory apparatus.

They remove and store foreign particles which enter the lungs. The olfactory organ serves to warn the organism of the presence of noxious substances in the air. The specialized respiratory epithelium of the lung alveoli is admirably suited for its function of gas exchange. The conducting tubules are constructed so as to maintain open passageways for gases under the widely fluctuating pressures produced in the ventilation process. These tubules gradually change in structure from thick-walled, rigid tubes to increasingly thinner and softer ones, a change similar to that occurring in blood vessels.

Upper parts of respiratory tract

NASAL PASSAGES

The nose consists of two passageways separated by the cartilage-containing *nasal septum*. Each passageway begins at the *external nares* as an inflection of the keratinized stratified squamous epithelium of the wings (alae) of the nose. The inflected portion forms the *vestibule* of the nose and is covered by numerous hairs (vibrissae). Large sebaceous glands and numerous sweat glands are also found in this region. The connective tissue papillae are deep, and scattered mixed serous and mucous glands may be observed. In the posterior region of the vestibule the epithelium becomes non-keratinized, or forms only small patches of nonhairy keratinized epithelium. The latter indicates the beginning of the so-called *respiratory part* of the nasal passage, which in turn terminates in a small orifice called the *choana* leading into the nasopharynx.

The respiratory portion of each nasal passage includes the sinuses, olfactory organ, the three conchae, including the meati, and the upper surface of the hard palate. In general the epithelium of this region is ciliated pseudostratified, usually exhibiting four to five rows of nuclei containing goblet cells. The underlying lamina propria, composed of both elastic and collagenous fibers, is usually adherent to a nearby periosteum or perichondrium. A basement membrane containing elastic fibers occurs irregulary.

The sinuses indicated are located in certain bones of the head and are usually viewed in decalcified sections of the head of an embryo or fetus. They are usually identified by their location rather than by histological characteristics. The epithelium is ciliated pseudostratified, of approximately one-half the thickness of other parts of the tract, exhibiting two to three rows of nuclei and very few goblet cells. The basement membrane is very thin and is rarely observed. The lamina propria is also thin, is mainly collagenous, and is closely adherent to the periosteum. It has few glands but is frequently supplied with lymphoid aggregations and other leukocytic forms.

The superior, middle, and inferior conchae are usually observed in frontal sections through the head of the human fetus as coiled and recurved projections arising from the walls opposite the septa (paraseptally). In animals like the pig only parts of the conchae are visible because the head is prolonged into a snout. The space inferior to each concha is, in sequence, the superior, middle, and inferior meatus.

The middle and inferior conchae bear the usual thick type of pseudostratified epithelium, containing many goblet cells. The basement membrane is thick and is readily demonstrated. The lamina propria exhibits both serous and mucous alveoli, as well as a large number of prominent venous passages. The latter may be either engorged with blood or collapsed, and their walls contain both circular and longitudinal bands of smooth muscle. Each meatus bears a thin epithelium containing a few goblet cells, which rests upon a very thin basement membrane. The superior concha, as well as parts of the roof of the nasal passage and adjacent septum, form part of the olfactory organ. The epithelium is extremely thick and, since the processes are almost impossible to trace in hematoxylin and eosin preparations, its appearance is like that of stratified columnar epithelia. The surface cells contain pigment granules when properly preserved, and the cilia present are covered by a coagulated secretion which gives the impression that the tissue is covered by a cuticle (see page 274).

NASOPHARYNX

In the parts of the nasopharynx which do not come into contact with surfaces of other tissues the epithelium is ciliated pseudostratified, and the lamina propria contains mixed or seromucous glands. In certain transitional zones stratified columnar epithelium may occur but is not easily distinguished from the pseudostratified variety. In the superior and posterior portions of the nasopharynx there are many aggregations of lymphoid cells, which may be extensions of the pharyngeal tonsils or adenoids. Similar aggregations forming the tubal tonsils are found surrounding the entrance of the eustachian tubes into the nasopharynx. The posterior wall of the nasopharynx, at about the lower level of the tonsils, is covered by a nonkeratinized stratified squamous epithelium with numerous low papillae. The superior surface of the soft palate and uvula also bear a nonkeratinized stratified squamous epithelium.

LARYNX

The uppermost portion of the larynx is known as the epiglottis. The lingual or anterior surface of the epiglottis is covered by a nonkeratinized stratified squamous epithelium and bears many seromucous glands in the lamina propria, especially near its connection with the base of the tongue. The upper part of the posterior surface of the epiglottis is covered by nonkeratinized stratified squamous epithelium which merges into a transition zone which appears irregularly as ciliated stratified columnar epithelium. The lower part of the posterior surface bears ciliated pseudostratified epithelium with goblet cells, and near the base one may observe scattered taste buds. The lamina propria includes some mucous and serous units. The zone between the two surfaces is occupied by a large piece of cartilage containing a number of thick elastic fibers, the so-called elastic cartilage. In the epiglottis of some animals the cartilage may contain a central zone invaded by fat cells. No perichondrium, however, occurs in the invaded zone.

The epithelium of the true vocal cords is of the nonkeratinized stratified squamous variety and does not contain mucous glands in the lamina propria. Above and below the true vocal cords the epithelium is ciliated pseudostratified with goblet cells, and many mucous glands are present in the lamina propria. Patches of the stratified squamous type are sometimes found in this region.

Lower parts of respiratory tract

Morphologists have divided the lower parts of the respiratory tract on the basis of gross dissection and by the injection of low melting point alloys into the passageways. Thus there are lobes and lobules of the lung, with their attendant blood and lymphatic circulation containing various air tubules. Ordinarily one does not utilize more than a small portion of a lobule for study. In addition the former tendency to utilize the diameter of a tubule as a criterion for identification is no more valid here than it is for blood vessels. In routine histology the salient features to observe in the tubules and lungs are (1) the epithelial make-up, (2) the presence or absense of cartilage and its disposition (that is, location, shape, and extent), (3) the glands and their disposition, (4) the disposition of the muscles, and (5) the relation of the parts to each other at the microscopic level. The student should attempt to visualize how each component appears in cross section and longitudinal section.

TRACHEA

The trachea consists of (1) mucosa, (2) submucosa, and (3) a layer of cartilage and muscle which corresponds to the muscularis of the digestive tract (Fig. 129). External to the perichondrium of the cartilage is a fibrosa or adventitious layer of connective tissue which fuses with the tissue of the mediastinum and the similar layer enclosing the esophagus. This layer is usually destroyed during dissection of the trachea.

The mucosa consists of (1) a ciliated pseudostratified epithelium with numerous goblet cells bounded by (2) a prominent basement membrane which is part of (3) the lamina propria (tunica propria), consisting mainly of reticular or fine areolar tissue containing a number of elastic fibers. At the outer edge of the lamina propria coarse elastic fibers are oriented longitudinally to form (4) a relatively compact elastic membrane or lamina. The latter is said to be comparable to the muscularis mucosae of the digestive tract and the similar elastic layer in the upper part of the esophagus. In the epithelium small patches of the stratified squamous variety are encountered, especially in older animals or those with chronic inflammations.

The submucosa is areolar tissue. It contains fat cells and the secreting portions of mixed glands with some units exhibiting prominent serous

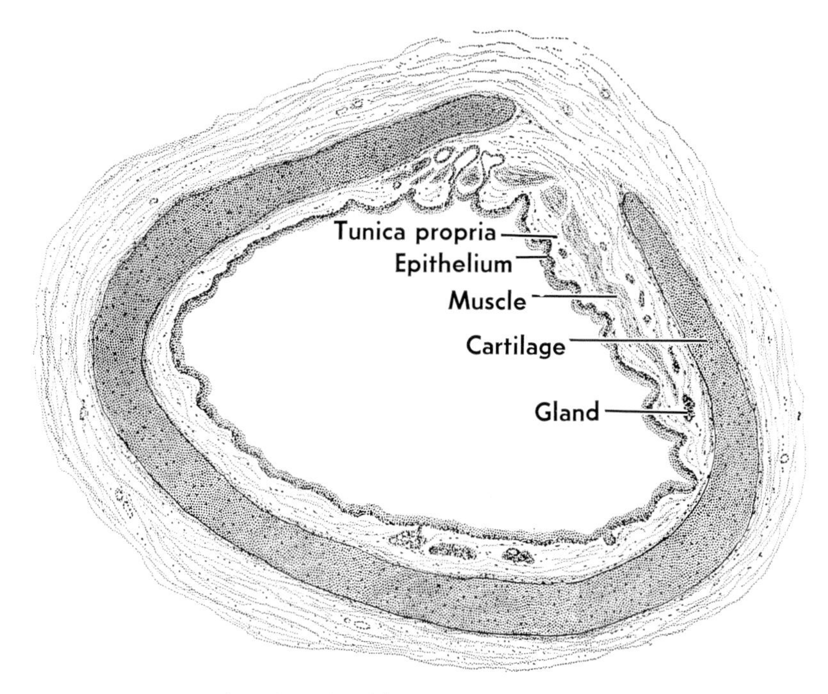

Fig. 129. Cross section of trachea of child.

crescents. In longitudinal sections dense clusters of these glands are seen in the triangular regions between the adjacent cartilage rings, to be described below.

In cross sections of the trachea the cartilages appear as a single C-shaped or U-shaped crescent with the open end or prongs directed posteriorly towards the esophagus. The prongs may branch so that more than one piece of cartilage may appear near the open side of the crescent. Bands of smooth muscle fibers transversely arranged appear between the prongs and at times may be observed inserting in the perichondrium either inside or outside the crescent. External to this muscle band one may observe the cut ends of longitudinally and obliquely arranged muscle fibers and their associated elastic fibers. The tracheal glands frequently penetrate the muscle layers. In longitudinal sections the cartilages appear as two rows of ovoid bodies. Occasionally two adjacent cartilages may fuse or be connected by a small longitudinal bar of cartilage. In the region between cartilages there are longitudinal bands of tough dense connective tissue which merge with the perichondria of the cartilages. In older animals some cartilages may appear to contain fibers or to be partly calcified.

BRONCHI

The extrapulmonary or primary bronchi are histologically identical with the trachea in practically all details except size. In the lungs the cartilages

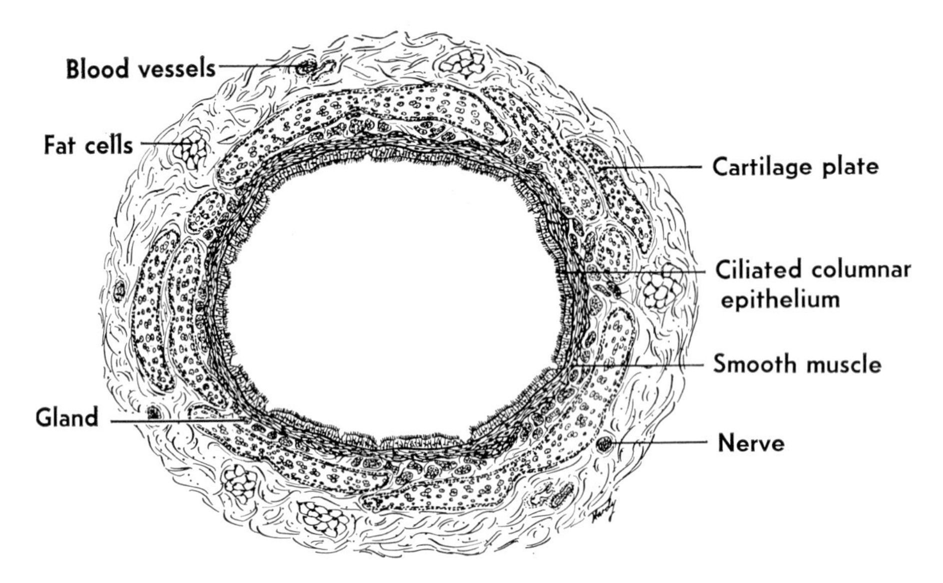

Fig. 130. Bronchus.

of the bronchi are arranged in a series of overlapping crescentic plates which completely encircle these structures. Deeper in the lung these soon give way to irregular masses of cartilage with more or less rounded edges (Fig. 130) and may or may not overlap when viewed in cross section. The intrapulmonary bronchi differ from the trachea as follows: (1) the elastic membrane of the tracheal lamina propria is replaced by a layer of smooth muscle which completely encircles both epithelium and the elastic fiber-containing lamina propria; (2) mucous and seromucous glands are more numerous and more generally distributed in the bronchi than in the trachea and often extend through the muscle and between adjacent cartilage plates; (3) the single crescent-shaped cartilage is replaced by a concentric ring of overlapping crescents. These eventually give way to smaller irregular masses of cartilage which continue to diminish in size until the tubules are completely devoid of cartilage. In the smallest bronchi only glands may be seen, and the cartilage is completely absent (Fig. 131). As the tubules become smaller the muscle bands which encircle the lumen become more prominent, with the concommitant reduction of the other structures. The muscles are arranged, however, as two opposing spirals which tend to form looser helices as the tubule branches and narrows. In cross section the looser spirals in smaller tubules appear as gaps between muscle bands at the same level. Upon death, contraction of the spiraling circular muscles throws the pseudostratified epithelium into longitudinal folds, carrying along with it folds of elastic lamina propria. Classification of large, medium-sized, and small bronchi on the basis of definitely overlapping crescentic plates of cartilage, circles of non-overlapping plates, or no cartilage at all introduces as many problems as it solves and is not a satisfactory criterion to use for identification.

BRONCHIOLES

In bronchioles there are neither glands nor cartilages (Fig. 131). The lumen is lined by ciliated simple columnar epithelium which lacks goblet cells. The lamina propria is elastic and very thin, and is surrounded by the same type of loosely spiraling smooth muscle bands found in the bronchi. It is interesting to note that ciliated cells are found beyond the point where glands are no longer in evidence. It has been postulated that this is a protection against the accumulation of mucus in the respiratory portion of the lungs. Subdivision of bronchioles into different types according to size is not histologically feasible and accordingly is not elaborated upon in this text.

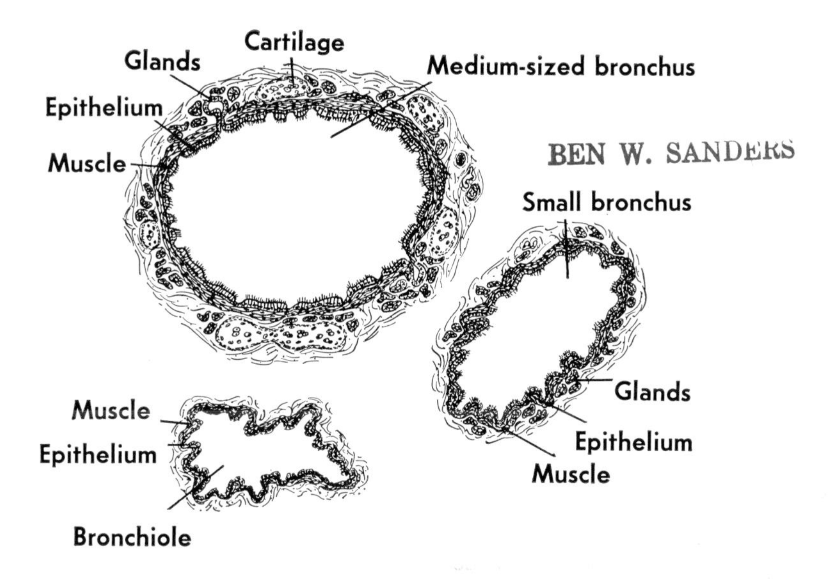

Fig. 131. Terminal intrapulmonary passageways of respiratory tract.

RESPIRATORY BRONCHIOLES

In the first part of the respiratory bronchiole the epithelium is of the ciliated low columnar or cuboidal type. Distally the epithelium becomes nonciliated cuboidal. The lamina propria is a very thin layer of diffuse reticular, collagenous, and elastic fibers. The spiraling muscle bands are quite prominent, but between adjacent muscle bands in the region where the lamina propria is not in evidence one can observe thin walls composed of simple cuboidal epithelium supported on a few helical elastic fibers. Some authors consider this to be respiratory epithelium, and from the

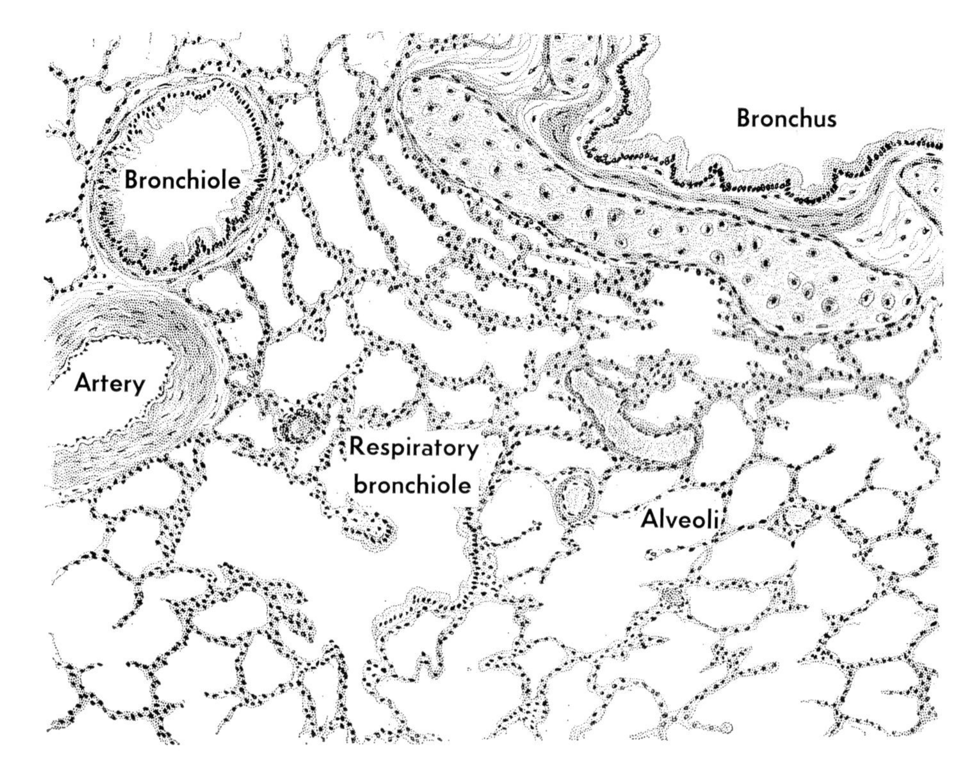

Fig. 132. Section of lung of dog.

appearance of these flattened plates the name respiratory bronchiole has arisen. It should be noted that in some sections the cells are so attenuated that the nuclei in these plates are not visible. In addition, pulmonary alveoli may arise directly from the walls of the respiratory bronchiole so that they appear as pockets in the tubule wall. Near their termini respiratory bronchioles flare out and give rise to two or more alveolar ducts.

ALVEOLAR DUCTS

The alveolar ducts are similar to the respiratory bronchioles from which they branch. The walls of the ducts are provided with so many openings into the alveoli that the wall appears discontinuous. Small bits of the branching, spiraling muscle fibers are seen around the openings into the alveoli or the chambers which lead into the alveoli.

In the alveoli of the lung there are respiratory epithelium and elastic tissue. To understand the arrangement of the former one must remember that all the tubules of the fetal lung are lined with cuboidal epithelium and are embedded in embryonic connective tissue. When respiration begins, at birth, some of the epithelium is stretched into the form of thin plates described previously in this discussion. There remain, however, at the angles between alveoli areas where the cells are not flattened. The surrounding connective tissue is reduced to a network of elastic fibers and a few fibroblasts between the alveoli. One may see, therefore, in a section of lung regions where the cells are reduced to a mere line and other regions where they are polygonal and evidently nucleated.

In human beings the atria are rare, and in other animals they are an inconstant feature, so we may well consider this term to be superfluous.

The original shape of each alveolus, or air sac, is round. The mutual pressure of adjacent sacs, however, alters the shape, and they appear as irregular polygonal spaces open on one side. They are so grouped that a number of them open into a common central space or atrium, which in turn opens into an alveolar duct.

The true relation of the parts described above is not often clear in a section of the lung. Occasionally one may have the good fortune to see an area in which the relations of respiratory bronchioles, alveolar ducts, atria, and alveoli appear, as in Fig. 134.

Under high magnification it may be seen that there are capillaries and some connective tissue between the air spaces of adjacent alveoli. The elements are not easily distinguished on a slide. Bounding the air space on each side are the thin plates of the respiratory epithelium. Beneath these

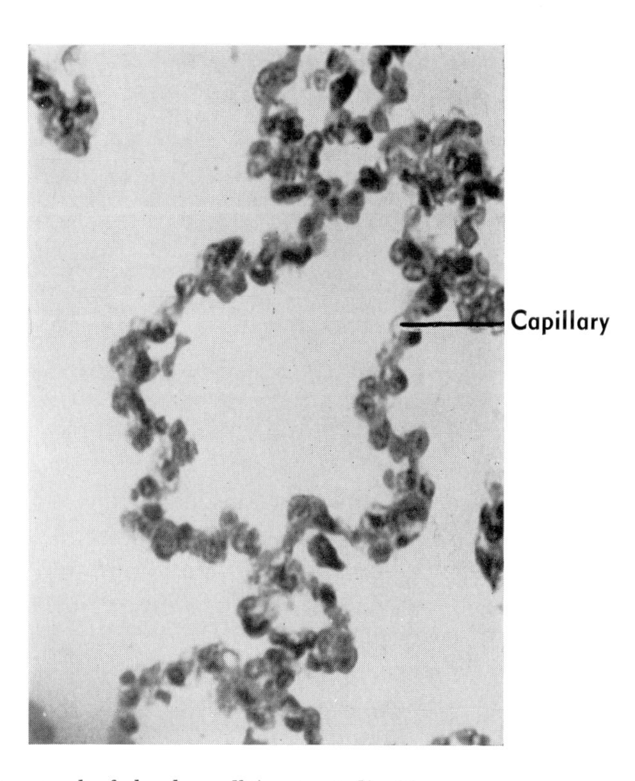

Fig. 133. Photomicrograph of alveolar wall (contracted) of lung.

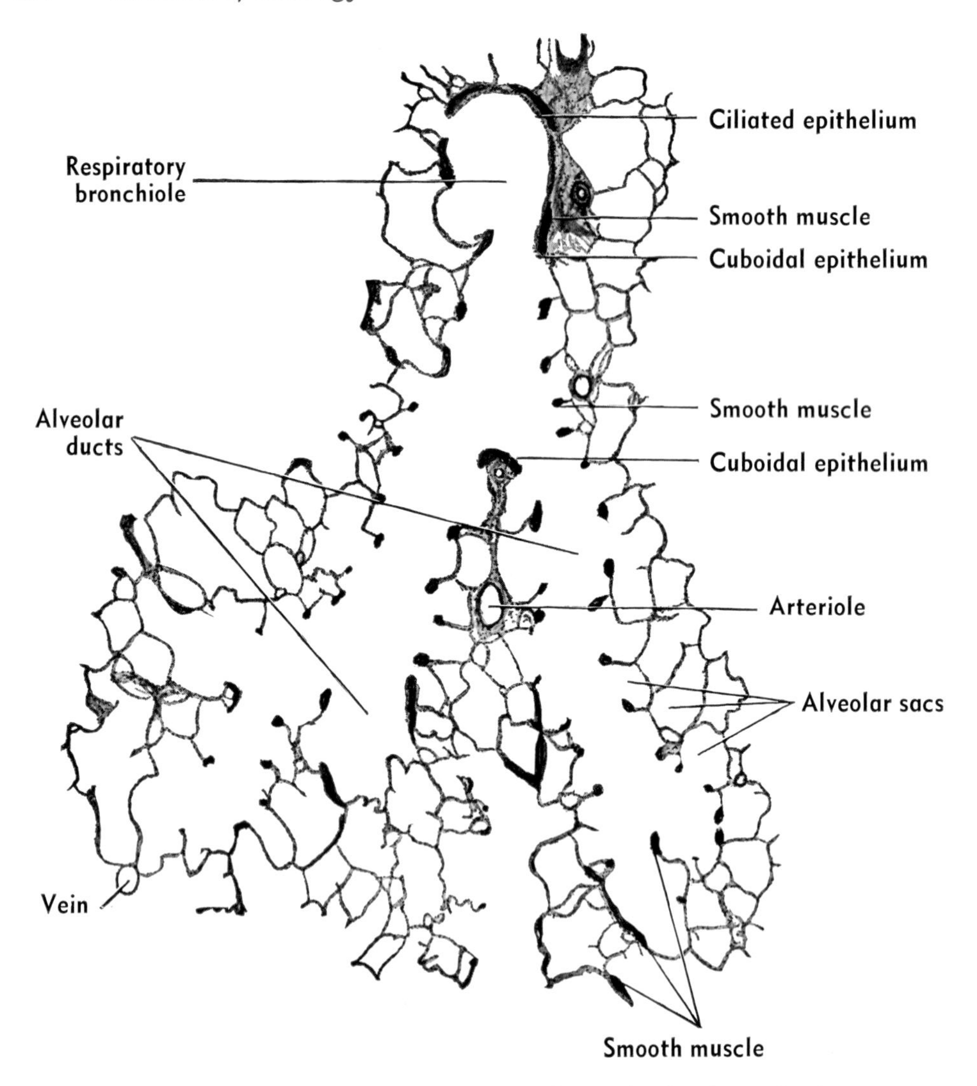

Fig. 134. Section through a respiratory bronchiole and two alveolar ducts of a human lung. (After Baltisberger; from Maximow and Bloom: Textbook of Histology, Philadelphia, W. B. Saunders Co.)

are the scattered cells and fibers of the connective tissue, and next to them is the endothelium of the capillaries. The red blood cells are thus separated from the air space by two very thin membranes, the endothelium and the respiratory epithelium, and by a scattering of connective tissue.

Blood supply of the lungs

The lungs receive most of their blood from the pulmonary arteries which eventually terminate in vessels of capillary size in the alveoli. In addition the lungs also receive some blood from the bronchial arteries.

Blood leaves the capillaries and is collected by venules which travel in the interstitial connective tissue and eventually fuse to form the pulmonary veins. There are two groups of lymphatic vessels: one group drains into the pleura, the other group drains toward the hilus and accompanies the large blood vessels.

Nerve supply of the lungs

The lungs are supplied by branches of the vagus and also fibers of the thoracic ganglia. The fibers which supply the constrictor elements are derived chiefly from the vagus. Those which innervate the dilators of the bronchi are, in the main, sympathetic in character; they are said to arise from the inferior cervical and upper thoracic ganglia.

CHAPTER XVIII

Urogenital system

Urinary system

KIDNEY

In mammals the main excretory pathways are the respiratory, integumentary, and urinary systems. The urine formed in the kidneys is transported with the aid of peristalsis through the ureters to a urinary bladder. As the sphincters leading out of the bladder relax, the whole bladder contracts and urine is forced out through the urethra.

The kidney offers two unusual opportunities to the student. (1) The gross structure of the dissected kidney correlates well with the pattern observed microscopically. (2) Instead of a vague mass of unnamed blood vessels, each one is named and exhibits definite microanatomical relations easily recognizable by beginning students. Because of its simplicity we will describe the rodent kidney first, then the human kidney.

Gross structure of the unilobar kidney. The kidney of a rodent, such as a rabbit, is a bean-shaped gland covered by a fibrous tunic or *renal capsule* which involutes into the kidney parenchyma along the medial aspect to form the *kidney sinus.* The external orifice of the sinus is called the *hilum* or hilus. The ureter expands into an *extrarenal pelvis,* which enters the kidney sinus and gives rise to an *intrarenal pelvis.* The distal portion of the latter is expanded into a trumpet-shaped cup or *calyx.* The lateral walls of the calyx fuse with the tissue lining the sinus. In addition to the ureter, the renal sinus contains a prominent fat pad, nerves, lymphatics, and branches of the renal artery and vein. (The highly vascularized perirenal fat body in the abdominal cavity functions to cushion and support the kidney.)

If one slices a rabbit kidney lengthwise it is seen to be composed of a single large mushroom-shaped lobe (unilobar kidney). The cap of the structure appears granular and is known as the kidney *cortex.* The stem-like portion appears triangular, striated, and in three dimensions resembles a *pyramid* (from which it derives its name). The tip of the pyramid is

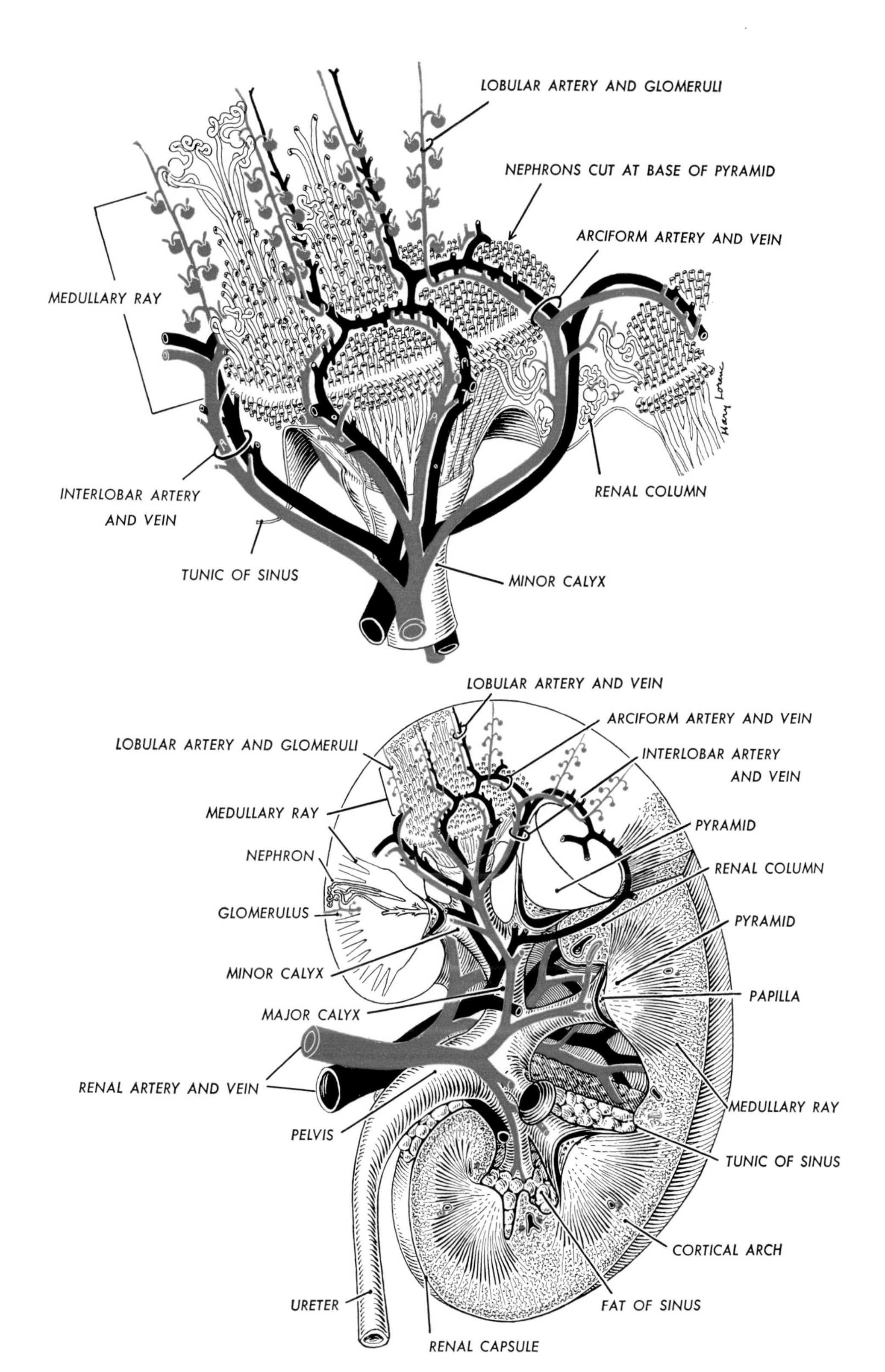

Plate 3. Circulatory plan of kidney. (From Smith: Principles of Renal Physiology, New York, 1956, Oxford University Press, Inc.)

called the *papilla* and it is this part which projects into and is received by the calyx. In the unilobar, unipyramidal kidney the term *medulla* applies to the pyramid itself, whereas the region near the base of the pyramid in the cortex is called the *juxtamedullary region.* Examination of the juxtamedullary region reveals fine strands of medullary substance penetrating and subdividing the cortical parenchyma. The former are called *medullary rays* (rays of Ferrein) and the latter are the *cortical labyrinths.* Also found in the juxtamedullary region are arched blood vessels running parallel to the base of the pyramid, which give rise to radial branches supplying and draining the cortical labyrinths.

Each lobe is subdivided into *lobules.* Most authors describe a lobule centered about a medullary ray and bounded by *interlobular arteries* running parallel to the ray in all the adjacent cortical labyrinths. (Plate 4, medullary ray lobule). Smith and others give valid reasons for supporting the idea that the artery located in the cortical labyrinth should be considered the center of the lobule (Plate 4, vascular lobule), which is then bounded by the centers of adjacent medullary rays. In the vascular lobule the artery becomes a *lobular artery,* which is synonymous with the interlobular artery of the previous system.

Gross structure of the multilobar kidney. Examination of the external aspect of the kidney of a six-month-old infant reveals remnants of a number of lobes (twelve to eighteen). With maturation the external evidence of lobation in man is obliterated. In the larger mammals, for example, ox, elephant, seal, etc., the lobes are externally visible, and each one appears to act like a separate kidney. Man has a multilobed, multipyramidal kidney.

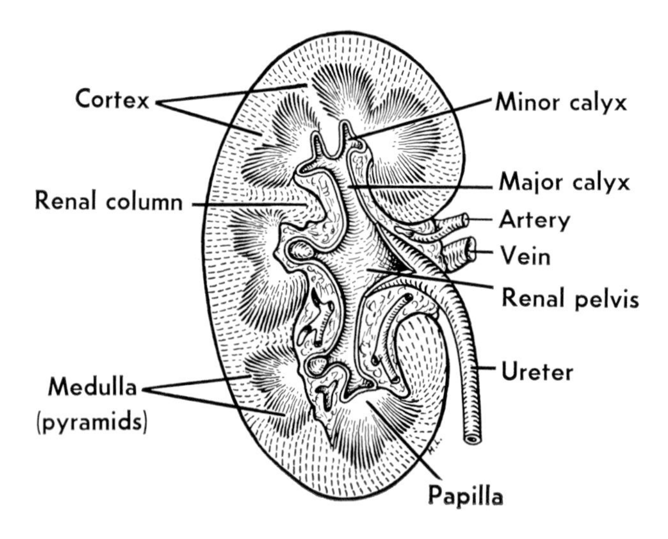

Fig. 135. Diagram showing topography of multipyramidal kidney. (Redrawn from Bailey.)

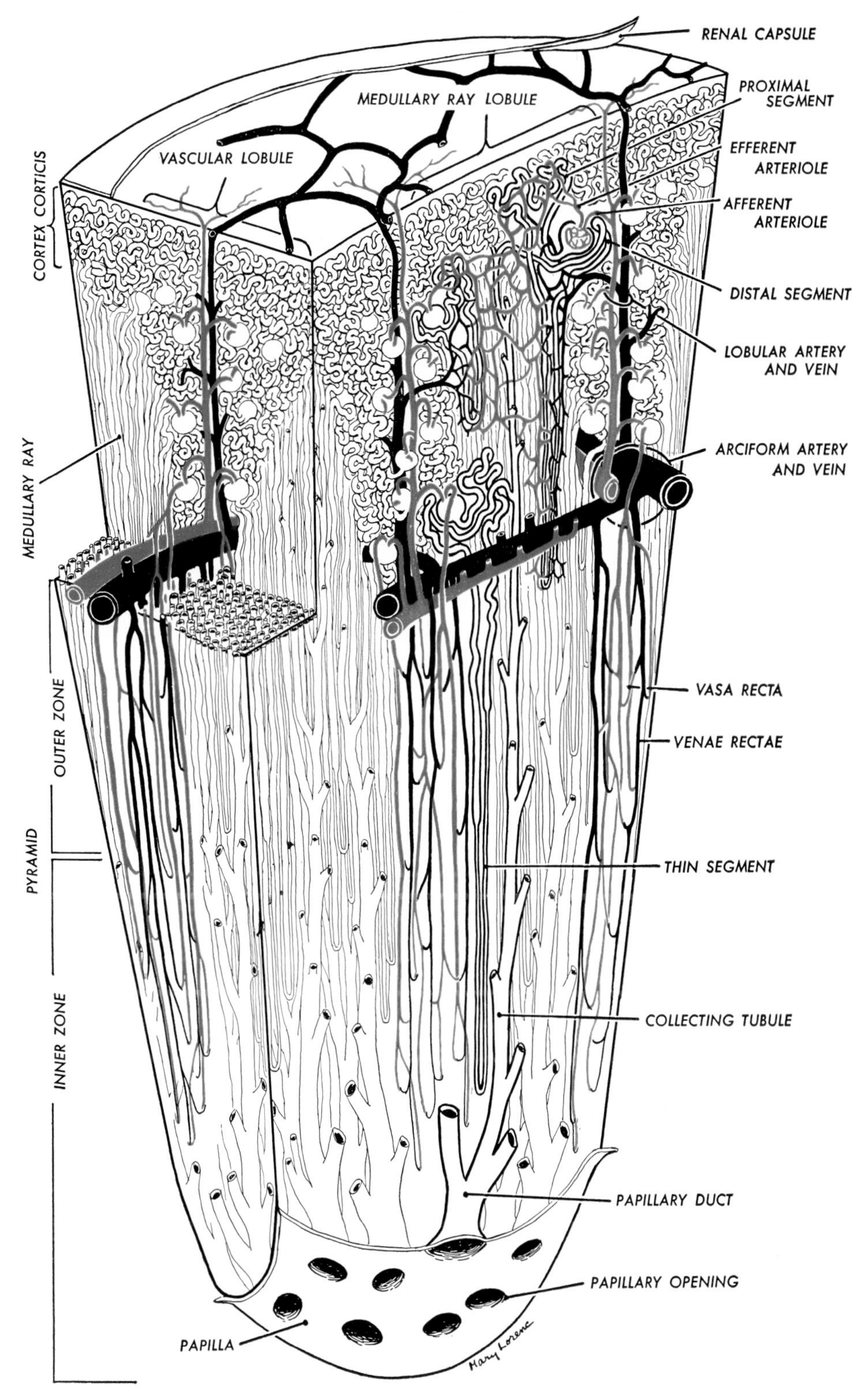

Plate 4. Details of a renal pyramid and cortex. (From Smith: Principles of Renal Physiology, New York, 1956, Oxford University Press, Inc.)

In man (Plate 3) the intrarenal pelvis branches into three anterior and posterior tubes called the *major calyces,* which in turn branch to form a total of eight *minor calyces* (Fig. 135). Each minor calyx receives a papilla from a single pyramid or a papilla formed by the fusion of two or more pyramids. As a result of fusion there are fewer papillae (four to thirteen) than pyramids (eight to eighteen). In multipyramidal kidneys trabeculae of the cortical parenchyma fill in the spaces between adjacent pyramids and are called the *renal columns* or columns of Bertini or Bertin. The physiologist considers only the renal pyramids and medullary rays as medulla and the cortical labyrinths and renal columns to constitute the cortex of the kidney.

Circulation. Each kidney (Plate 3) is supplied by a single *renal artery,* which divides in the renal sinus into two sets of *secondary renal arteries.* One set supplies the anterior two-thirds of the kidney, whereas the other supplies the posterior one-third. As they pass through the fat body of the sinus they divide again prior to penetrating between adjacent pyramids or between a pyramid and an adjacent renal column. The latter are called *interlobar arteries* (a term obviously not suited to unilobar kidneys). Each lobe is supplied by a number of interlobar arteries (six to fourteen) which curve abruptly in the juxtamedullary region to form incomplete arterial arches known as *arciform arteries* (arcuate arteries). Along their entire path over the base of the pyramid the arciform arteries give rise to radial or perpendicular *lobular arteries* (interlobular arteries) which supply the cortical labyrinths. In the cortical labyrinths the lobular arteries give rise to numerous short straight *afferent arterioles* which supply small tufts of blood vessels called *glomeruli.* The lobular arteries become progressively smaller and terminate in the subcapsular region in a plexus of arterioles and capillaries which supply part of the capsule.

The blood flow leaving the glomeruli differs according to the location of the latter. Each of the *cortical glomeruli* (outer two-thirds of the cortex) give rise to an *efferent arteriole* of a diameter equal to that of the afferent vessel. The efferent arterioles divide shortly to form a *peritubular capillary network* within the cortical labyrinths and medullary rays found in the cortical region. Each *juxtamedullary glomerulus* (located in the inner one-third of the cortex) gives rise to an efferent arteriole whose diameter is equal to or larger than the afferent vessel. The efferent arterioles of these glomeruli penetrate the pyramid and divide there into a series of long straight parallel blood vessels passing into the papilla and are collectively referred to as the *vasa recta.* Their diameter is roughly equal to that of the efferent vessels, and the presence of intermittent circularly arranged smooth muscle elements indicates the source of the name *arteriolae rectae.* Careful observation is necessary to differentiate these from ordinary capillaries. An incomplete inner elastic membrane may occur in afferent arterioles but not in the efferent or glomerular vessels. The smooth muscle elements of the efferent arterioles may be lacking or replaced at intervals by groups of contractile pericytes or Rouget cells.

If the renal capsule is stripped away carefully, one may observe that a series of subcapsular blood vessels merge at certain points. These give the impression that the kidney surface is covered by a number of star-shaped blood vessels. These are the so-called *stellate veins,* and the central point of fusion marks the beginning of the *lobular vein* (interlobular vein). The lobular veins pass through the cortical labyrinths in company with the lobular arteries. The freely anastomosing peritubular capillaries drain into short cortical veins (intralobular veins), which in turn join the lobular veins. In the juxtamedullary region the lobular veins join the *arcuate veins* (arciform veins). In contrast with the arcuate arteries the arcuate veins form complete arches over the surface of the pyramidal base (see Plates 3 and 4). The papilla is drained by a series of straight blood vessels, *venae rectae.* The walls of these veins contain smooth muscle spirally arranged. The venae rectae drain directly into the arcuate veins in the juxtamedullary region.

The renal artery sends a branch to the adrenal gland as well as much smaller branches to the ureter, renal pelvis, adipose tissue, and nerves of the sinus, calyces, and the vasa vasorum of the larger blood vessels entering the kidney parenchyma. The collateral circulation of the kidney is described in more advanced texts. In the literature one finds references to blood circuits from the lobular arteries which do not pass through any recognizable glomerulus. These conditions seem to exist more often in infected or chronically afflicted kidneys or in the kidneys of very old individuals. If the glomerulus is destroyed, then the afferent arteriole and efferent arteriole remain as a single continuous structure. With a loss of cortical glomeruli the so-called Ludwig's arteriole is formed in the manner just described and leads directly to a capillary bed. If the glomerulus is lost in the juxtamedullary region, then the afferent and efferent vessels form a single arteriole penetrating the pyramidal tissue. Several of these give rise to the so-called *arteriolae rectae verae* (the true straight arterioles). These pathways are relatively infrequent in normal young kidneys and are described in detail in pathological texts. Occasionally one finds mention of intralobular arteries which give rise to two or three afferent arterioles. These are relatively infrequent and have been described primarily in the juxtamedullary region.

Finer structure of the kidney. The urinary functions of the kidney are carried out by three groups of structures. These are (1) the glomeruli, (2) the nephrons, and (3) the collecting tubules and papillary ducts. It is by the activity of nephrons that urine is formed, and nephrons are described as the functional units of the kidney. There are about one million nephrons in each human kidney.

Glomeruli. In tissue sections each glomerulus is observed as an oval or

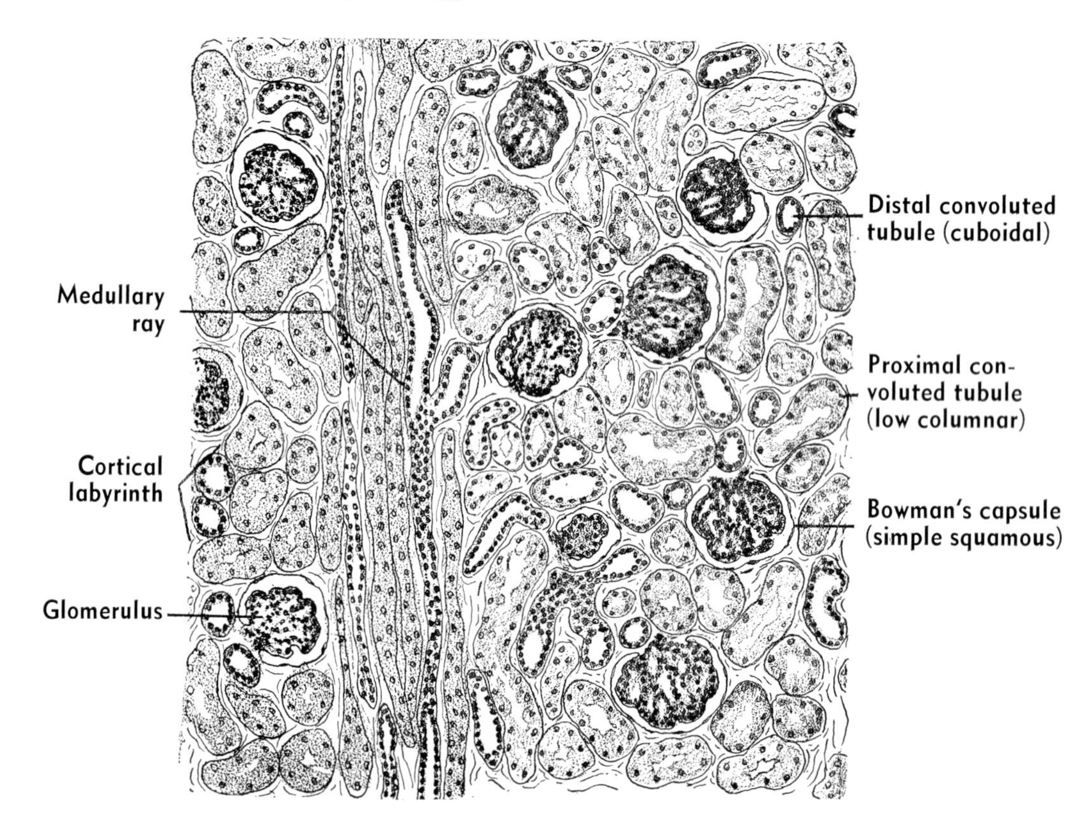

Fig. 136. Section of part of cortex of human kidney.

rounded body consisting of a mass of capillaries containing many red blood cells and bounded by a small space (Figs. 136 and 138). The space is the cavity of Bowman's capsule, formed by invagination of the capillary into an enlargement of the end of the nephron. Thus Bowman's capsule is a double-layered structure composed of simple squamous epithelium, with nuclei bulging into the capsular space. The inner layer of Bowman's capsule is known as the *visceral layer* and is in intimate contact with all the exposed surfaces of the glomerular tuft. The *parietal layer* forms the outer boundary of the capsule. A prominent basement membrane is visualized by the PAS technique and is located around the parietal layer of the capsule and between the visceral layer and the glomerular capillaries.

The side of the glomerulus where the afferent and efferent arterioles enter and leave and approximate each other forms the vascular pole of the glomerulus. The end directed towards the tubular portion of the nephron is known as the urinary pole of the glomerulus (Fig. 138).

As the afferent arteriole approaches the vascular pole it gives rise to the juxtaglomerular apparatus (Fig. 138). As it enters Bowman's capsule the afferent arteriole loses its inner elastic membrane and gives rise to four to eight primary capillaries which branch and form a number of anastomosing secondary capillaries. They in turn merge to form primary capillaries draining into the efferent arteriole. As a result of this arrangement of capillaries, the glomerulus is described as *lobulated* (Fig. 136). In section, however, the mass of capillaries observed in glomeruli rarely appear lobulated.

The glomerulus and its enveloping Bowman's capsule form the *malpighian corpuscle* or renal corpuscle. Although there is considerable variation in size, the juxtamedullary glomeruli appear to be larger and in man may average approximately 0.2 mm. in diameter. Glomeruli are limited to the cortical labyrinths and renal columns and are not ordinarily found in the medullary rays or pyramidal tissue of the kidney (Plates 3 and 4). *Note:* Many lower chordates, for example, certain fishes, possess aglomerular kidneys.

Nephron. On an anatomical basis the nephron consists of four parts: Bowman's capsule, proximal convoluted tubule, loop of Henle, and the distal convoluted tubule (Fig. 137). Bowman's capsule has been described previously as an invaginated dilation of the nephric tubule. The parietal layer leads into a small necklike constriction which contains ciliated cells in submammalian forms but not in human beings. The tubule leading from the capsule almost immediately begins a twisted and tortuous path through the cortical labyrinth and is accordingly named the proximal convoluted tubule. In sections this is indicated by tubules cut in several planes (Fig. 136), most however appear in transverse or in tangential section.

The proximal tubule enters a medullary ray at the site where it bends towards the papilla and forms a relatively straight tube, the *descending arm* of Henle's loop, which extends for a variable distance and then reverses its direction to form the so-called *ascending arm* of Henle's loop, which is approximately parallel to the descending arm. In the region of the actual curvature the tubule becomes extremely thin, giving rise to the *thin segment* of Henle's loop. The thin segment is a variable structure, since it may be located on the ascending side, the descending side, or both. Thin segments of nephrons arising from cortical glomeruli are abbreviated or lacking entirely, whereas nephrons originating in the juxtamedullary region bear long thin segments penetrating deeply into the pyramids (see Plate 3). In summary, the loops of Henle are located entirely within the medullary rays and pyramids. They consist of a thick descending limb, a thin segment which varies in location and length, and a thick ascending limb.

The ascending limb enters the cortical labyrinth slightly below the level of the glomerulus of origin and passes between the afferent and efferent vessels and makes tangential contact with the vascular pole of the glomerulus. The region of tangential contact gives rise to the *macula densa* (Fig.

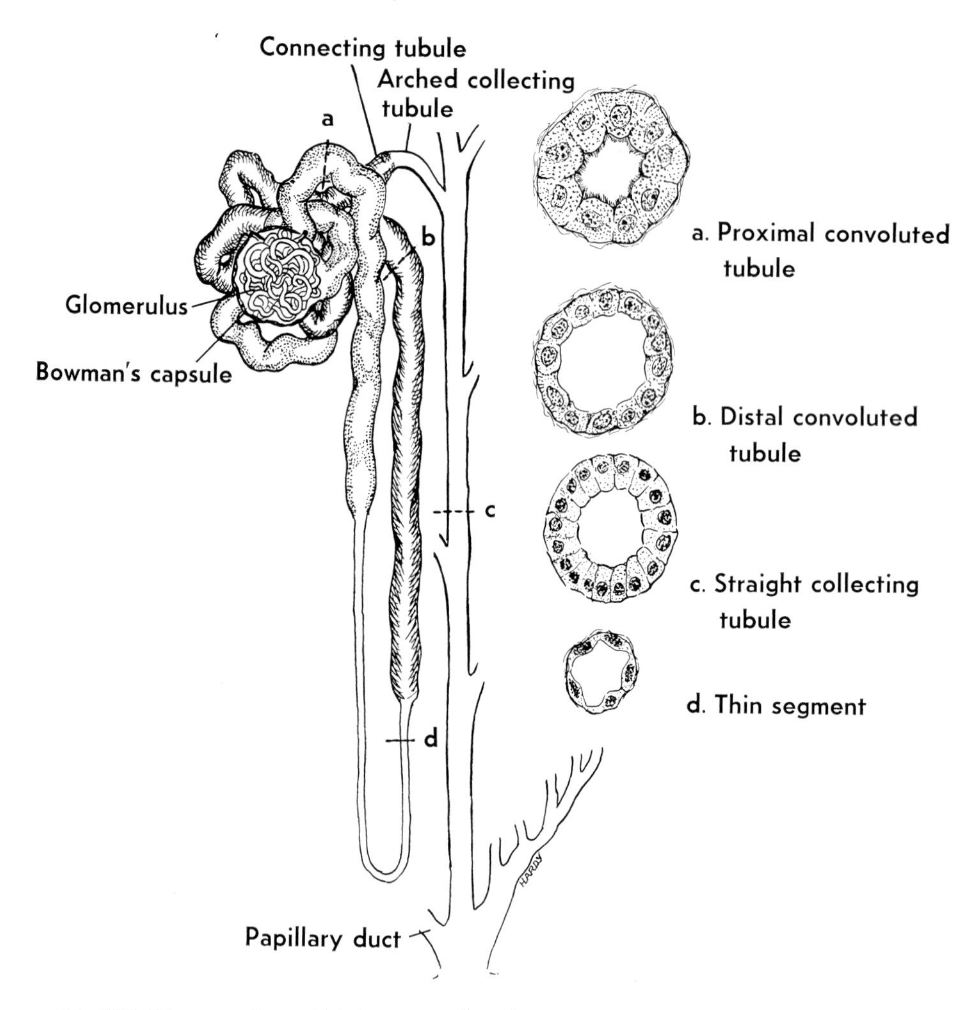

Fig. 137. Diagram of essential structures of nephron.

138). The portion of tubule extending beyond the vascular pole is known as the *distal convoluted tubule.* It is less convoluted than the proximal tubule. The distal tubule leads to an arched tubule which enters the medullary ray to join the system of collecting tubules.

On a cytological-physiological basis only four subdivisions of the nephron are designated: Bowman's capsule, a proximal segment, a thin segment, and a distal segment.

BOWMAN'S CAPSULE. Consists of simple squamous epithelium with a prominent basement membrane (Fig. 138).

THE PROXIMAL SEGMENT. Consists of tubules with low columnar epithelium (Fig. 137) bearing a brush border at the free surface and basal striations in the subnuclear position. The latter represent infoldings of the cell membrane along which mitochondria may be visualized by special methods.

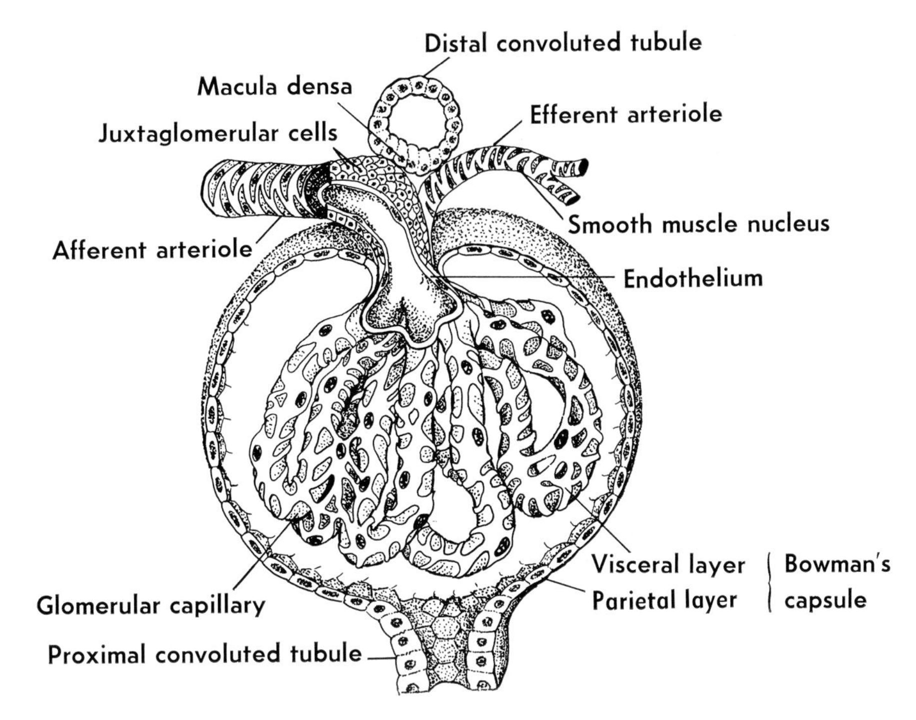

Fig. 138. Representative drawing of renal corpuscle. (Redrawn and modified from Bailey.)

Inasmuch as adjacent cells interdigitate freely, the cell outlines are rarely seen in cross sections of the tubule. The coarsely granular eosinophilic cytoplasm bulges into the lumen and the nuclei are basally located. The brush border is not ordinarily well preserved, accordingly the free edge of the cell appears rounded and slightly ragged. Similarly mitochondria and basal striations are not well preserved in routine preparations and are not usually apparent to the novice. The basal striations become less distinct as the thin segment is approached. Despite considerable post-mortem degeneration, these cells are considerably more eosinophilic than those found in adjacent tubules.

The proximal segment consists of a convoluted portion in the cortical labyrinth and a straight descending limb in the medullary ray and pyramid.

THE THIN SEGMENTS. Are tubular structures consisting of squamous cells. The cytoplasm appears agranular and the nucleus is slightly compressed. In cross section they may be confused with capillaries and arteriolae rectae, especially since red blood cells are sometimes forced into the thin segments during preparation of the tissue. They are distinguished from capillaries by (1) the more extensive protrusion of nuclei into the lumen and (2) the greater number of cells visible in cross section through a tubule.

Thin segments are demonstrable in profusion in the deeper portions of the pyramids since they extend almost to the papillae. Thin segments of the kind described are lacking in reptiles, most birds, amphibians, and fishes.

THE DISTAL SEGMENT. The thin segment joins the distal segment, the latter being composed initially of low cuboidal cells with indistinct boundaries. As the ascending limb approaches the cortex the cells are taller but are still cuboidal and bear irregular projections into the lumen. Upon entering the cortical labyrinths the tubule passes the vascular pole of the glomerulus of origin and makes tangential contact with the afferent arteriole. At the point of contact the cuboidal cells become more closely packed so that the cells appear taller (sometimes columnar), and many nuclei are visible and crowded together to form the *macula densa* (Fig. 139). Beyond this structure the tubule becomes convoluted, consisting of smaller cuboidal cells, the free surfaces of which are smooth. These cells are less eosinophilic (or more basophilic) than those found in the proximal tubule. The cells do not bear a striated border or brush border, basal striations, nor do they exhibit definite cell boundaries in sectioned material. The basement membrane is prominent along all parts of the tubule except in the region of the macula densa. Since the convoluted portion is short, fewer sections through this segment are seen in the cortical labyrinths.

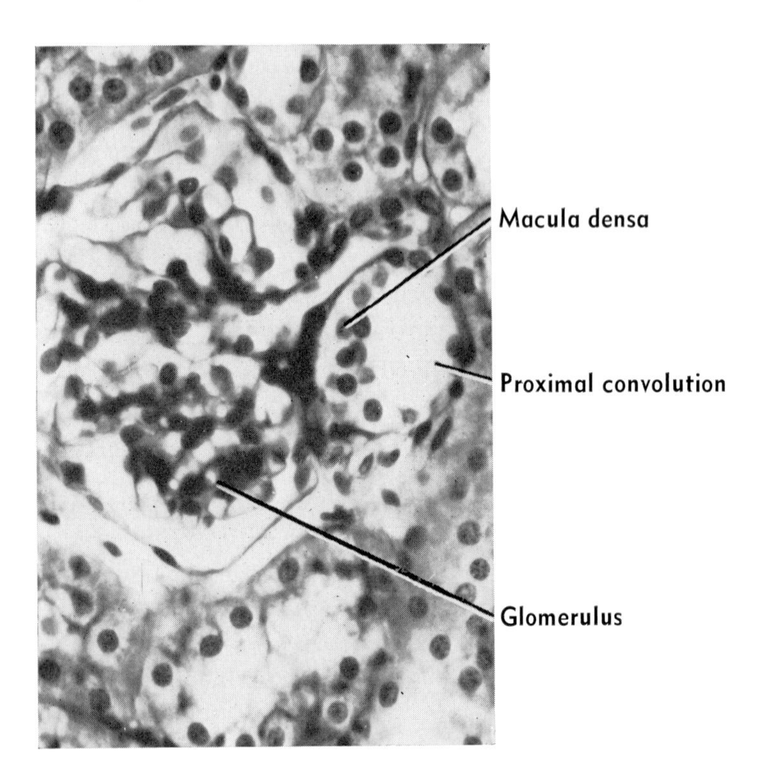

Fig. 139. Section of cortex of kidney of rabbit. (PAS and hematoxylin stain.)

Collecting tubules and papillary ducts. At the termination of the distal convoluted tubule one may sometimes observe a short connecting tubule. It contains a mixture of the cuboidal cells characteristic of the distal segment and occasional isolated large granular cells (intercalated cells). This is supposedly the region of embryonic fusion between the nephron and the collecting tubule.

The connecting tubule is continuous with the *arched collecting tubule* which passes into the medullary ray, where it joins the *straight collecting tubule.* The straight tubules, along with Henle's loops, lie in parallel bundles and occupy most of the medulla, with the exception of the papilla. The cells of the collecting tubules are noted for their distinct boundaries, spherical nuclei at approximately the same level in the cell, and relatively agranular cytoplasm. Eventually the straight tubules (Plate 4) reach the papillary region and fuse to form relatively large ducts, the *papillary ducts* (ducts of Bellini). The latter consist of tall columnar cells. In each papilla sixteen to twenty papillary ducts are formed which penetrate the apex of the papilla to form a sievelike region or *area cribosa.* From this site the urine formed in the nephrons is drained into a minor calyx.

Juxtaglomerular apparatus. At the vascular pole of the glomerulus (Fig. 138) the media and adventitial reticulum of the afferent arteriole are replaced by cells which vary from cuboidal to columnar. These form a thickening or cuff around the arteriole (periarteriolar pad). A number of cells may spill over into the cleft between the afferent and efferent vessels to form an asymmetrical cap (polkissen or polar cushion). This complex of cells is referred to as the *juxtaglomerular apparatus.* The polkissen and periarteriolar pad both may be in contact with the macula densa, and their region of contact is marked by the absence of a PAS-positive basement membrane. The polkissen cells of certain rodents exhibit some large epithelioid cells containing brilliant fuchsinophil granules. In canines and man the cells are small and agranular. In addition the juxtaglomerular apparatus is not demonstrable in man for the first two years of postnatal life. The presence of epithelioid cells similar to those found in certain endocrine organs suggests an endocrine function. Physiological experiments have failed to produce consistent changes in the juxtaglomerular apparatus and thus the status of this structure remains to be elucidated.

Lymphatic circulation. The lymphatic plexi are found in three main regions as follows: (1) A network of lymphatic capillaries permeates the cortex and renal columns; these capillaries form an anastomosing network around blood vessels, especially the larger arteries; the plexus drains into the lymphatic vessels leaving the hilum of the kidney, and thence goes into the lateral aortic nodes (2) beneath the renal capsule in intimate association with the stellate veins and subcapsular plexus of blood capillaries. This group communicates with (3) the lymphatics draining the perirenal fat body. The perirenal lymphatic plexus drains into the lateral aortic nodes.

Lymphatics are lacking in the renal pyramids and glomeruli and do not enter the tubules. No specific function has been demonstrated for the kidney lymphatics.

Connective tissue. The renal capsule is formed of a dense fibrous connective tissue which is primarily collagenous, with some elastic fibers and a few scattered smooth muscle cells. A thin inflexion of this capsule lines the renal sinus and fuses with the adventitia of the blood vessels and epineurium of the larger nerves. It also disperses into fine strands in the fat body of the renal sinus. The renal capsule is easily stripped from normal kidneys due to a lack of trabeculi from the capsule.

The basement membrane entirely envelops all parts of the nephron and collecting tubules except as noted previously. The ground substance of the basement membrane is PAS positive, and the reticular fibers are typically argyrophile and quite fine. In the pyramids the reticular fibers form an extensive network binding ducts and blood vessels together.

URETER

Urine collects in the pelvis of the kidney and passes out through the ureter. This is a thin duct, composed of the following layers: mucosa, submucosa, muscularis, and adventitia.

Mucosa. The mucosa includes an epithelium of the transitional type

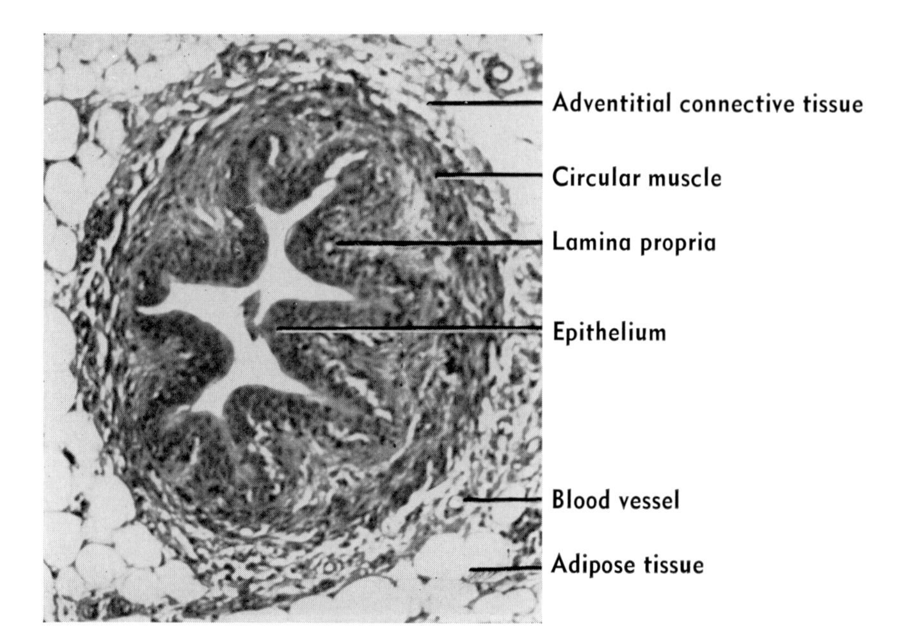

Fig. 140. Transverse section of ureter of rat.

resting on a tunica propria of reticular and fine areolar tissue. There is no muscularis mucosae.

Submucosa. The submucosa consists of loose areolar tissue and blends with the tunica propria on one side and with the intermuscular connective tissue of the muscularis on the other. It contains blood vessels and lymphatics.

Muscularis. In the muscularis there is a reversal of the usual arrangement of coats, there being an inner longitudinal and an outer circular layer. In the lower portion of the ureter there is a third layer of muscle, longitudinally disposed, outside the circular layer. All three layers are somewhat loosely arranged, with a great deal of areolar tissue among the muscle fibers.

Adventitia. The adventitia is formed of loose connective tissue.

URINARY BLADDER

The wall of the urinary bladder is composed of the same elements as that of the lower part of the ureter, namely, transitional epithelium, tunica propria, submucosa, three layers of muscle, and adventitia (Fig.

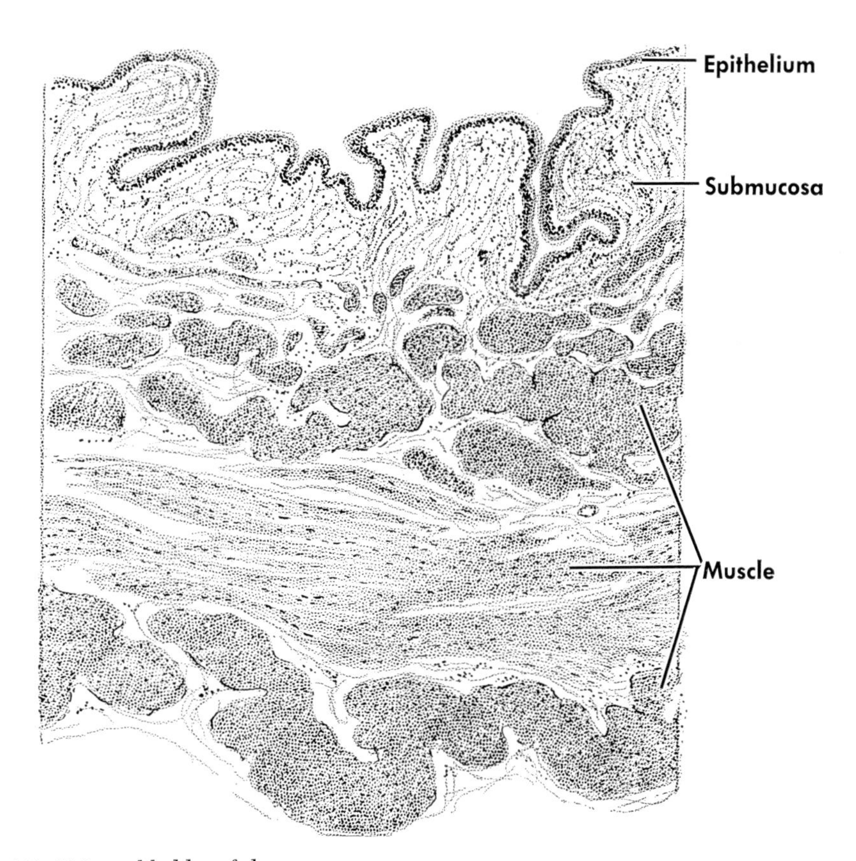

Fig. 141. Urinary bladder of dog.

141). In the bladder the epithelium varies in thickness according to the degree of distention of the organ (see discussion on transitional epithelium, Chapter II). The muscular layers of the bladder are not so regular in their arrangements as those of the ureter but they form a thicker layer.

URETHRA

The urethra of the female serves as an outlet for urine from the bladder, whereas that of the male functions also as the terminal portion of the ducts of the reproductive system. The organ is, therefore, somewhat different in the two sexes.

Female urethra

In the female the tube is composed of an epithelial lining, a connective tissue layer, and a muscular coat. The epithelium of the proximal part is like that of the bladder. This type is replaced further down the tube first by stratified columnar or pseudostratified epithelium and later by stratified squamous toward the distal end.

The connective tissue layer contains elastic fibers and a rich plexus of veins which may be compared with the corpus cavernosum of the male urethra (see below) though it is much less extensive. The lumen of the organ is irregular, since the connective tissue and epithelium are thrown into longitudinal rugae. There are also small diverticula from the lumen (lacunae) into which open the mucous-secreting glands of Littre.

The muscularis consists of two sets of smooth muscle fibers intermingled with connective tissue. The fibers of the inner set are longitudinally placed, the outer have a circular direction. At the distal end of the urethra there is, in addition, a sphincter of striated muscle.

Male urethra

The male urethra shows modifications of the structure described above. It is divided into three portions.

Prostatic portion. The proximal end of the prostatic urethra is homologous to the female urethra and resembles it in structure as well as in function. As the tube passes through the prostate gland it receives the openings of the ducts from the testes and numerous small ducts from the prostate.

Membranous portion. The membranous portion of the urethra, which passes through the urogenital diaphragm, is also somewhat like the female urethra. The epithelium changes in or about this region from transitional to stratified columnar or pseudostratified, but the location of the change varies considerably in different individuals. Glands are more common than in the female urethra. The bulbourethral (mucous) glands of Cowper are situated in the muscle near the distal part of the membranous urethra, but their ducts enter the cavernous urethra.

Cavernous portion. The cavernous portion is the longest segment of the urethra, lying in the penis. The tissues surrounding it will be discussed more fully in the section on the male reproductive system. The epithelial lining of the urethra changes at the distal end to stratified squamous with well-developed connective tissue papillae. The tunica propria contains an extensive plexus of blood vessels which forms the corpus cavernosum urethrae, and the glands of Littre are most numerous in this portion of the tube. The muscular coat is broken up into scattered groups of fibers.

Blood and nerve supply of the excretory passages

The blood supply of the ureter, bladder, and urethra comes from arteries which penetrate the muscular coats of the organs and form plexuses in the deeper layers of the tunica propria. From here vessels continue inward, forming other plexuses just below the epithelium. The deeper layers of the connective tissue and probably the muscular layers have a rich lymphatic supply.

Plexuses of medullated and nonmedullated nerves occur in the walls of the ureter and the bladder. The nonmedullated nerves supply the muscles; the medullated, the mucosa. Numerous ganglia are present in the connective tissue.

Male reproductive system

TESTIS

The testis in the adult man lies in the scrotum, partly surrounded by a serous sac, the tunica vaginalis, which is a diverticulum from the peritoneum. The testis is covered by a two-layered connective tissue capsule. The outer layer or tunica albuginea is composed of dense white fibrous tissue; the inner or vasculosa layer is of looser areolar tissue richly supplied with blood vessels. From the capsule trabeculae extend inward to a central mass of connective tissue, the mediastinum which contains the proximal portions of the duct system. The parenchyma of the testis is thus divided into many pyramidal lobules which contain the closely packed coils of the seminiferous tubules and a stroma of interstitial connective tissue (Fig. 142). In the connective tissue there are blood vessels and groups of endocrine cells called the interstitial cells of the testis.

The convoluted seminiferous tubules are lined with germinal epithelium, which may contain as many as five layers of cells. Each layer represents a different stage in the development of the spermatozoa or male sex cells. Nearest the outside of the wall of the tubule lie the spermatogonia or primordial germ cells. These are small cuboidal or rounded cells with

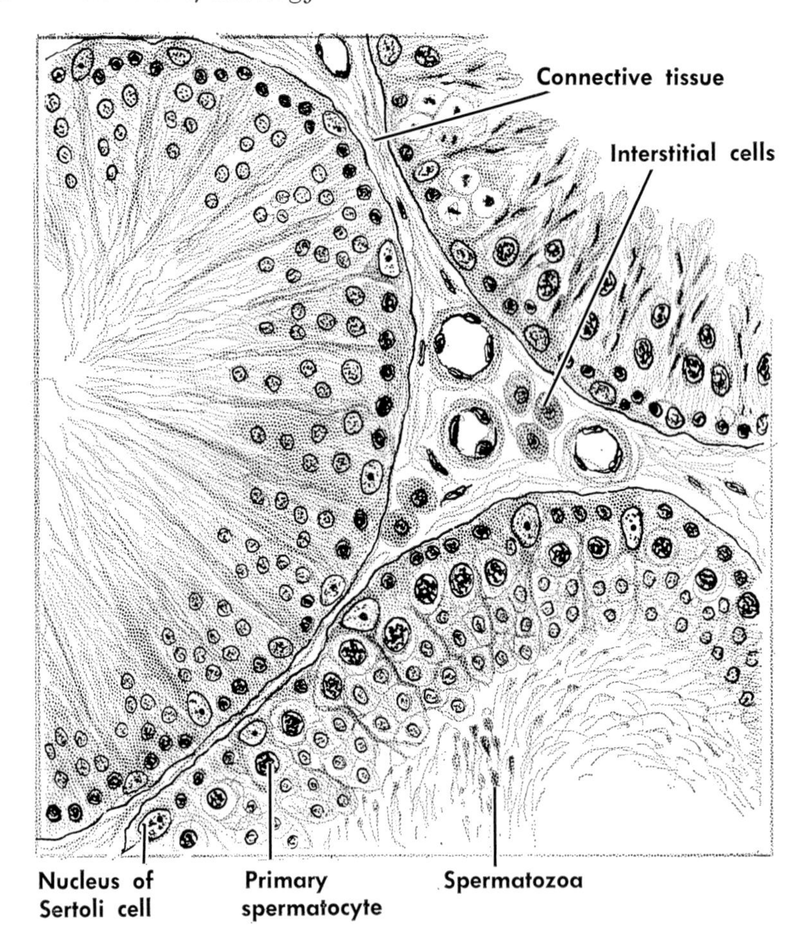

Fig. 142. Seminiferous tubules and interstitial cells of testes of rat. The different appearance of the germinal epithelium in three sections of tubules represented is indicative of differences in stages of spermatogenesis.

vesicular nuclei. Next to them toward the lumen are the primary spermatocytes, larger cells, in the nuclei of which the chromatin is collected in dense clumps. Then follow the secondary spermatocytes, similar in appearance but somewhat smaller than the primary spermatocytes. Superimposed on these are the spermatids, which are much smaller cells with vesicular nuclei, and bordering on the lumen are the fully formed spermatozoa. These have dark, elongated nuclei and flagella.

The process involved in the development of the spermatoza consists of (1) a rearrangement of the chromatin material of the nucleus and (2) the formation of motile cells. In ordinary mitoses, or cell divisions, the chromatin condenses into a number of small bodies, the chromosomes. Each chromosome divides so that one-half of it goes to one daughter cell and one-half to the other. The number of chromosomes formed at each

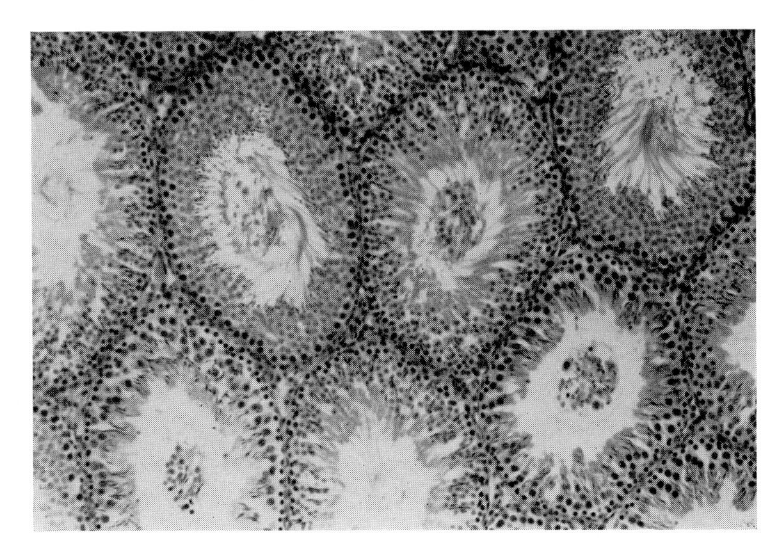

Fig. 143. Section of seminiferous tubules of rat, showing mature sperm.

mitosis is constant and is characteristic for each species of animal (probably forty-eight in man). This number also appears in the division of the spermatogonia. When, however, the primary spermatocytes divide the individual chromosomes do not split. One-half of them go undivided to one secondary spermatocyte, one-half to the other. This is known as maturation or the reduction of chromatin. A similar process takes place in the development of the ovum or female sexual cell. Its result is obvious: the spermatozoon, containing twenty-four chromosomes, unites with the ovum which also contains only twenty-four, and the resulting new individual is thus provided with forty-eight of these bodies, one-half of which are derived from each parent. Since the chromosomes are believed to be the bearers of hereditary characteristics, their distribution is of great interest to geneticists. The details of maturation are not, however, to be observed in ordinary slides. This is true also of the second part of the development of the spermatozoa, that is, the formation of motile cells from nonmotile cells. The stages mentioned may be identified in most slides of the testis.

The process of spermatogenesis is not in the same stage in all parts of the tubule at a given time. The completion of spermatozoa occurs in a series of waves which pass down the tubule. For this reason a lobule of the testis when sectioned will show some portions of the tubules in which all five stages are present and others in which only three or four can be demonstrated.

It will be noticed that the germinal epithelium of the testis, while it is stratified, is not to be classed with any other type of epithelium. In those already studied the stratification has as its purpose the formation of a protective layer. In the germinal epithelium it is simply the accidental result of the piling of one stage of development on another. The tissue differs from other epithelia also in the relation of the cells to each other. In stratified squamous epithelium, for instance, the cells are closely applied to each other and are held together by cement substance. In germinal epithelium the cells are so loosely piled that many of them retain their spherical shape.

Besides the cells which represent stages of spermatogenesis, the seminiferous tubule has in its wall a number of supporting cells, the sustentacular or Sertoli cells. These are irregular elongated elements, the bases of which lie against the basement membrane, while their apices border on the lumen. Because of the pallor of their cytoplasm and the crowding of the germinal cells, it is difficult to see the outlines of a sustentacular cell. Its nucleus may be identified by its elongated shape and lack of chromatin; it is much paler than the nucleus of any of the stages of spermatogenesis. When mature spermatozoa are present they tend to gather in groups with their heads (nuclei) embedded in the free end of the Sertoli cell, and this fact will aid the student, as the groups of spermatozoa are easily seen. It is supposed that the sustentacular cells furnish nourishment to the spermatozoa and also form a supporting framework for the other germinal cells.

As has been said, the spermatogenic tubules lie coiled in a stroma of loose connective tissue in which, entirely separated from the tubules, are groups of cells which are not concerned with the formation of spermatozoa. These are the interstitial cells, which are believed to produce the hormone responsible for the development and maintenance of secondary sexual characteristics. They are fairly large cells with abundant reddish cytoplasm. They occur in small groups not surrounded by a connective tissue capsule and not obviously in close connection with a blood vessel. They are readily distinguished from fibroblasts by the color and amount of their cytoplasm.

From the convoluted tubules the spermatozoa pass into the proximal part of the duct system of the testis, which lies in the mediastinum of the organ. They go through the tubuli recti, or straight tubules, into the rete testis, which is a network of fine tubules occupying a part of the mediastinum. The walls of the tubuli recti and the rete testis consist of low cuboidal epithelium. From the rete testis a number of spiral tubules lead to the epididymis. These are called tubuli efferentes and are lined with a peculiar epithelium in which groups of ciliated columnar cells are interspersed among the cuboidal elements, giving the border of the lumen an irregular outline.

EPIDIDYMIS

The epididymis lies near the testis, partly surrounded by a fold of the tunica vaginalis and enclosed in a connective tissue capsule (Fig. 144). It

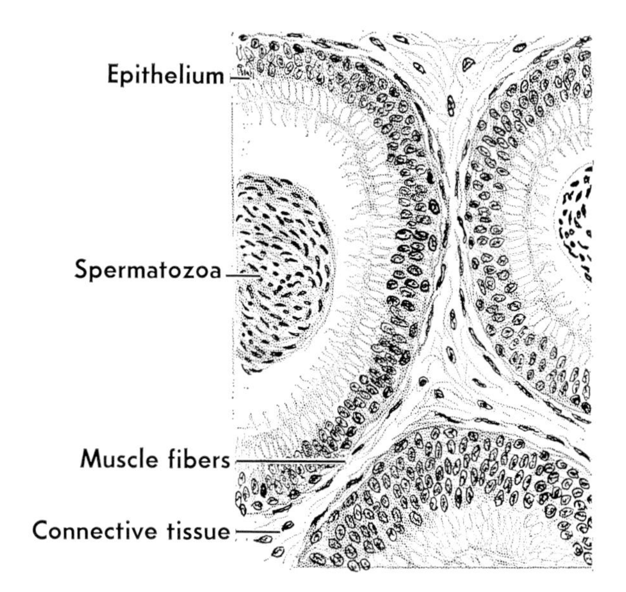

Fig. 144. Tubules of epididymis of dog.

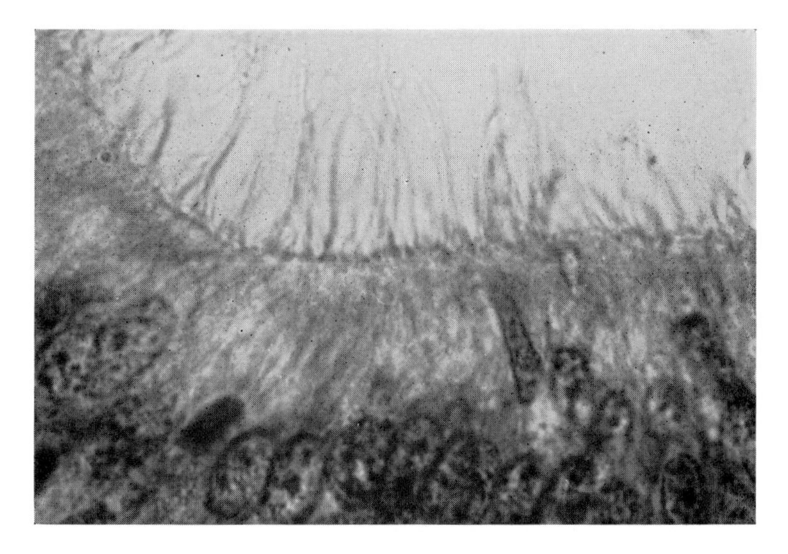

Fig. 145. Epithelium of epididymis, showing stereocilia.

contains only one tubule, the ductus epididymidis. It is, however, much coiled, so that a slide made from a piece of this organ presents a great number of sections of it cut longitudinally, transversely, or tangenitally. The duct is lined with ciliated epithelium described as pseudostratified by some and as stratified columnar by others. The epithelium is surrounded by smooth muscle circularly arranged.

DUCTUS DEFERENS

The ductus deferens is a continuation of the ductus epididymidis. It is lined with a somewhat lower epithelium, without cilia. This rests on a well-developed tunica propria. The muscularis has three layers: a thick circular one and one thin longitudinal layer on either side of it. Just before reaching the prostate gland the ductus deferens is dilated to form the ampulla. As it passes into the substance of the prostate, it is constricted again to form the narrow ejaculatory duct which opens into the prostatic part of the urethra.

SEMINAL VESICLE

The seminal vesicle is an elongated saccular organ lying near the ampulla of the ductus deferens and opening into the latter at the point where it narrows to form the ejaculatory duct. The most striking histological characteristic of the seminal vesicle is the folding of its mucosa (Fig. 146). This produces a great number of projections and pockets, and, since the latter are often tangentially cut, there appear to be follicles in the mucosa. The appearance is much like that of the gallbladder. The epithelium of the seminal vesicle is, however, pseudostratified or stratified columnar and it has a thinner muscular coat than that of the gallbladder.

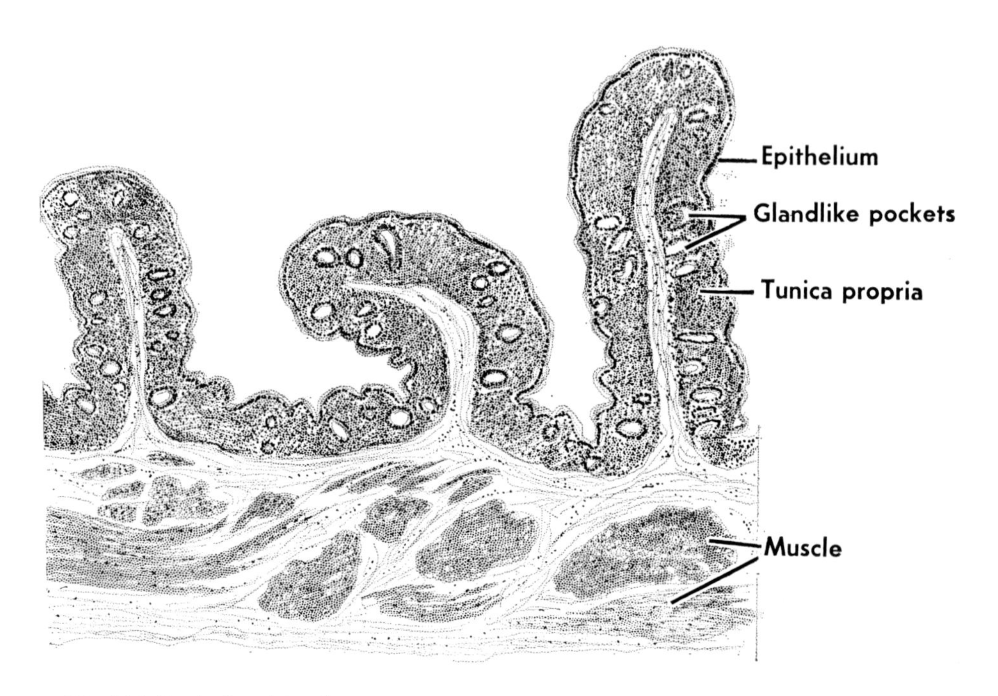

Fig. 146. Seminal vesicle of cat.

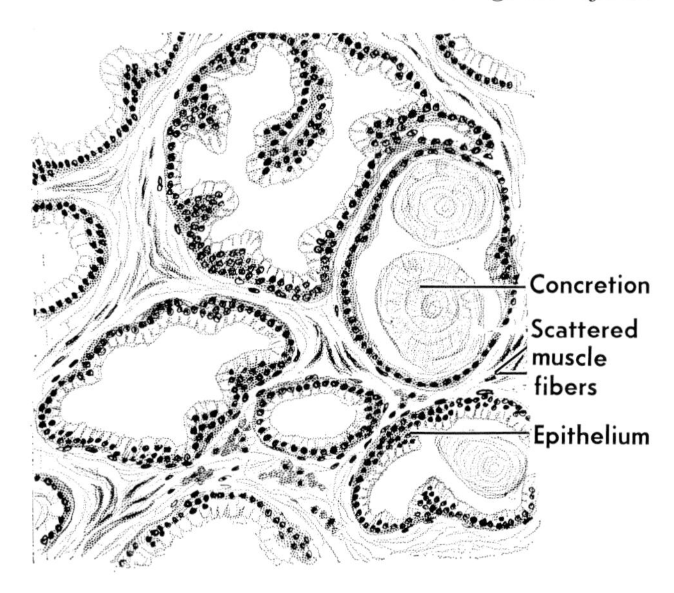

Fig. 147. Human prostate gland.

PROSTATE

The prostate is a much-branched follicular gland which surrounds the urethra as the latter emerges from the bladder. Its secreting portions are lined with columnar epithelium and have large irregular lumina (Fig. 147). They may contain lamellar bodies which stain red with eosin and are called prostatic concretions. If a follicle is somewhat distended by such a mass, the epithelium is flattened to the cuboidal type. A characteristic feature of the prostate is the presence of scattered fibers of smooth muscle in the connective tissue surrounding the follicles. The muscle does not form layers about the glandular portions but is distributed in groups of a few fibers running in various directions.

PENIS

A section of the penis shows, under the low power, three large masses of erectile tissue, each of which contains a great number of anastomosing blood vessels (Fig. 148). The two dorsal masses, connected by a bridge of the same kind of tissue, are the corpora cavernosa penis. The smaller ventral mass surrounding the urethra is the corpus cavernosum urethrae, called also the corpus spongiosum.

The cavernous bodies are surrounded by a sheath of dense connective tissue, the tunica albuginea. Outside this is a stroma of loose connective tissue containing blood vessels, nerves, and lamellar corpuscles. There is no well-defined corium of the skin covering the penis, and it has a thin epidermis.

Blood is brought to the penis by the arteria penis, which branches to

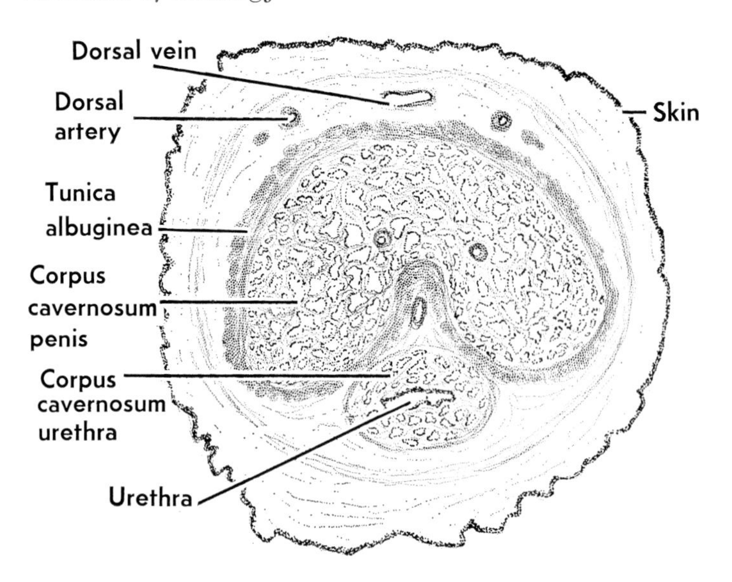

Fig. 148. Transverse section of penis of newborn infant.

form the dorsal artery and the paired deep arteries. The dorsal artery sends branches to the tunica albuginea and to the large trabeculae of the cavernous bodies. Such branches break up into capillaries from which blood passes into the lacunae of the erectile tissue, and thence to a plexus of veins in the albuginea. The deep arteries run lengthwise, giving off branches which open into the cavernous spaces. During times of sexual excitement the flow of blood into the cavernous spaces is greatly increased, especially that coming from the deep arteries. The veins which drain the blood spaces leave at an oblique angle. The central spaces are filled first, and their distention compresses the peripheral spaces and obstructs the flow of blood through the angular openings into the veins, thus producing rigidity of the penis. In the flaccid condition of the organ the incoming flow of blood is less and the passage into the veins remains open.

Nerve supply. The penis has an abundant supply of spinal, sympathetic, and parasympathetic fibers and many sensory end organs.

Female reproductive system

The female reproductive system consists of the ovaries, the fallopian tubes (oviducts), the uterus, and the vagina. Because of its functional relation to the reproductive tract the mammary gland is discussed with the group of genital organs.

OVARY

The ovary differs greatly from the testis in its appearance, although it has the functions of forming sexual cells and of maintaining secondary

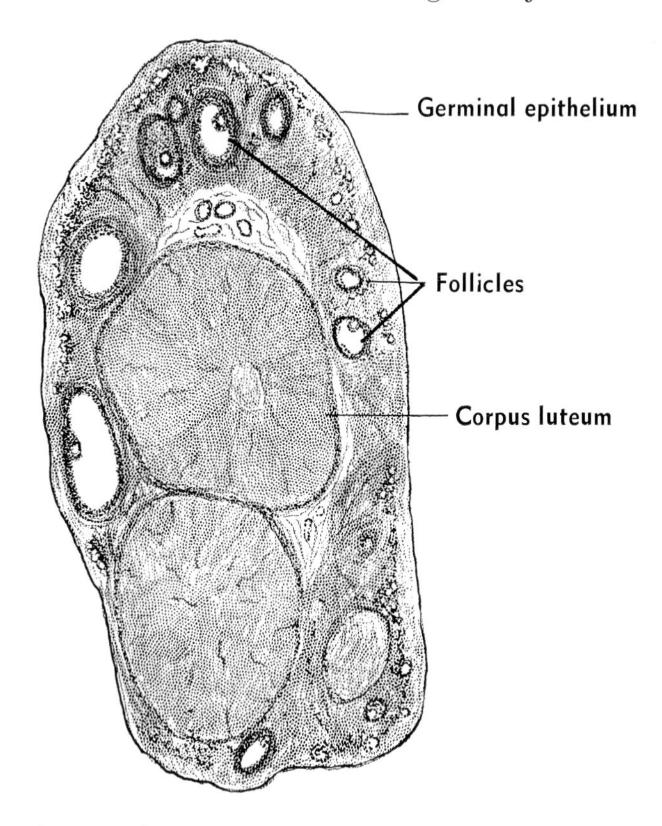

Fig. 149. Ovary of cat, low magnification.

sexual characteristics. In the testis the germinal epithelium forms the lining of a series of tubules, and the process of maturation is completed within the organ. In the ovary, on the contrary, the germinal epithelium forms the outer covering of the whole organ, and the only part of the development of ova which takes place in this part of the tract is growth. Maturation of ova occurs in most forms only after insemination, while the egg is passing from the ovary to the uterus.

The ovary is a small ovid body consisting of a mass of cellular connective tissue covered by germinal epithelium (Fig. 149). In the adult it contains interstitial cells and various stages of development and atrophy of the ova and their follicles. The entire organ is very vascular.

During embryonic life the germinal epithelium forms a many-layered mass at the periphery of the ovary proliferating cells downward into the underlying connective tissue. Some of these cells are destined to develop into oogonia, while others are to form the follicles. The mass of cells is broken up by invading connective tissue into smaller clumps, the egg nests or cords of Pflüger. Later the egg nests are subdivided into units, in each of which one may recognize a large central cell, the ovum, and a surround-

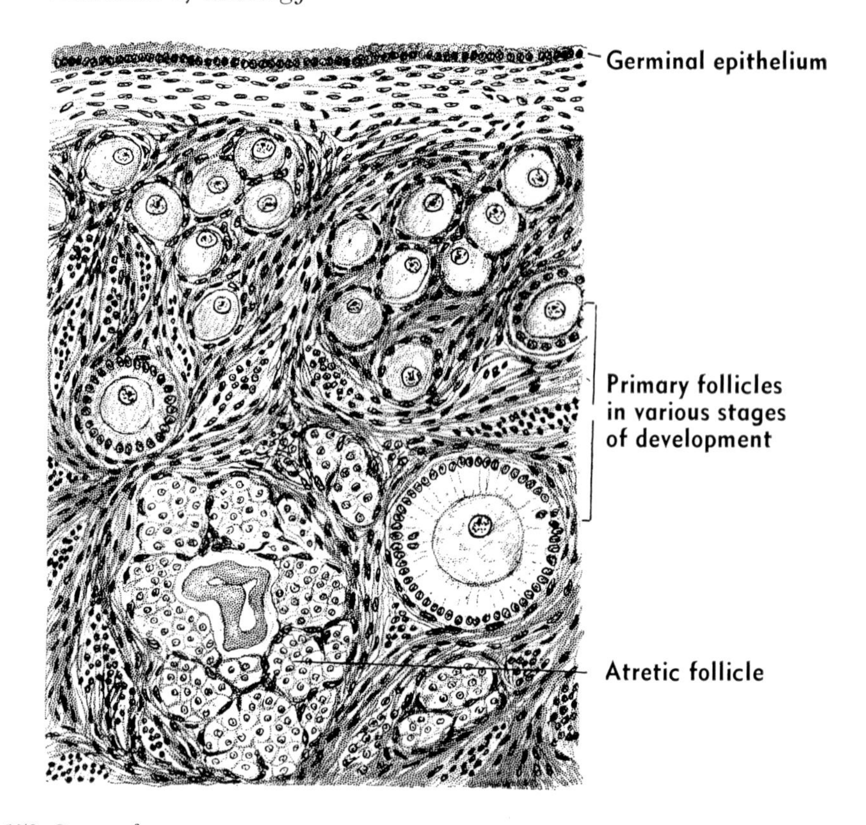

Fig. 150. Cortex of ovary.

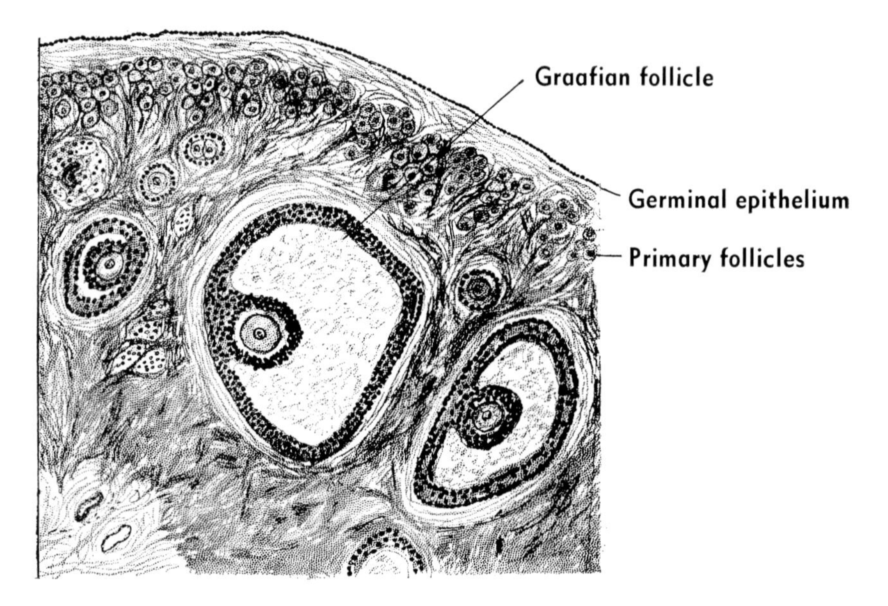

Fig. 151. Cortex of ovary.

ing group of flat follicular cells (Fig. 150). Such units are called primary follicles and are found in the ovary at birth. The connective tissue forms a thick sheath, the tunica albuginea, just beneath the germinal epithelium, and the latter is reduced to a single layer of cells which are columnar at first and cuboidal later.

At this stage of development the ovum is a spherical cell about 50μ in diameter. It contains a vesicular nucleus, and the granular cytoplasm stains red with eosin. The flattened cells of the follicle multiply and change in form from squamous to cuboidal and then to columnar. Finally a layer of stratified columnar epithelium surrounds the ovum. The latter enlarges, and the outer part of its cytoplasm is modified to form a hyaline coating called the zona pellucida. Later stages involve chiefly the development of the follicle; the ovum attains a diameter of about 100μ, but its appearance is otherwise unchanged.

As the follicle sinks still deeper into the cortex of the ovary its cells come to form a many-layered covering for the ovum. This is, at first, solid; in a later stage a cleft appears in the substance of it, and this cavity increases as the follicle grows (Fig. 151). At the end of its ovarian development the ovum is surrounded by a relatively enormous structure, the graafian follicle, in which one may distinguish the following parts (Fig. 152): the follicle, which is covered by a capsule of connective tissue, and the theca folliculi. The outer part of this (theca externa) is dense fibrous tissue and the inner part (theca interna) is looser, more vascular, and contains cells, the abundant cytoplasm, form, and arrangement of which suggest glandular rather than fiber-forming function. Internal to the theca are the follicular cells, the derivatives of the cells of the primary follicle. These form a coating approximately fifteen cells deep around the whole follicle. At one point there is a mound of follicular cells which bulges into the cavity of the follicle. This is the cumulus oophorus, at the center

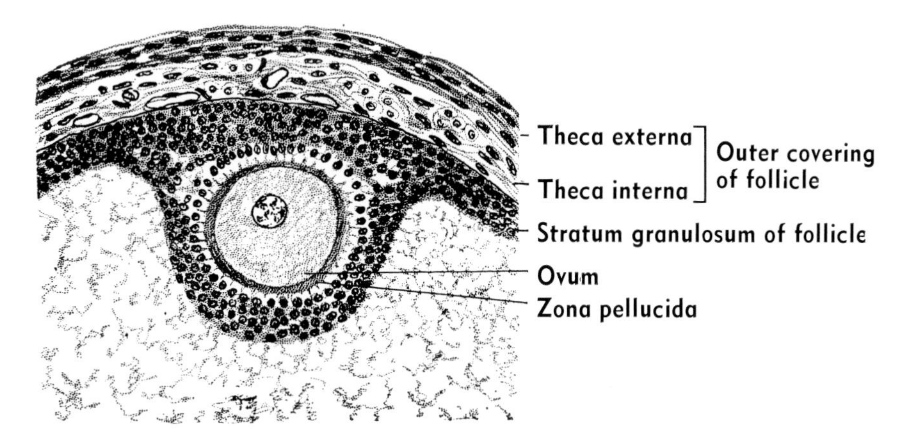

Fig. 152. Part of graafian follicle, showing ovum and surrounding structures.

of which is the ovum. The rest of the follicular cavity is filled with a fluid, the liquor folliculi. This is sometimes seen in sections as a pinkish granular coagulum. The cells of the cumulus which immediately surround the ovum are columnar in form (zona radiata).

The ovum and its follicle are now ready for the extrusion of the egg from the ovary (ovulation). The entire structure has moved out to the periphery of the cortex and lies so near the surface that it produces an elevation. At the end of intra-ovarian development the follicle ruptures, and the ovum is washed into the oviduct by the liquor folliculi. The number of ova discharged at one time and the interval between ovulations varies in different animals. In the human ovary there is usually one ovum discharged from one ovary or the other at intervals of four weeks.

It has been supposed that in human ovaries the first step of this development of follicles, namely, the separation of ova from the germinal epithelium, has been completed during embryonic life. If that is so, the time required for the maturation of a follicle would vary from thirteen to forty-five years, according to whether they rupture at the first or the last ovulation of sexual life. It has been shown that in the mouse, cells may be found detaching themselves from the germinal epithelium at any time between puberty and menopause, and it seems probable that the process occurs in this way in other mammals also.

At ovulation the majority of the follicular cells remain in the ovary and the follicle undergoes changes leading to the formation of the corpus luteum. The first of these is the formation of a blood clot, the blood coming from the vessels of the theca interna which ruptured at ovulation. The

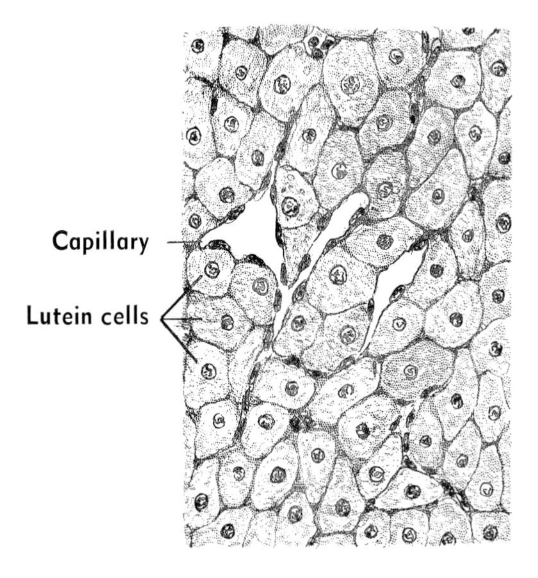

Fig. 153. Part of corpus luteum.

next change involves the alteration of the character of the follicular cells and the cells of the theca interna. In the mature graafian follicle the former are rather small elements with relatively little cytoplasm. They now enlarge and begin to invade and resorb the blood clot. Ultimately they fill the center of the follicle with large, pale cells (Figs. 149 and 153). Each cell has an abundant amount of cytoplasm in which may be seen granules and fat droplets. The theca cells also enlarge and invade the mass at its periphery along with connective tissue elements and blood vessels. The structure in a fresh specimen has a yellow color and is called the corpus luteum. The length of life of the corpus luteum and the size to which it grows depend upon the fate of the ovum which was discharged from the follicle. If the ovum is fertilized and becomes implanted in the uterine wall the corpus luteum continues to grow and is called a "true" corpus luteum (of pregnancy). If the ovum is not fertilized the corpus luteum begins to degenerate about fourteen days after ovulation. Such corpora lutea are "false" and are soon replaced by scar tissue (corpus albicans). These relations will be discussed more fully.

Atretic follicles. In the preceding paragraphs we have discussed the normal development of an ovum and its follicle. It often happens, however, that follicles which have developed to the graafian stage degenerate instead of going on to ovulation. The first step in atresia is the death of the ovum itself, which is followed by the degeneration of the follicular cells; the result is a mass of detritus left at the center of the follicle. The cells of the theca interna undergo a hypertrophy similar at first to that occurring in corpus luteum formation. It is, however, carried further, so that the striking characteristic of an atretic follicle is the ring of enlarged theca cells surrounding it (Fig. 150). These cells have at this stage some resemblance to the cells of the corpus luteum but are smaller, less eosinophilic, and not conspicuously vacuolated.

The theca cells gradually come to fill the space left by the degenerating ovum and follicular cells, thus forming a solid mass. In this condition they may remain in the stroma of the ovary for some time. Such masses or strands of theca cells have been called the interstitial cells of the ovary, and they were originally supposed to have a function comparable to that assigned to the interstitial cells of the testis. Experimental work, however, has not offered any proof that they secrete the hormone responsible for the maintenance of secondary sexual characteristics.

In summary, besides the connective tissue stroma, one may find in the ovary, the following elements:

1. Germinal epithelium
2. Interstitial cells
3. Primary follicles
4. Growing follicles
5. Graafian follicles
6. Blood clots
7. Corpora lutea
8. Scars
9. Atretic follicles

FALLOPIAN TUBE (OVIDUCT)

The ova, when they are extruded from the ovary, pass into the open end of the oviduct. The relation of the ovary to its duct differs from that of the testis to the ductus deferens. In the latter case the lumina of the convoluted tubules are continuous with that of the duct, and there is no possibility of the spermatozoa escaping from the system into the body cavity. The ova, on the contrary, come out to the surface of the ovary, and the latter is not completely enclosed in the lumen of the oviduct. The end of the oviduct is funnel shaped with a convoluted, ciliated mucosa. It sweeps over the surface of the ovary, the beat of its cilia pulling the ova into its lumen. Occasionally, however, an egg cell falls out of the open end of the tube, resulting, if it becomes fertilized, in an abdominal or ectopic pregnancy.

Sections of the oviduct vary somewhat in appearance according to the region from which they are cut. At the funnel-shaped end of the tube the folding of the mucosa attains its greatest development, and the lumen is reduced to a narrow channel between the fimbriae (Fig. 154). Farther down the tube the height of the fimbriae is reduced and the lumen enlarged. The mucosa consists of a ciliated columnar epithelium resting on a tunica propria. It is said that special preparations show some cells of the epithelium to be nonciliated and glandular. There is no muscularis mucosa, so that the tunica propria blends with the submucosa and the two layers

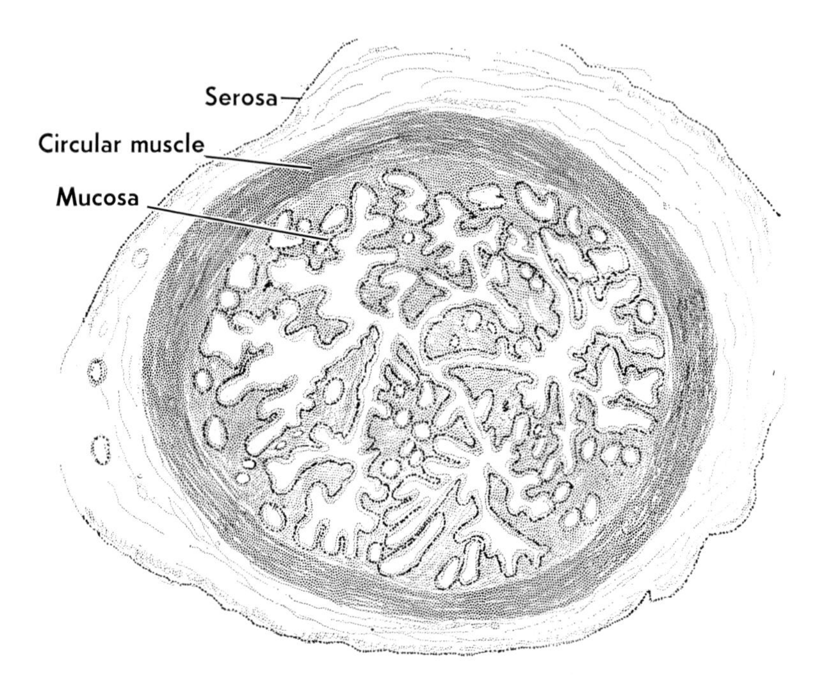

Fig. 154. Fimbriated end of oviduct of cat. Note extremely irregular outline of mucosa.

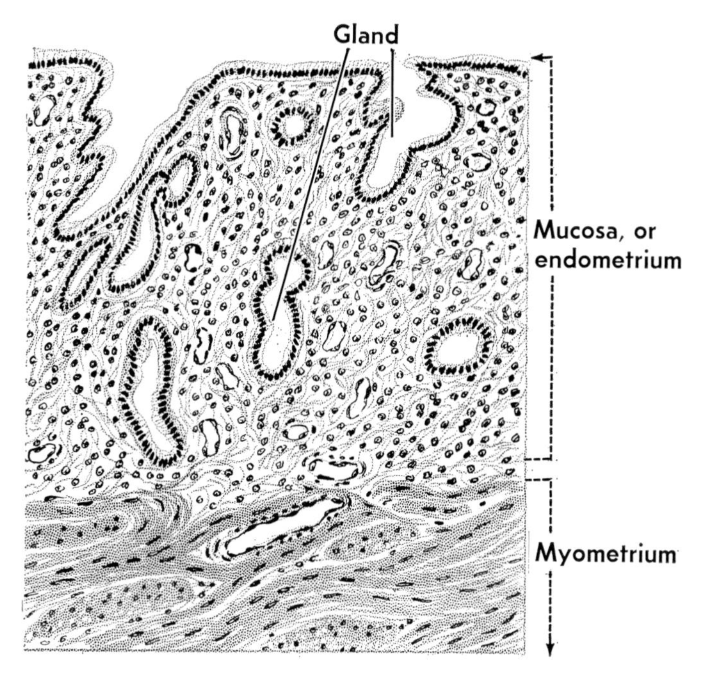

Fig. 155. Mucosa and part of muscularis of human uterus.

are sometimes called one. The muscularis has two layers, an inner circular and an outer longitudinal, the two being indistinctly separated.

UTERUS

The human uterus is a pear-shaped muscular organ having two parts, a body and a neck or cervix. At its upper, broader end it receives the oviducts; its lower end opens into the vagina.

Its wall consists of three layers: (1) the endometrium, which corresponds to the mucosa and submucosa; (2) the myometrium, or muscularis; and (3) the perimetrium or serous membrane. The myometrium is a very thick layer of interwoven bundles of smooth muscle, forming three-fourths of the uterine wall. At the lower end or cervix of the uterus the fibers are arranged in three fairly distinct layers; the middle layer is circular, and the outer and inner layers are longitudinal.

Endometrium

The endometrium is lined by columnar epithelium and contains numerous tubular glands which open at the surface. The mucosa undergoes a number of cyclic variations which are related to changes occurring during the ovulatory and menstrual cycle. While the changes which occur in the endometrium are not abrupt, structural differences occur which have resulted in the classification of four morphologically distinct stages: (1) the proliferative, also known as the estrogenic stage, (2) the progravid or secretory stage, (3) the premenstrual stage, and (4) the menstrual stage.

Proliferative stage. This phase of the cycle begins at the termination of the menstrual phase and continues until the thirteenth or fourteenth day of the cycle. It is characterized by the rapid regeneration of the endometrial wall and a replacement of epithelial cells to cover the surface of the mucosa. Also the gland cells increase in number and the glands themselves increase in length. Vascularity of the tissue becomes more pronounced, and indications of edema are also evident.

Secretory (progravid) stage. This stage is characterized by a marked increase in the hypertrophy of the endometrium, which is the result of proliferation of the glandular tissue, and a marked increase in edema and vascularity of the mucosa. The secretory stage begins on the thirteenth or fourteenth day of the cycle and continues until the twenty-sixth or twenty-seventh day.

Premenstrual stage. In this part of the cycle changes occur in the vascular components which result in a loss of the superficial portion of the mucosa. During this time fragmentation of the glands and the extrusion of blood and tissue debris into the lumen of the uterus occur. The premenstrual stage is confined to one or two days and is said to terminate at the first external signs of bleeding.

Menstrual stage. The menstrual stage usually occupies three to five days of the cycle and is characterized by a considerable amount of endometrial destruction which consists essentially in the sloughing off of the upper three-fourths of the endometrium. It involves the destruction of the epithelium and connective tissue and the rupture of blood vessels.

Pregnancy. During pregnancy the structure of the endometrium undergoes marked hypertrophy to provide for the nutrition of the embryo. For a full description of the placenta the student should consult a textbook of embryology. We shall consider here only as much as will explain the place of pregnancy in the female sexual cycle. The changes which take place in the secretory stage are preparations for the implantation of a fertilized ovum. The endometrium is full of large irregular pockets, and in one of these the fertilized ovum becomes embedded. The surrounding tissues encloses it in a sac, from the walls of which the placenta develops. At first, while the embryo is small, the sac surrounding it is smaller than the cavity of the uterus. Later the embryo and its membranes increase in size so as completely to occlude the uterine cavity. The part of the endometrium which first covered the ovum fuses with the wall of the opposite side, and the only space in the uterus is that immediately surrounding the fetus.

At the end of pregnancy (parturition) the muscles of the uterus contract and the fetus is expelled. Shortly after this another series of con-

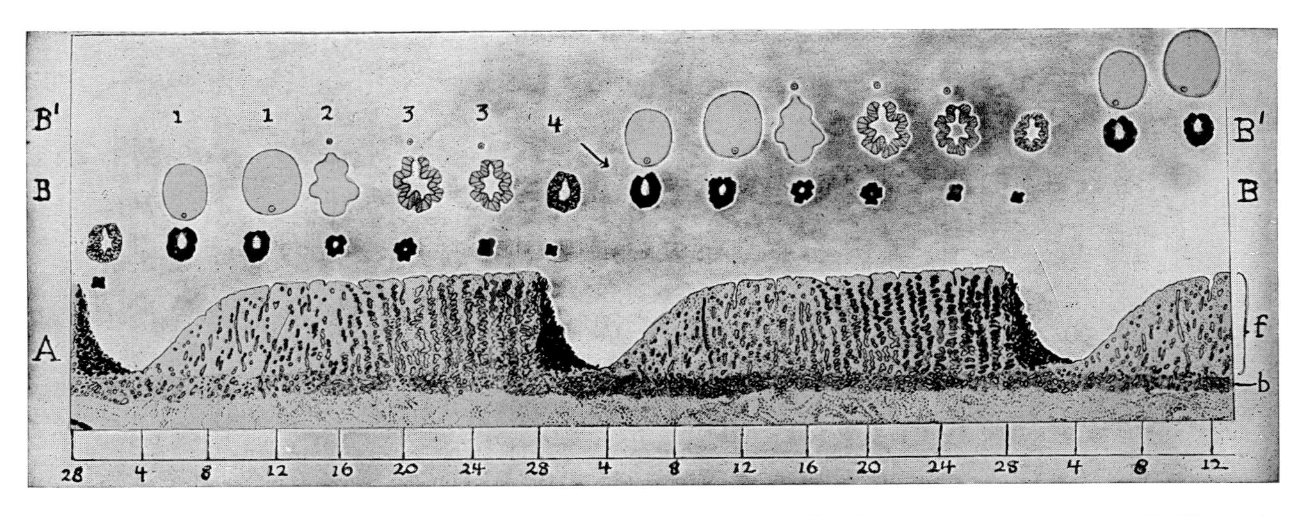

Fig. 156. Diagram illustrating relation of menstruation to ovluation. **A**, Cyclic changes in uterine mucosa; **B**, **B′**, ovarian cycles; **b**, basal layer of mucosa; **f**, functional layer of mucosa; **1**, **1**, maturing follicle; **2**, rupture of follicle and discharge of ovum (ovulation); **3**, **3**, corpus luteum in full function; **4** and remaining figures, degenerating corpus luteum. Numbers at base indicate days of menstrual cycle. (After Schroeder.)

tractions empty the organ of the so-called afterbirth. This includes the placenta and the upper layers of the endometrium. After parturition the uterus is in a condition such as that which follows each menstruation, and it enters a period of repair similar to that of the postmenstrual period. From this stage it goes on to the proliferate stage and to a renewal of the menstrual cycle. In Fig. 156 are shown the probable relations between the uterine cycle and the changes which take place in the ovary (ovulation and the formation of corpora lutea). The cycle represented is one in which there is no coitus and consequently no fertilization of the ovum. Ovulation probably occurs about the middle of the latter part of the interval between menstrual periods (sixteen to twenty days after the beginning of the last menstrual flow). The unfertilized ovum travels slowly down the fallopian tube, reaching the uterus in from eight to twelve days. In the meantime the ruptured follicle is being transformed into a corpus luteum, and the endometrium is undergoing the progravid hyperplasia. The ovum reaches the uterus when the latter is ready to receive a fertilized egg. But in the cycle under consideration the ovum is dead, and the endometrium enters the menstrual period, during which a part of its mucosa is sloughed off. The ovum also is expelled with the menstrual flow, and the corpus luteum begins to degenerate. If the ovum has been fertilized, it reaches the uterus, as before, when the latter is in the progravid condition. The endometrium provides a suitable place for the embedding of the ovum which remains in the uterus for the nine months of the gestation period. If pregnancy occurs the corpus luteum does not undergo involution but grows larger and persists throughout pregnancy.

The foregoing account is supported by a considerable body of evidence, though it is not definitely proved to be accurate. It appears quite certain that the regulating mechanism of the cycle is in the ovary, not in the uterus, and that it is of endocrine nature. The time of ovulation is not definitely established, nor is it known whether the growing follicle or the corpus luteum provides the controlling hormone.

VAGINA

The wall of the vagina includes a mucosa, submucosa, and muscularis (Fig. 157). As in the oviduct and uterus, the mucosa and submucosa are blended. The epithelium is of the stratified squamous variety; the muscularis is of interlacing fibers of smooth muscle which form somewhat indefinite circular (inner) and longitudinal coats.

The epithelium of the human vagina undergoes changes during the menstrual cycle, although these are less marked than those of the uterine mucosa. During the premenstrual period a zone of keratinized cells is formed in the middle layers of the epithelium. At the menstrual period the cells above this zone are sloughed off, and the keratinized cells are thus

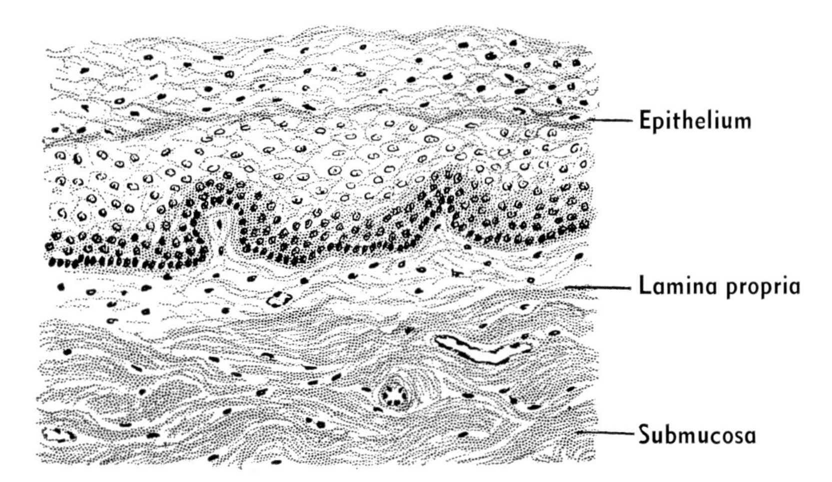

Fig. 157. Human vagina. Epithelium shows layer of cornification about midway between its base and its surface.

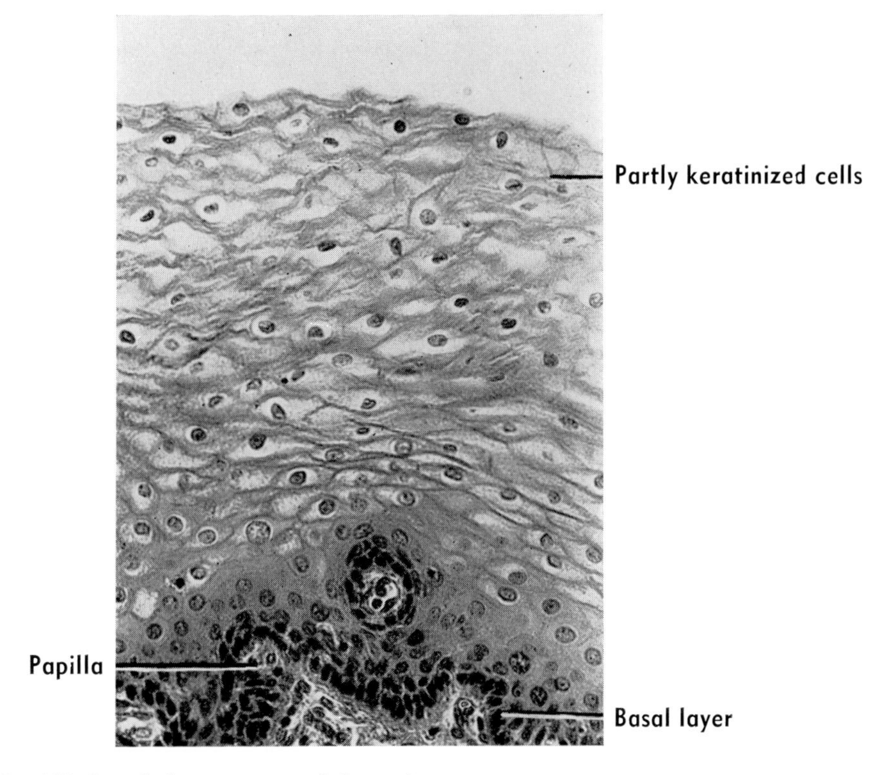

Fig. 158. Stratified squamous epithelium of vagina.

brought to the surface. In some mammals the changes are more marked, so that vaginal smears furnish an indication of the stage of the oestrus cycle of the animal from which they are made.

MAMMARY GLAND

The mammary gland is a compound alveolar gland which develops from the lower layers of the epidermis. It consists of from fifteen to twenty lobes separated by broad bands of dense connective tissue. The lobes are divided into lobules by connective tissue septa, from which strands extend into secreting units. The intralobular connective tissue is fine areolar. The alveoli of each lobule open into small intralobular ducts which unite to form interlobular ducts, and these in turn lead to the main excretory (lactiferous) ducts. The inactive and active phases of the gland are marked by difference in appearance.

Resting gland. A section of the mammary gland during a period of inactivity hardly resembles a gland at all on first inspection (Fig. 159). The secreting tissue is represented by scattered ducts, around the terminal portions of which one may see a few collapsed or very small follicles and a few solid cords of epithelial cells (Fig. 160). Such groups of intralobular epithelial tissue lie in a thin investment of loose connective tissue, and this is surrounded by a dense mass of collagenous fibers. The connective tissue occupies by far the greater portion of the section. Examined under high power the ducts are seen to be lined with two or three layers of cuboidal cells, whereas such follicles as may be found are composed of simple cuboidal epithelium.

Active gland. During pregnancy the epithelial portions of the mammary gland undergo a pronounced hypertrophy, so that by the fifth month of the period of gestation the organ presents a histological picture very different from that of the resting gland (Fig. 161). Alveoli have developed

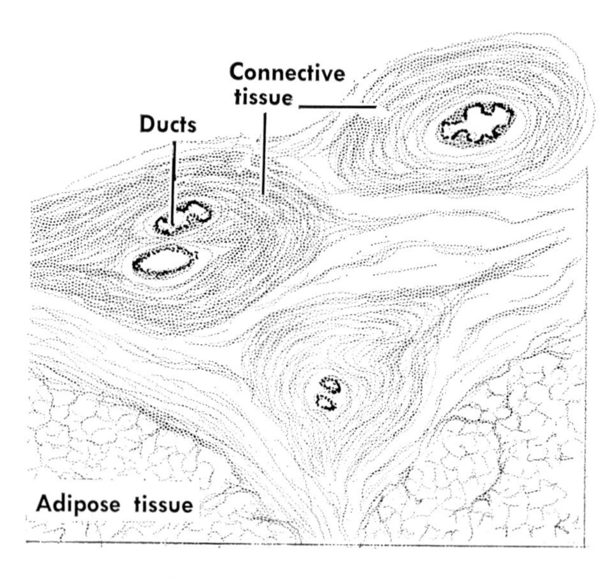

Fig. 159. Human mammary gland, resting condition (low magnification).

from the cords of tissue which were to be seen before. The small areas of intralobular connective tissue have expanded and the lobules appear as relatively large areas filled with alveoli and ducts. The interlobular connective tissue is correspondingly reduced in amount.

During the later part of the gestation period the development of alveoli and ducts continues, so that at childbirth they occupy the greater part

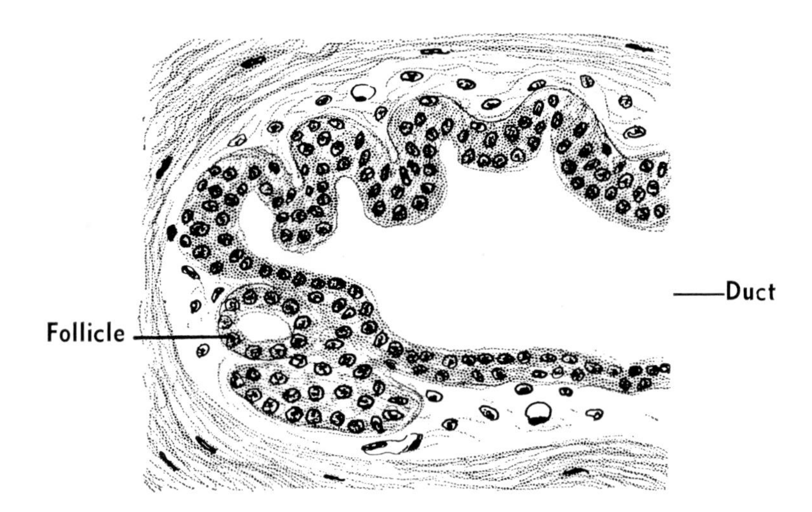

Fig. 160. Resting mammary gland.

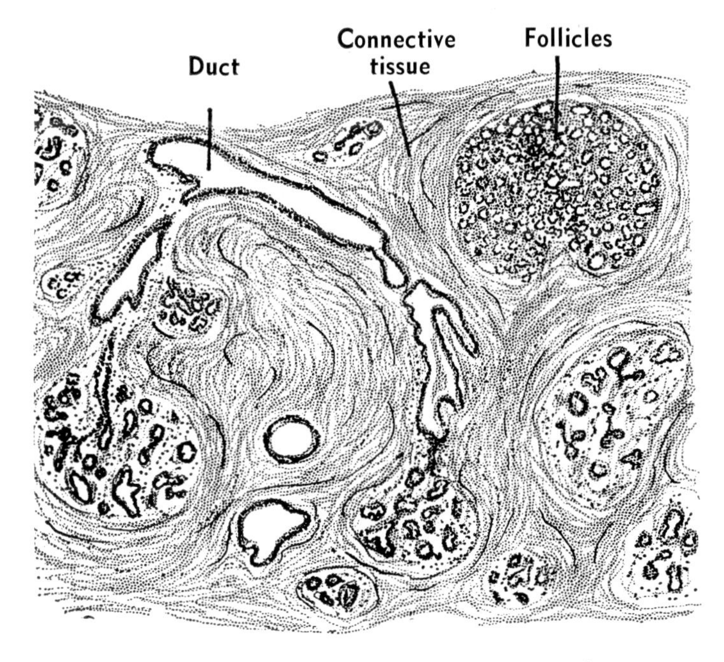

Fig. 161. Human mammary gland in fifth month of pregnancy, showing great increase in numbers of ducts and follicles.

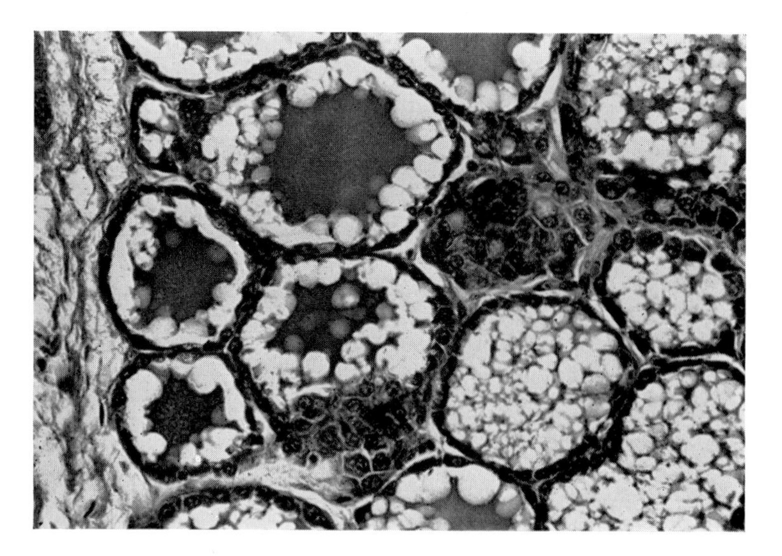

Fig. 162. Lactating mammary gland, showing follicles and secretion.

of the section. They are lined with an epithelium which varies from tall columnar in actively secreting units to low cuboidal in those which have been drained of milk (Fig. 162). The cells in active alveoli are filled with fat droplets which distend them at the free surface and give an irregular outline to the lumen. The ducts leading from the alveoli are lined with low columnar cells, which are replaced by pseudostratified epithelium in the excretory ducts. Near the nipple the epithelium changes to stratified squamous, which is continuous with the skin.

The mammary gland remains in the active condition for a variable period after childbirth and then returns to the resting stage. After the menopause it undergoes involution in which the alveoli and parts of the ducts degenerate and their places are taken by connective tissue.

Blood vessels, lymphatics, and nerves. Blood is brought to the mammary gland by the intercostal, internal mammary, and thoracic branches of the axillary artery. The terminal branches of these vessels lie among the alveoli. Lymph vessels, which are numerous, drain chiefly toward the axilla. Nerves come from both cerebrospinal and sympathetic systems to supply the epithelial tissue and the blood vessels.

CHAPTER XIX

Endocrine organs

Endocrine glands may be defined as collections of epithelial cells which are not provided with ducts but which deliver their secretion (hormone) into the blood stream. There are, however, not many organs which clearly fit this definition. The absence of ducts is easily determined, but the presence of secretion is more difficult to prove. Two methods of experimentation are used in this field: operative removal of the gland in question and injection of substance extracted from it. The first of these is not always practicable. To the second method there may be objections on the ground that extracts from organs do not necessarily represent the secretion elaborated by them. The use of the two methods may be illustrated by the work on the thyroid which has yielded fairly clear-cut results. If this gland is removed from a laboratory animal, there follows a marked retardation of the metabolic rate, but this becomes normal again when thyroid extract is administered. The extract also raises the metabolic rate of normal (unoperated) animals. Clinical and post-mortem evidence also supports the belief that the thyroid contains a substance which influences, directly or indirectly, the rate of metabolism of the body. This effect is not produced by extracts of other glands. Moreover, the thyroid is a ductless organ composed of secreting epithelial cells, so that its morphology supports the conclusion derived from experimental and clinical work that it secretes a hormone.

Unfortunately, results are not so clear-cut in the cases of some other organs. In some instances the results of physiological experiments are contradictory; in others they are unsupported by morphological evidences of secretion. One may group in the following way the organs which have been thought to have an endocrine function.

Thyroid gland, parathyroid glands, hypophysis, adrenal glands, and islands of Langerhans. These five organs are composed of cells which have the appearance of glandular tissue. Clinical and experimental evidence is preponderantly in favor of the view that each secretes a specific substance or substances which influence some phase of the metabolic activity of the body.

Gonads. There is ample experimental evidence that the testis and ovary produce hormones which control the development and maintenance of secondary sexual characteristics and that the ovarian secretion influences the oestrus cycle. It is believed that the first of these functions is regulated by the interstitial cells of the two organs, but this point is not definitely proved. Similarly, doubt exists as to the respective roles of the graafian follicles and the corpus luteum in the regulation of oestrus. The difficulty in establishing the connecting link between physiological and morphological evidence is obvious; it is impossible to extirpate the interstitial cells completely while leaving the other tissues of the gonads intact.

Thymus and pineal glands. Evidence of the endocrine function of the thymus and pineal glands is weak. The results of physiological experimentation are contradictory, and there is little in the morphology of the organs to suggest that they are secretory in function. They are placed in the endocrine group chiefly because their function is not known. This is true also of various other groups of cells in the body.

Organs from which hormones isolated. A fourth group may be made of organs from which, at various times, investigators have claimed they have isolated hormones. For instance, a substance called secretin has been extracted from the wall of the duodenum, and it has been shown that this substance stimulates the alveoli of the pancreas. There are, however, no cells in this region to which the elaboration of secretin can be assigned. In other words, we have a "secretion" without a gland to form it.

Liver. The liver, as previously mentioned, is sometimes grouped with the endocrine organs.

The grouping of organs just described indicates a part, at least, of the confusion existing in this field. The complications of the physiological side of the science are great, owing to the fact that all members of the endocrine group are closely interrelated, and disturbance of one may be expected to affect some or all of the others. Fortunately the histology is less complicated than the physiology. We shall now discuss the thyroid, parathyroid, hypophysis, and adrenal glands. The islands of Langerhans and the gonads, also in good standing as endocrines, have already been described (see discussions on pancreas, testis, and ovary).

THYROID GLAND

The thyroid gland consists of two lobes and a connecting isthmus. It lies in the neck in contact with the upper part of the trachea and the lower end of the pharynx. The thyroid is enclosed in a connective tissue sheath derived from the cervical fasciae.

Trabeculae arising from this fascial sheath penetrate the gland, subdivid-

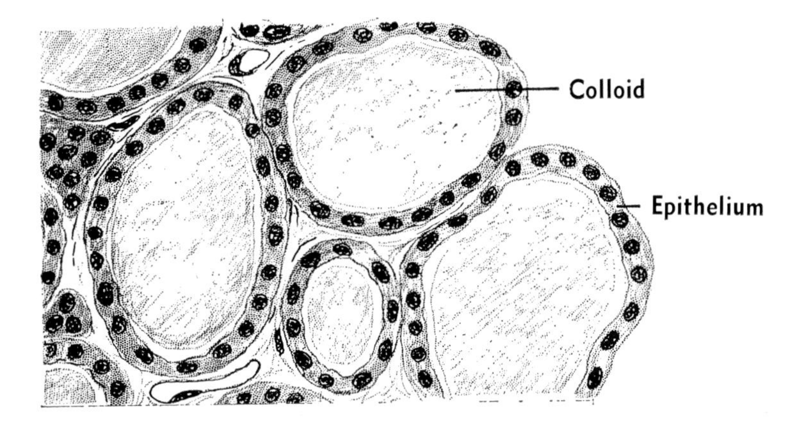

Fig. 163. Follicles of thyroid gland in inactive condition. Note low cuboidal epithelium and large masses of colloid.

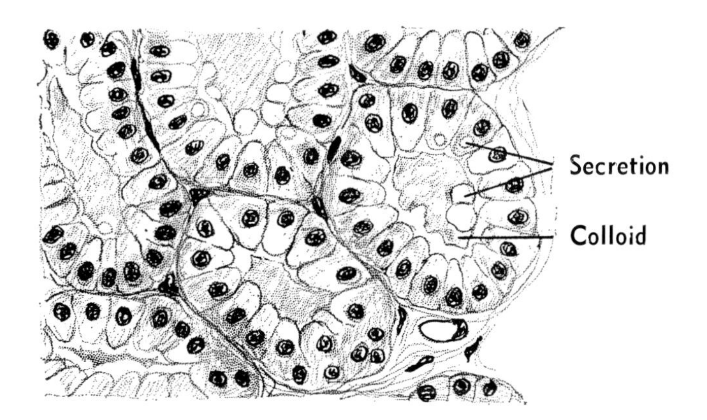

Fig. 164. Follicles from thyroid gland in active condition. Note droplets of colorless secretion in the cytoplasm of the tall columnar cells and at the borders of the masses of the colloid.

ing it into lobules, and provide a pathway for the vascular and nerve supply of the gland. The connective tissue which makes up the stroma of the gland is largely reticular in nature and is extremely rich in nerve and vascular plexuses.

The structural unit of the thyroid is the follicle, which consists of a layer of simple epithelium enclosing a cavity (follicular cavity) containing a colloid secretion. The colloid elaborated by the cells is usually rich in iodine and contains the thyroid hormone. The shapes of the follicles, their contents, and the character of their epithelium vary with the functional condition of the gland. In the hypoactive condition the follicles are round or oval with regular outlines (Fig. 163). They are lined with low cuboidal epithelium, which stains deeply with eosin and has indistinct cell walls. The lumen of each follicle is filled with colloid which appears as a structureless red mass in hematoxylin and eosin preparations. In the hyperactive state, on the other hand, the follicles may have a folded, irregular shape. In this condition they are lined with tall columnar cells, the cytoplasm of which stains lightly (Fig. 164). The colloid is pale in color during the active phase of glandular activity, and many follicles may be found which contain little or none of this substance. The two conditions described represent the extremes. A normal thyroid may contain some follicles of each kind, but the majority will be in a condition intermediate between the two. The secretion of the thyroid gland is a compound rich in iodine. It is probable that the colloid represents stored secretion. The hormone is carried away from the gland through the capillaries in the connective tissue surrounding the follicles.

The primary function of the thyroid is to regulate the rate of metabolism. Hyperfunction results in increased bodily metabolism; conversely hypofunction in decreased metabolism. The number and variety of functions affected by the thyroid are extensive and diverse. Hypothyroidism frequently results in the enlargement of the gland, a condition referred to as goiter. Other functions regulated by the thyroid, which has intricate interrelationships with other endocrine glands, affect carbohydrate metabolism, heart rate, bodily growth, and mental activity.

PARATHYROID GLANDS

The parathyroid glands are small glands lying near the thyroid or embedded in its substance (Fig. 165). They consist of light-colored polygonal cells arranged in irregular cords and supplied with a rich capillary network (Fig. 166). These cells are surrounded by a framework of reticular connective tissue. The arrangement in cords becomes more definite as the age of the animal advances; sometimes the grouping of cells is such as to suggest the presence of small follicles. The appearance of the gland does not vary with fluctuations in its activity, as does that of the thyroid. In human parathyroid glands and in those of some other mammals there are groups of eosinophilic cells. These are larger than the pale "chief" cells and have small dark nuclei. It has been claimed that their presence is an indication of activity on the part of the gland, but experimental evidence does not support this view. It seems more probable that they are degenerating chief cells. Small colloid follicles frequently occur in the parenchyma of the parathyroid. The origin and function of this substance are not known. It has been established, however, that the colloid is not functionally related to that of the thyroid.

The parathyroids are believed by some investigators to be concerned with the regulation of calcium metabolism. Surgical removal of the glands results in a decrease in blood calcium which may be accompanied

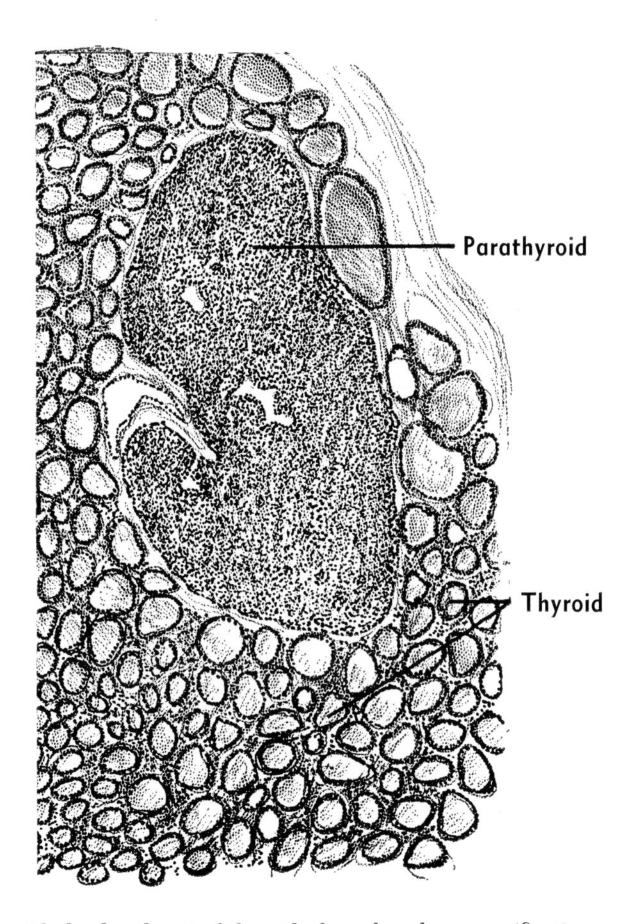

Fig. 165. Parathyroid gland and part of thyroid of monkey, low magnification.

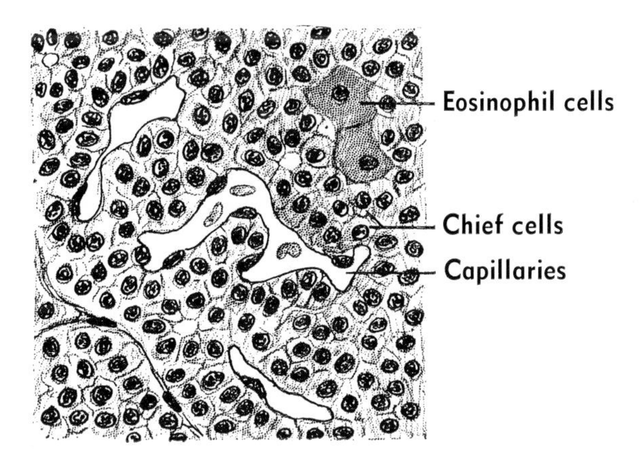

Fig. 166. Parathyroid gland of monkey.

by tetany, hyperexcitability, and eventually death. These conditions can be relieved by the administration of calcium or parathyroid extract.

HYPOPHYSIS

The hypophysis or pituitary gland consists of two lobes, each of which is again subdivided (Fig. 167). These parts, unlike the lobes of a secretory gland such as the parotid, are composed of tissues which differ from each other in function and (partially) in origin. The gland is actually two organs intimately associated. One part of it develops from the roof of the oral cavity of the embryo; the other forms as an outgrowth from the floor of the brain. The buccal portion loses its connection with the oral cavity and becomes a solid mass of cells. The nervous portion retains, in some animals, a cavity at its center. In the adult the relations are as follows:

Pars buccalis { Pars tuberalis
Pars distalis—Anterior lobe
Pars intermedia }
Pars nervosa } Posterior lobe

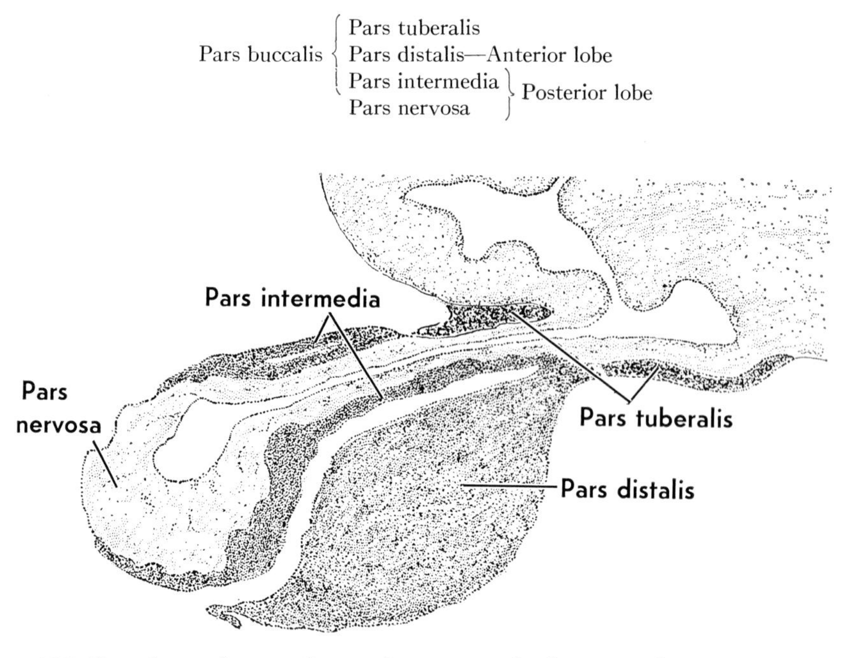

Fig. 167. Hypophysis of cat, mid-sagittal section, under low magnification, to show topography.

Anterior lobe

The anterior lobe is surrounded by a connective tissue capsule from which fine strands penetrate the gland to form the stroma. Many of the connective tissue fibers of the stroma are of the reticular variety and support an extensive capillary network. Sinusoids containing macrophages are of frequent occurrence; these cells are part of the reticuloendothelial system.

The cells occur in clumps or cords arranged in close association with

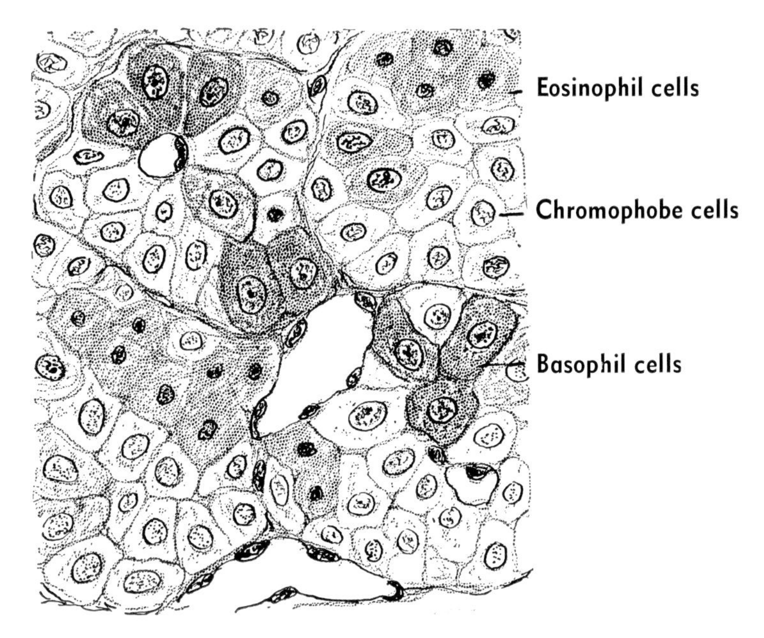

Fig. 168. Portion of pars distalis of hypophysis of cat.

the capillaries and sinusoids. They present three different appearances which may be expressions of permanent functional differences or of transient variations in condition. The three kinds are chromophobe cells and two types of chromophil cells (acidophilic and basophilic).

Chromophobe cells. These, as their name indicates, are the cells which do not stain readily. They are scattered throughout the anterior lobe but are most numerous in the pars intermedia and pars tuberalis. The cell outlines are indistinct, and the cytoplasm contains few granules.

Chromophil cells. Chromophil cells are of two types: acidophilic (alpha) and basophilic (beta) cells. These cells are characterized by the presence of distinct cell walls and by the morphology and staining reactions of the cytoplasmic granules. The alpha cells contain large, closely packed, acid-staining granules and are somewhat smaller than beta cells. The beta cells contain granules which stain basically and are finer and less discrete than those of the alpha cells.

Posterior lobe

Pars intermedia. The pars intermedia, a thin strip of darkly staining cells, is obviously epithelial in nature. This portion, like the pars tuberalis, contains follicles.

Pars nervosa. The pars nervosa, the lobe arising from the brain, consists of a fibrous mass in which there are scattered branching cells supposed to be ependymal in origin (see discussion on neuroglia). There are no perikarya of nerve cells in this region and no cells which look like secreting elements.

Functions

This gland is sometimes referred to as the master gland. It gives rise to several different secretions or hormones. The anterior lobe secretes a growth-promoting hormone. Excessive secretion in young individuals causes gigantism and in adults acromegaly, a thickening of the bones. Some of the other secretions produced by the anterior lobe are the thyrotropic, gonadotropic, corticotropic, and lactogenic hormones. The organs such as the thyroid, gonads, and adrenals are referred to as "target" organs, since they respond in a selective manner to the stimulative effects of the hormonal secretion. The neural portion of the lobe gives rise to secretions, one of which is known as oxytocin. This hormone causes the contraction of uterine muscle. The second, known as Pitressin or vasopressin, raises blood pressure and also produces an antidiuretic effect upon the kidneys.

ADRENAL GLAND

The adrenal (suprarenal) gland is like the hypophysis in that it is, in reality, two glands having different functions and arising from different sources. One of these is the cortex, which is derived from mesodermal tissue. The boundary between cortex and medulla is irregular (Fig. 169).

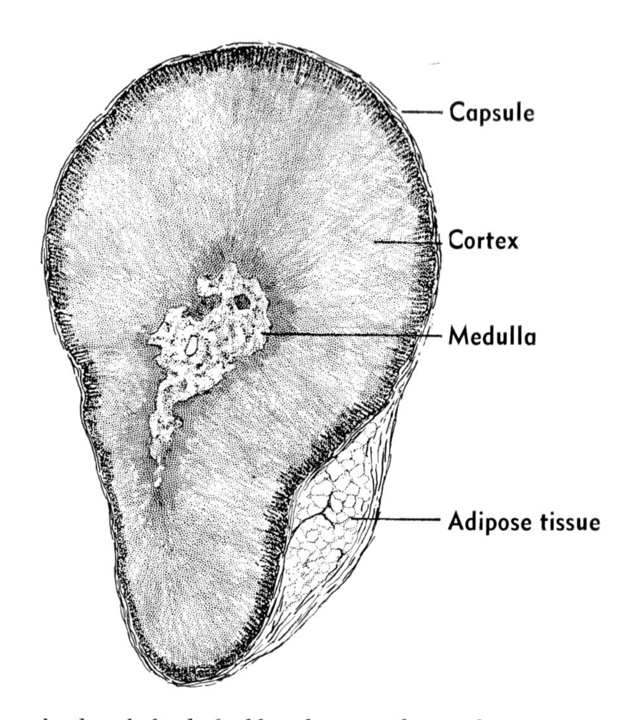

Fig. 169. Section through adrenal gland of rabbit, showing relation of its parts.

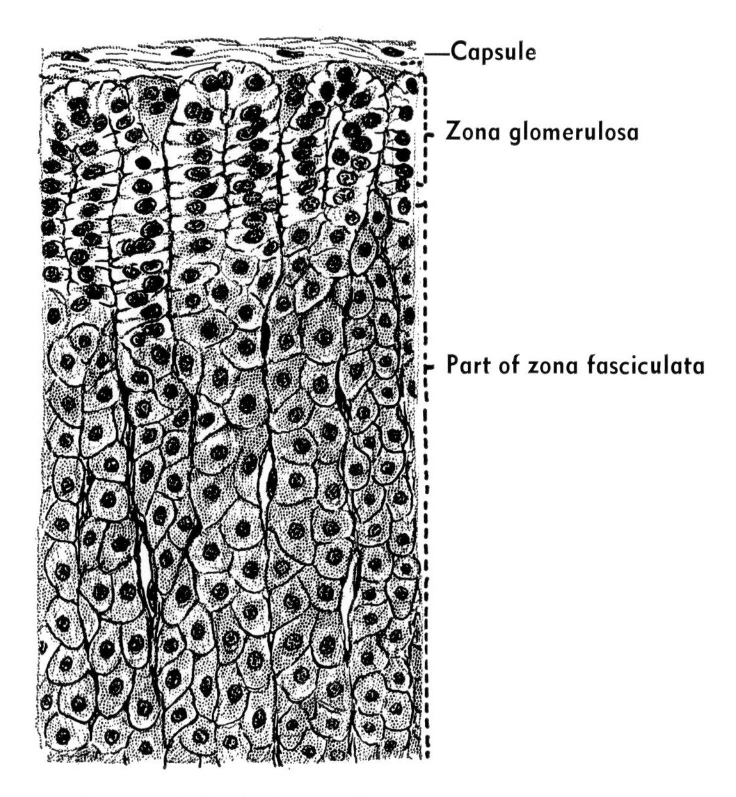

Fig. 170. Outer portion of cortex of adrenal gland of rabbit.

The other is the medulla of the organ, which comes from the same group of cells as those which form the sympathetic ganglia.

The entire gland is surrounded by a capsule of connective tissue (Fig. 170). From the capsule delicate connective tissue fibers pass into the cortex at the hilus. They continue into the stroma of gland as reticular fibers supporting the arterioles and capillaries of the cortex and the sinusoidal vessels of the medulla. The capsule also gives rise to cells which replace the cells of the cortex.

Cortex

The cortex is composed of cords of cells, between which lie capillaries in a fine network of reticular tissue. Three zones are distinguishable, though they are not sharply delimited one from another. The zones are as follows: (1) Zona glomerulosa–in this region the cells are pale in color and columnar in form (Fig. 170); they are arranged in oval groups separated from each other by fine vascular connective tissue. (2) Zona fasciculata–this is the widest zone of the cortex and is composed of polygonal cells, in the cytoplasm of which fat (lipoid) droplets are present; cells in the zone are arranged in cords which radiate from the center of the gland (Fig. 171); the

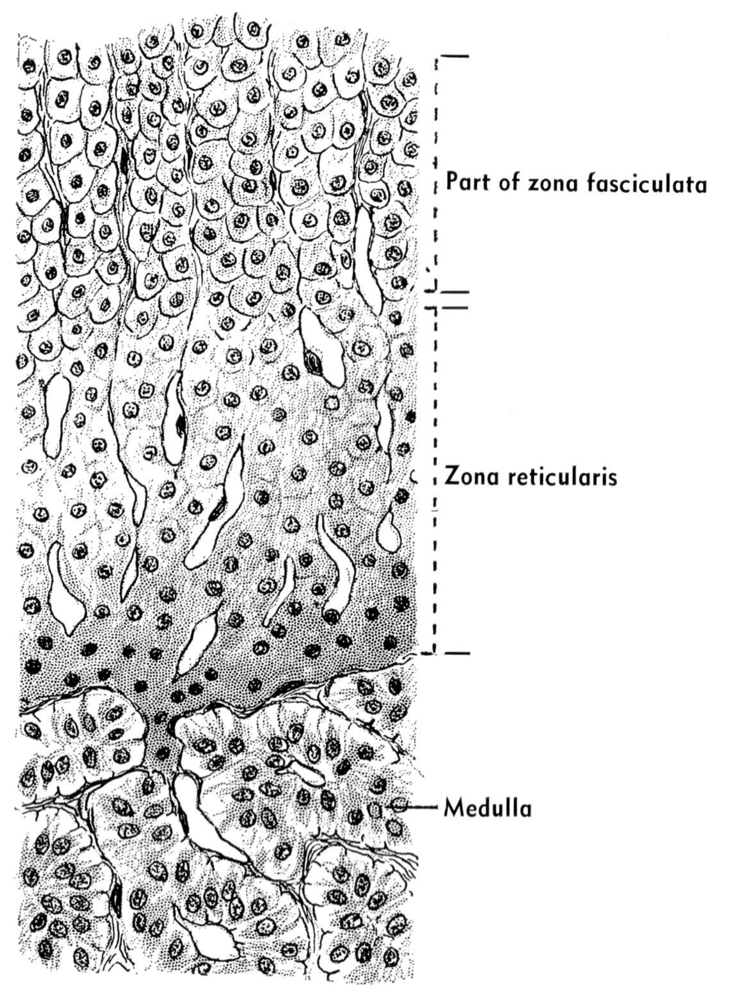

Fig. 171. Inner portion of cortex and part of medulla of adrenal gland of rabbit.

cords are usually two cells in width, being cuboidal and often binucleate. In the outer portion of the fasciculata the cells contain droplets of cholesterol and other fats. In the usual preparations these areas appear as vacuoles, giving the cell a spongy appearance. (3) Zona reticularis—in the innermost zone of the cortex the cords of cells, instead of running in a radial direction, break up into a network, in the spaces of which the capillaries are to be found; the cells of the reticular zone are somewhat smaller and darker than those of the fascicular zone. (Fig. 171.)

The function of the cortex is complex. Addison's disease is a fatal syndrome resulting from the destruction of the adrenal cortex. The cortex regulates sodium and potassium balance. It contains appreciable amounts of cholesterol and vitamin C. Phagocytic activity occurs in the zona reticularis. The normal activity of the cortex is said to be regulated by the corticotropic hormone secreted by the hypophysis. The relationship of the cortex of the adrenal to the other endocrine glands is, however, also important.

Medulla

The medulla consists of irregularly arranged groups of cells which have a granular cytoplasm and polygonal outlines (Fig. 171). With hematoxylin and eosin their color is faintly purple. They react strongly to chromium salts and are therefore called chromaffin cells. Even without this specific stain they are readily distinguished from the cortical cells by their basophilic reaction, their larger size, and their arrangement. Among the cords is a network of capillaries such as is characteristic of endocrine organs.

The adrenal medulla, or chromaffin tissue, is not essential for life. From it a substance is extracted (epinephrine) which causes the contraction of the smooth muscles of blood vessels through its action on the sympathetic nerve terminations. The granules in the chromaffin cells vary with physiological activity; when the medulla is depleted the granules disappear, reappearing again when secretion is restored.

CHAPTER XX

Brain and special sense organs

THE BRAIN

Cerebrum

The cerebrum consists of two large symmetrically arranged lobes or hemispheres which are connected by a bridge of white matter, the corpus callosum. Each hemisphere contains a central mass of white matter, the medulla, in which are to be found aggregations of cells known as the internal nuclei and a covering of gray substance known as the cortex.

The cortex is thrown into many folds which are marked by convolutions separated by intervening fissures and sulci. The cells located within the cortex are arranged in layers which are parallel to the surface of the convolutions. Different areas of the cortex vary in the number of cell layers. Some areas contain as few as four, while others contain as many as eight cell layers. The neurons of the cerebral cortex are believed to consist of two main physiological types: (1) neurons whose axons enter projection pathways which connect the cortex with the spinal cord and other lower centers; (2) neurons whose axons enter association pathways which connect different areas of the same or opposite hemisphere.

Inasmuch as the arrangement of cells differs slightly in different areas of the cortex, a general description will be presented (Fig. 172).

The outer molecular layer consists of a network of fine fibers which is composed chiefly of dendrites derived from cells in the deep layers. These fibers are arranged in tangenital meshes below the pia. Small polymorphous cells are sometimes observed among the fibers. They are believed to be displaced from the deeper layers.

The most characteristic type of neuron found in the cerebral cortex is the so-called pyramidal cell (Fig. 173). Pyramidal cells are distributed in two strata. The stratum located below the molecular layer contains small pyramidal cells which are about 10 to 12μ in width; the second stratum is adjacent to that containing small pyramidal cells on the one hand and to the white matter on the other. The neurons in this stratum,

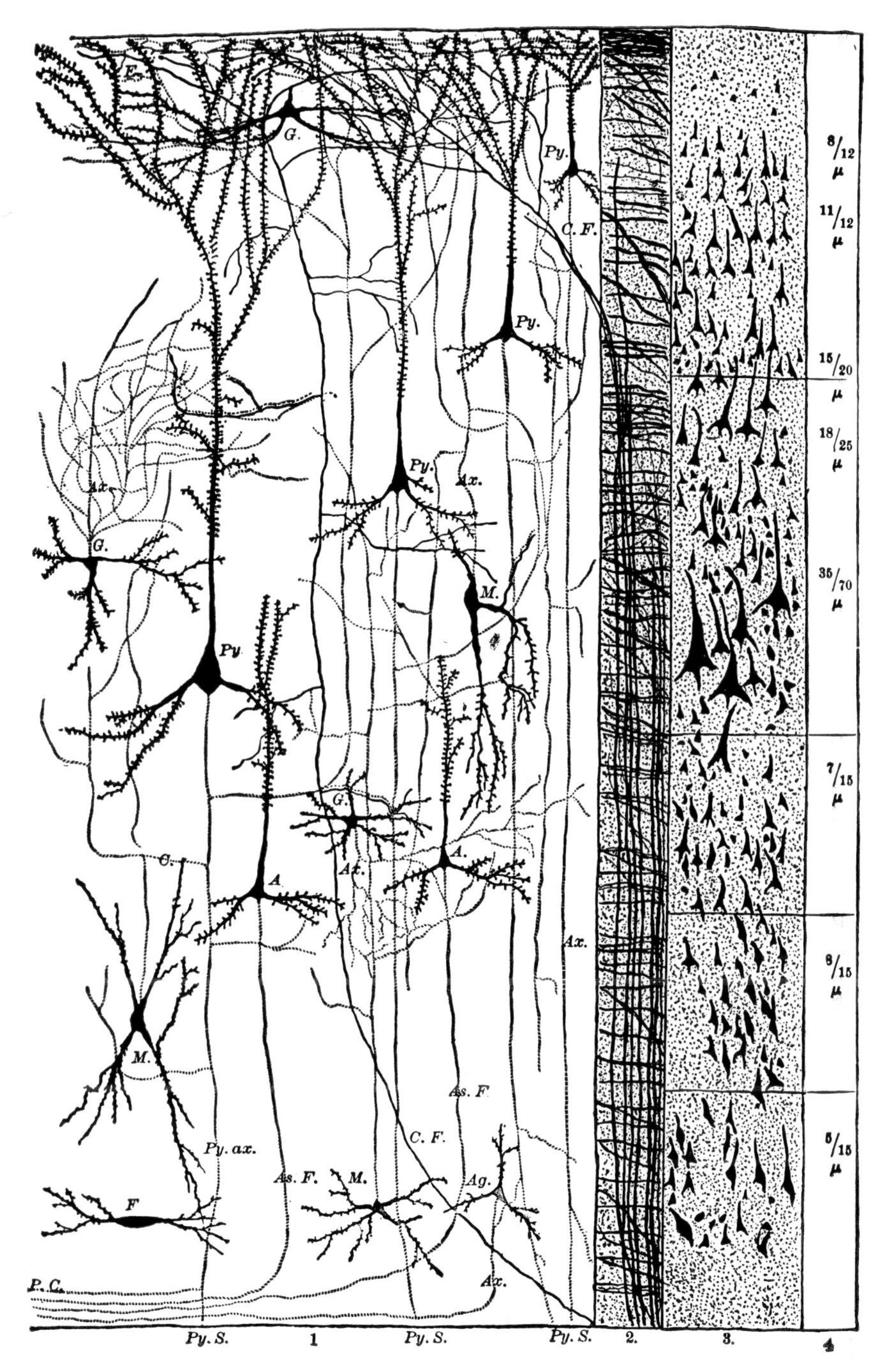

Fig. 172. Scheme of motor area of cerebral cortex, showing effect of various staining methods. **1,** Golgi's stain; **2,** Weigert's stain; **3,** hematoxylin and eosin; **4,** relative depth of each layer. **A.,** Association neurons; **Ag.,** angular cells of polymorphous layer; **As.F.,** association fibers; **Ax.,** axons; **C.,** collateral; **C.F.,** centripetal fibers; **E.,** terminal fibers; **F.,** fusiform cell of polymorphous layer; **G.,** Golgi cells, type II; **M.,** cells of Martinotti; **P.C.,** collateral of pyramidal cell; **Py.,** pyramidal cell; **Py.ax.,** axon of pyramidal cell; **Py.S.,** pyramidal axons passing to cerebral medulla. (After Berkley; from Jordan: Textbook of Histology, Philadelphia, D. Appleton-Century Co., Inc.)

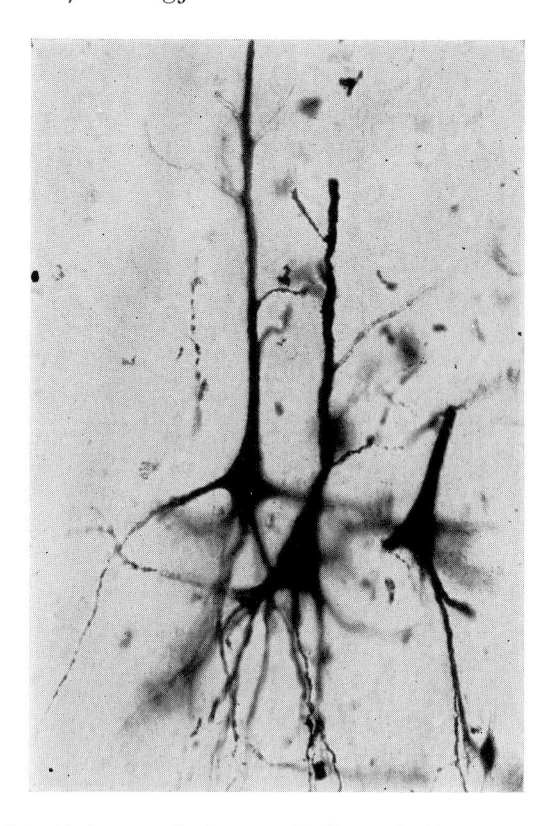

Fig. 173. Pyramidal cells from cerebral cortex (Golgi method).

which is known as the layer of large pyramidal cells, vary in both size and form. The smaller cells in this layer are approximately 20μ in width, whereas the largest, which are located in the motor cortex, attain a size of from 60 to 80μ. In the motor cortex they are known as the cells of Betz. The shape of the cell body is also variable and has been described as pyramidal, triangular, or pyriform.

The pyramidal cells are so arranged in the cortex that their pointed apices are directed toward the surface. The pyramidal cells usually exhibit two sets of dendrites. The largest leaves the cell at the apex and passes to the outer molecular layer. The second set leaves the cell at the sides of the basal part. These dendrites are distributed in the same plane as that in which the cell bodies are located. The axon of the pyramidal cell usually originates at the base of the cell and, after giving off several collateral branches, enters the white matter.

The polymorphous layer, sometimes referred to as the inner polymorphous layer, is somewhat thicker than the layer of large pyramidal neurons and consists of cells which may appear stellate, fusiform, or granular. The cells in this layer are less densely distributed than in the other layers and are somewhat smaller than the small pyramidal cells. The axons of these cells pass for the most part to the white matter of the medulla, some reaching the neighboring convolutions. Some of the dendrites are distributed within the layer in which they arise, but most of them pass to the outer pyramidal layers. The granule cells located within this layer are extremely small.

In general, it has been observed that the dendrites of cells in all the layers of the cerebral cortex are either distributed in the same plane as the cell body or pass to the surface of the convolutions. The axons, on the other hand, are directed toward the white matter of the medulla where they continue as association or projection fibers to distant parts of the nervous system.

Cerebellum

The cerebellum is made up of two main lobes or hemispheres which are connected by a third lobe known as the vermis. Each lobe consists of a number of subdivisions, the lobules, which are thrown into several

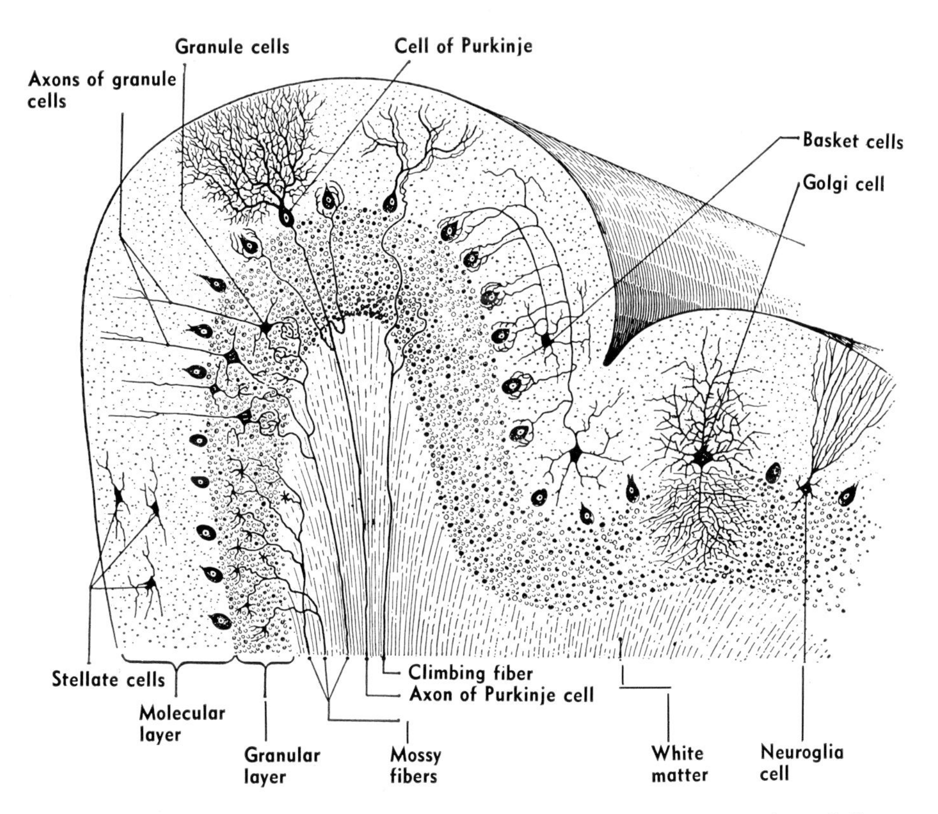

Fig. 174. Diagrammatic drawing of cell forms and fiber arrangement of cerebellum. (After Cajal; from Globus: Practical Neuroanatomy, Baltimore, The Williams & Wilkins Co.)

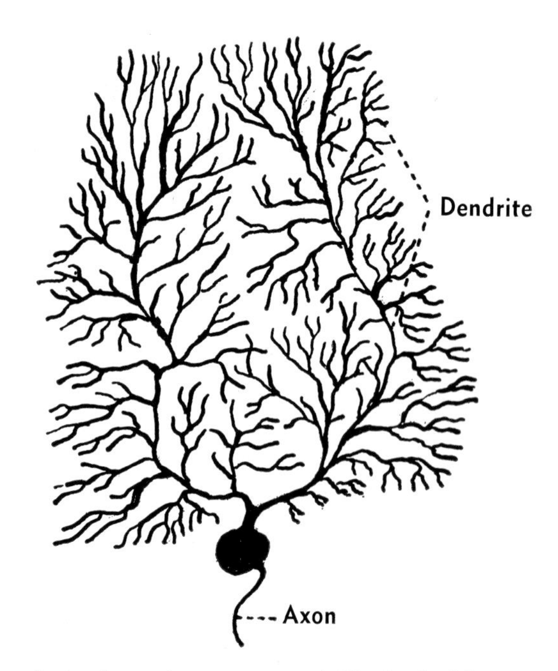

Fig. 175. Purkinje cell. (Redrawn from Bremer and Weatherford.)

transverse convolutions or folia. Like the cerebrum, the cerebellum consists of a central core of white matter, the medulla, and a thick external covering of gray matter, the cortex.

The cerebellar cortex is made up of an inner granular layer and an outer molecular layer. Between these two zones there is a single layer of large conspicuous cells known as Purkinje cells (Figs. 174 and 175).

The molecular layer contains two types of neurons, the small cortical and the large cortical or basket cells.

The basket cells are relatively large multipolar cells with short, thick, branching dendrites and a long axon which passes horizontally in the same plane as that occupied by the dendrites of the Purkinje cells. In its course it gives off five or six collaterals which pass centrally to end in basketlike arborizations around the Purkinje cells. The basket cells are confined for the most part to the middle and outer part of the molecular layer. They are believed to be association neurons.

The small cortical cells are also multipolar neurons but smaller than those just described; in addition they are more variable in size. They send out from two to five dendrites which are distributed mainly in the same plane as the Purkinje cells. A single short, slender axon which is horizontally placed is characteristically looped and usually sends out several collaterals. These cells are found to be distributed throughout the molecular layer; they are, however, most numerous in the outer half of this part of the cortex.

The Purkinje cells form a single layer of conspicuous neurons which is interposed between the molecular and granular layers. These cells are histologically the most distinctive neurons which occur in the cerebellar cortex (Fig. 175). They are large, flask-shaped, multipolar cells which possess a thick dendrite directed toward the surface of the convolution. Immediately on leaving the cell body the dendrite divides into two thick branches, each of which undergoes many successive dichotomous branchings. They appear at the surface as a dense profusion of fine fibrils. When viewed in its entirety, the dendrite appears fan-shaped, and its characteristic expansions are placed at right angles to the long axis of the convolution. When these dendrites are examined in sections of the convolutions which are cut lengthwise, they are relatively much less extensive. The single axon arises from the deep surface of the cell and passes through the granular layer to the medulla. Before reaching the medulla the axons send out several collaterals which turn back into the molecular layer and end in association with adjacent Purkinje cells.

The granular or nuclear layer contains three types of cells: (1) granule cells, (2) large stellate cells, and (3) solitary cells which are extremely small and fusiform in shape.

Granule cells are small multipolar nerve cells which are distributed throughout the granular layer. These cells have from two to four short dendrites which pass toward the surface and terminate in peculiar claw-like processes which are in intimate association with small granular spheroidal masses known as eosin bodies. On reaching the surface the axon divides into a T-shaped process, the fibers of which pass parallel to the long axis of the convolutions.

The large stellate cells are also multipolar neurons with profuse dendritic processes which contribute to the molecular layer. The axons and collaterals of these cells are also profuse and contribute to the granular layer where they end in association with the granule cells.

The medulla contains three main types of fibers: (1) the axons of the Purkinje cells, which are the main efferent fibers from the cortex; (2) the climbing fibers, which are afferent and end in association with the Purkinje cells; and (3) mossy fibers, which are afferent fibers ending in mossy terminations with the granular layer.

Meninges

The brain and spinal cord are enclosed by connective tissue coverings known as the meninges. The meninges (Fig. 176) consist of three membranes which are known as the dura mater, the arachnoid, and the pia mater. In the spinal cord the dura is separated from the periosteum of the vertebrae by a space which is occupied by a loose fibrous and adipose tissue. This region is known as the epidural space.

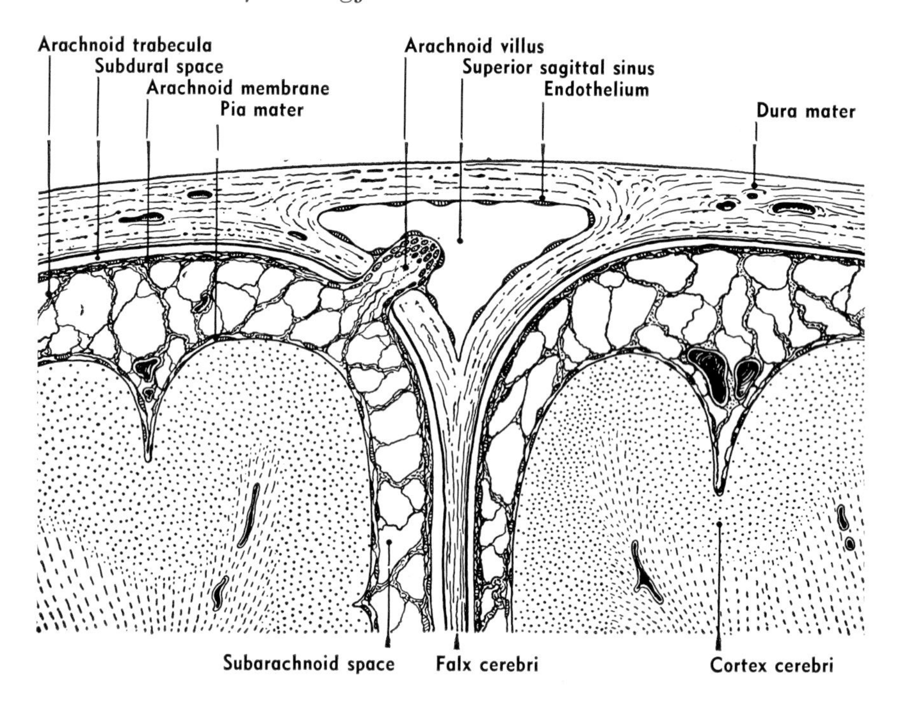

Fig. 176. Diagram of arachnoid and subdural spaces. (After Weed; from Bremer and Weatherford: A Text-Book of Histology, New York, 1948, The Blakiston Co.)

The dura of the spinal cord is a single-layered structure made up of fibrous tissue containing a few elastic fibers. The fibers in this part of the dura are longitudinally disposed. The cranial dura consists of two layers: an outer vascular portion serving as the periosteum and an inner layer, the dura proper. The cranial dura forms reduplications which extend between the cerebral hemispheres and between the hemispheres and the cerebellum. The two layers of the dura separate along the lines of attachment to form the venous dural sinuses which receive blood from veins of the brain.

In the cord where the outer surface of the dura is not attached to the adjacent bone, the covering consists of a layer of thin mesenchymal epithelium which serves as the lining of the epidural space. The inner surface is also lined with a layer of mesenchymal epithelium. This forms the outer wall of the subdural space.

The arachnoid is a loose netlike membrane which intervenes between the dura and the pia. The outer surface consists of a thin fibrous sheath which is covered by a layer of epithelium. Numerous delicate strands of this membrane pass to the outer surface of the pia.

In the cranial part of the arachnoid numerous fingerlike structures are to be found which project into the venous sinuses. They are known as the arachnoid villi.

The pia mater is a delicate, vascular, fibrous layer which is closely adherent to the brain and spinal cord. In the region of the roof of the third and fourth ventricles the vascular membranes which cover them are in some areas invaginated to form the choroid plexuses. Similar invaginations also occur in the lateral ventricles. The vessels of the plexuses are enclosed in connective tissue which in turn is covered by a granular cuboidal epithelium. The entire complex is known as the tela choroidea. The choroid plexuses are believed to be one of the main sources of the cerebrospinal fluid.

EYE

On cutting the eye in a meridional horizontal plane, one may readily see the following features.

The eye is a hollow globular structure with a thick, fairly elastic wall, the inner lining of which appears darker than the remainder. It is divided into two unequal parts by a transversely placed structure, the iris. The portion between the iris and the cornea is the anterior chamber; the remainder is divided by the lens and its capsule into the small posterior chamber and the large vitreal space (Fig. 177).

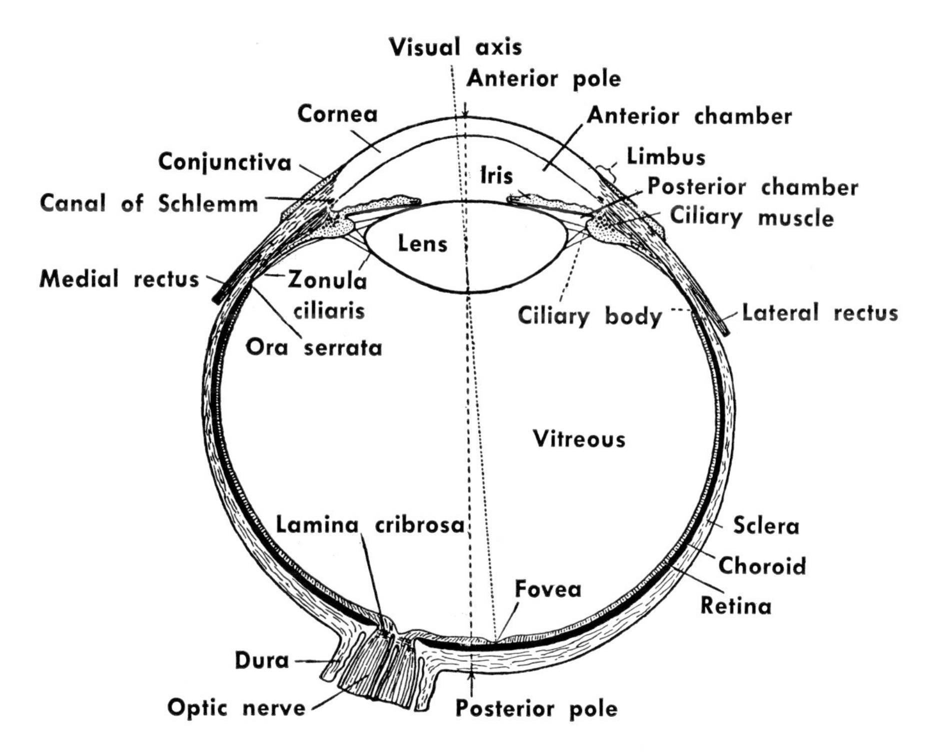

Fig. 177. Schematic horizontal meridional section of right eye. (×3.) (Redrawn and modified from Salzmann.)

The curvature of the outer coat as it passes over the anterior chamber is sharper than that around the posterior part of the eye, so that the eyeball is not a perfect sphere. The coat is modified in structure also in its anterior portion, forming the transparent cornea. The anterior chamber contains a fluid, the aqueous humor.

The iris does not lie flat in the transverse plane. Its center is slightly anterior to its periphery so that it has the form of a low truncated cone. It is pierced at the center by the pupil, which is a round aperture of varying dimensions.

The posterior part of the eye contains the lens and the vitreous body or humor. The latter is a jellylike mass; the former a smaller and more solid body lying just posterior to the iris. The lens is suspended in this position by a group of fine fibers, the suspensory ligament. The fibers of the ligament are attached at one end to the lens capsule and at the other to the ciliary body. This is macroscopically visible as a thickening of tissue posterior to the periphery of the iris.

The optic nerve is seen as a stalk leaving the eye at a point slightly medial to the posterior pole. The thick covering of the eye extends over this stalk, and in a complete dissection of the eye, the optic nerve, and the brain one would find that the sheath of the eye extends to and is continuous with the dura mater of the brain.

Coats of the eye

On microscopic examination it is apparent that the coating of the eye has three parts as follows: (1) The fibrous coat includes the sclera covering the vitreal cavity and the transparent cornea of the anterior chamber. (2) The vascular layer extends around the posterior chamber inside the sclera and turns inward to form the iris. The choroid is thickened to form the ciliary body. (3) The retina lines the vitreal cavity. A part of the retina extends over the ciliary body and the posterior surface of the iris.

Fibrous coat. The fibrous coat consists of the sclera and cornea.

Sclera. The sclera surrounds the vitreal cavity and extends a short distance anterior to the margin of the iris. It consists mainly of closely packed fibers and fibroblasts. At its inner margin there is a layer of looser connective tissue containing pigment cells (lamina fusca). Elastic fibers are abundant in the sclera, especially at the points of insertion of the muscles which move the eye.

Cornea. The corneal portion also consists mainly of fibers arranged in flat lamellae parallel to the surface. It has, in addition, two epithelial layers. The outer one is a thin stratified squamous epithelium (from four to six layers of cells) which rests on a relatively thick basement membrane called the anterior basal membrane (of Bowman). The posterior surface of the cornea is covered with a mesenchymal epithelium which

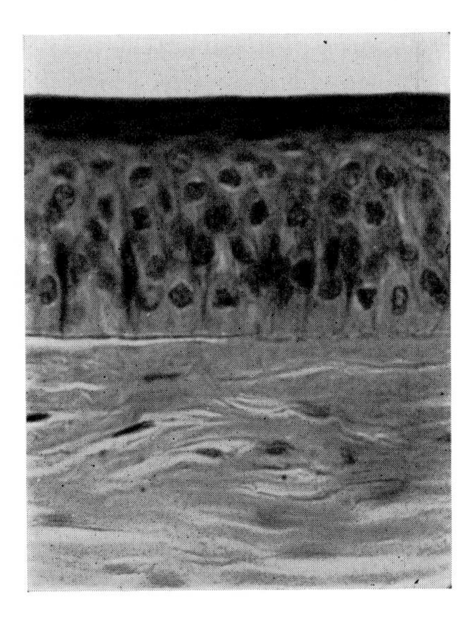

Fig. 178. Cornea showing stratified epithelium.

consists of one layer of flattened cells and rests on an exceptionally transparent membrane called the posterior basal or Descemet's membrane.

Vascular layer. The vascular layer corresponds to the pia mater of the brain and is fundamentally a layer of loose connective tissue containing blood vessels. The part surrounding the posterior chamber is called the choroid. The anterior part forms two structures, the ciliary body and the iris.

Choroid coat. Blood vessels and connective tissue are not evenly distributed throughout the choroid. Nearest to the sclera is a layer of connective tissue with few, if any, blood vessels. The next layer contains the largest arteries and veins; the innermost a plexus of capillaries. The choroid is bounded on the inside (next to the retina) by the hyaline membrane of Bruch, part of which is said to be a cuticular formation of the cells of the retina.

Ciliary body. The ciliary body is a thickening of the vascular layer to which the suspensory ligament of the lens is attached. It extends into the posterior chamber in a series of from seventy to eighty radially arranged ridges, the ciliary processes. It contains all the elements of the choroid coat except the capillary layer. In addition there are smooth muscle fibers in it, the contraction of which alters the shape of the lens. The muscles form three groups: meridional, radial, and circular. The ciliary body is covered by a forward extension of the retina, and fibers extend from it to the capsule of the lens. These two elements will be discussed with the retina and the lens, respectively.

Iris. Anterior to the ciliary body the vascular layer forms the iris which acts as a diaphragm to control the amount of light falling on the retina. The anterior surface of the iris is covered by flattened mesenchymal epithelium similar to the innermost layer of the cornea. The epithelium is interrupted by irregular crypts which extend into the underlying stroma. The connective tissue of the anterior part of the stroma is a loose network of stellate cells and fine fibers. Some of the stellate cells are pigmented. Fibers are more numerous in the posterior layers of the stroma, and the cells may or may not contain pigment. In this part there are a few elastic fibers, radially arranged, and two groups of muscle fibers. One group of muscles forms the dilator, the other the sphincter, by which the size of the pupil is altered. A part of the retinal layer extends over the posterior surface of the iris.

Retina. The structures described thus far are concerned with the protection of the retina or with focusing light upon it. The retina is the nervous mechanism for the reception and transmission of light stimuli.

The retina arises embryologically as a vesicular outgrowth from the forebrain. As development proceeds the distal surface of the optic vesicle is invaginated, resulting in a two-layered, cup-shaped structure. The outer layer forms the pigmented epithelium; the invaginated portion gives rise to the remaining layers of the retina which are, in most of its extent, nine in number.

Three main regions of the retina may be distinguished histologically and topographically. They are (1) pars optica, lining most of the vitreal space; (2) pars ciliaris, covering the ciliary body; and (3) pars iridica, covering the posterior surface of the iris.

Pars optica (Fig. 179). It is in the pars optica, the largest part of the retina, that ten layers have been distinguished and named as follows:

	Layer	Group
1.	Pigmented epithelium	a
2.	Rods and cones	b
3.	External limiting membrane	b
4.	Outer nuclear (granular) layer	b
5.	Outer plexiform (molecular) layer	b
6.	Inner nuclear (granular) layer	c
7.	Inner plexiform (molecular) layer	c
8.	Ganglion cell layer	d
9.	Nerve fiber layer	d
10.	Internal limiting membrane	

The pars optica is, however, more easily understood if we consider that it is composed of a layer of pigmented epithelium and three layers of nervous elements with intervening strata between the perikarya of the latter, which are occupied by axons and dendrites. This division into four kinds of elements is indicated by a, b, c, and d in the list. Among the nervous elements are found supporting cells which lie among the nervous elements and form the fibers composing the two limiting mem-

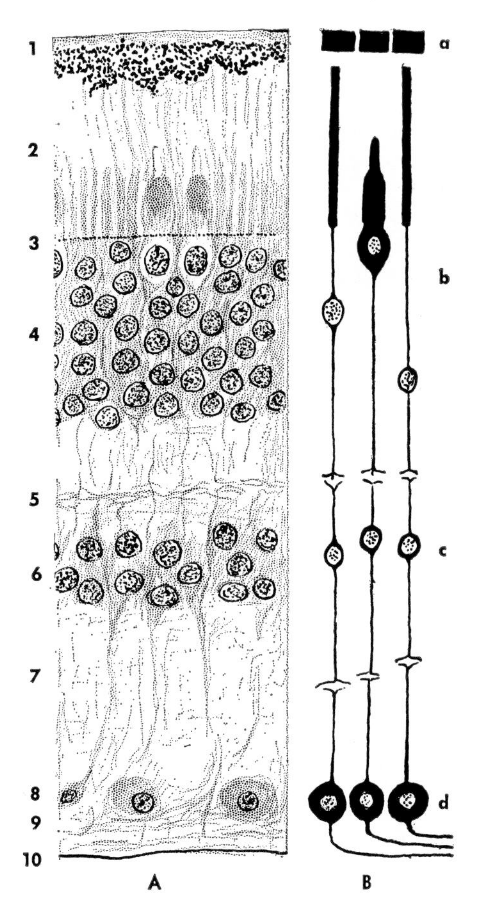

Fig. 179. Human retina. **A,** Section of retina. **B,** Isolated cells, diagrammatically presented. Numbers to left of illustration and letters to right correspond to numbers and letters in outline on page 264.

branes (3 and 10 in accompanying list). Since cells of this group are scattered throughout all layers of the retina except the first and the tenth, they cannot well be included in the list.

(a) The pigmented epithelium is a single layer of cuboidal cells, the cytoplasm of which contains melanin in the form of rod-shaped granules. The cells are said to send out processes among the subjacent rods and cones. In some of the lower vertebrates variations in the extent of such processes can be observed and correlated with differences in the amount of light falling on the retina, but such morphological variations have not been established as occurring in the mammalian eye.

(b) Immediately next to the pigmented epithelium lie the rods and cones which are the light receptors. They are part of the first nervous elements involved in the transmission of stimuli. The nuclei of the rod and cone cells form the outer nuclear layer of the retina. Between this

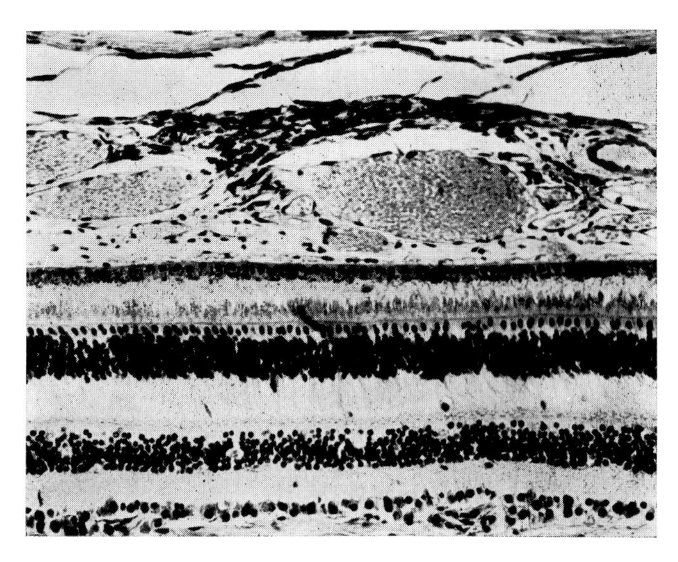

Fig. 180. Vertical section of human retina. (Courtesy Dr. E. O. Butcher, New York, N.Y.)

layer and the pigmented epithelium the cytoplasm of the cell assumes one of two forms. In the rod cells the outer segment of the cell is an elongated cylinder 60μ in length and 2μ in width. This portion, the rod, is homogeneous in appearance. It rests upon an inner segment which contains fine cytoplasmic granules. As it passes through the outer limiting membrane, the cytoplasm of the cell narrows to a thin strand which traverses part of the outer granular layer till it reaches the nucleus and expands again to form a thin perinuclear film. The nucleus is characterized by the presence in it of from one to three definite bands of chromatin. Beyond the perikaryon the cytoplasm of the rod cells forms a fiber which extends into the outer plexiform layer, ending there in a club-shaped enlargement.

The cone cells are less numerous than the rods in most parts of the retina. Their outer segments are relatively short and thick, tapering to a blunted point. The inner segment is broader than that of a rod cell and passes to the perinuclear portion without any marked constriction. The inner process or fiber of the cone cell ends in a pyramidal base in the outer plexiform layer.

(c) The cells of the second layer are bipolar. Each has a dendrite located in the outer plexiform layer, a perikaryon in the inner nuclear layer, and an axon which extends to the inner plexiform layer. Among the perikarya of these cells one may find association neurons which lie entirely within the inner nuclear layer and serve as horizontal lines of communication between different parts of the retina.

(d) The ganglion cells are typical multipolar nerve cells. Their dendrites synapse with the axons of the bipolar cells, whereas their axons run in a plane parallel to the surface of the retina to the optic disc. This part of the axon is nonmedullated.

(e) Throughout the retina, as in other parts of the nervous system, there is a network of supporting tissue. Concentrations of the fibers elaborated (Müller's fibers) form the external and internal limiting membranes.

The structure of the pars optica is modified in two regions: the optic disc and the macula lutea. The former is the point at which the axons of the ganglion cells meet and turn at right angles to their previous course to leave the eye and form the optic nerve. In the optic disc the outer layers of the retina are interrupted, and the area does not receive stimuli ("blind spot").

The macula lutea is an area near the posterior pole of the eye which appears yellow in the fresh specimen and has the shape of a shallow funnel. The center, where the retina is thinnest, is the fovea centralis. From the periphery of the macula to its center there is a gradual reduction of all the retinal elements except the cones, and at the fovea the retina consists of a layer of small cone cells and a few scattered ganglion cells. The fovea is the spot of most acute vision.

The foregoing account of the structure of the retina is based on facts to be observed in special preparations. The ordinary section shows differentiation into ten layers, but the forms and connections of many of the cells are difficult to see.

It is of interest to note that light entering the eye does not fall directly upon the rods and cones. It must first pass through the thickness of the greater part of the retina to the pigmented epithelium. The pigment absorbs the light in the rods and cones.

Pars ciliaris. The pars optica of the retina ends at a point slightly posterior to the ciliary body in a thick irregular margin called the ora serrata. As it approaches this point, the retina undergoes a gradual loss of visual elements, and beyond the margin these disappear entirely. The pars ciliaris of the retina consists of two layers: the pigmented epithelium continues unchanged, and beneath it lies a layer of sustentacular cells arranged in the form of a columnar epithelium. The sustentacular cells produce fibers, some of which are gathered in a hyaline membrane bordering the cavity of the posterior chamber. Other fibers enter into the formation of the ligament of the lens.

Pars iridica. The pigmented epithelium is the only part of the retina which continues beyond the ciliary body to cover the posterior surface of the iris (pars iridica). It becomes somewhat thicker in this region and the amount of pigment contained in the cells is so great as to obscure nuclei and cell boundaries.

Contents of the eye

The anterior chamber and the small posterior chamber are filled with a fluid, the aqueous humor, whereas the large vitreal cavity encloses the vitreous body. Between the posterior chamber and the vitreal cavity lie the lens and its capsule.

Aqueous humor. The aqueous humor is a colorless fluid which is probably derived partly by transudation from the blood vessels of the region and partly from secretion of the cells covering the anterior surface of the iris and the ciliary body.

Vitreous body or humor. The vitreous body or humor is a mass of jelly-like connective tissue which resembles the mucous connective tissue of the umbilical cord. It consists of fine fibers and fibroblasts in a semisolid matrix. The periphery of the vitreous body is covered by a thin membrane of fibers (hyaloid membrane), which some authors consider as merely a surface condensation. Others believe it to be a definite membrane uniting the vitreous body to the retina in the posterior part of the eye, turning inward at the ciliary body to contribute part of the suspensory ligament of the lens.

Lens. The lens is an ectodermal structure which was originally cut off as a hollow vesicle from the epithelium. The space within the lens vesicle is filled, as development proceeds, by the growth of the cells on its posterior aspect. These cells elongate until they are fibrous in shape, then lose their nuclei and undergo cornification. The anterior surface of the lens is covered by a layer of cuboidal cells. The whole lens is enclosed in a hyaline capsule which is a specialized basement membrane, and to the capsule are attached the fibers of the suspensory ligament. As we have seen, the fibers of the ligament are supposed to be derived from the basal (sustentacular) cells of the retina and perhaps also from the hyaloid membrane of the vitreous body.

Optic nerve or stalk. The optic nerve consists of the axons of the cells of the ganglionic layer of the retina. These fibers have neither myelin or neurilemma as long as they remain in the retina. At the optic disc, as we have already seen, they turn and leave the eyeball, and at this point they acquire a myelin sheath but not a neurilemma. The optic nerve is enclosed in extensions of the pia mater and dura mater of the brain which join the fibrous coat of the eye. The optic nerve is, in fact, an extension of the substance of the central nervous system rather than a true sensory nerve, and it is more correct to call it the optic stalk.

Circulation and innervation of the eye

The retina and the optic nerve are supplied by the central artery which passes in the optic stalk. The remainder of the eye receives blood from the ophthalmic artery which forms three ciliary vessels. The latter enter the wall at different levels, supplying the choroid, sclera, iris, and ciliary bodies. Motor nerves form a plexus in the region of the ciliary body, from which are innervated the smooth muscles of the ciliary body and the iris.

THE EAR

The ear develops from three sources embryologically and retains throughout life its division into three parts: external ear, middle ear, and inner ear. The last-named part develops early in the course of embryonic life as a vesicle which is cut off from the ectodermal covering of the head region and lies in the mesenchyme between the surface and the wall of the developing hindbrain. In this situation it becomes surrounded by bony tissue as the latter develops from the mesenchyme of the region. The middle ear develops from a diverticulum of the pharynx (first pharyngeal pouch), its ossicles being formed in the surrounding mesenchyme. The external ear is a secondary ingrowth of ectoderm from the surface plus a projection on the surface which forms the pinna.

External ear

The pinna is an irregularly shaped flap of elastic cartilage covered by skin which is set on the side of the head around the opening of the external auditory meatus. The latter is a tubular channel leading to the eardrum or tympanic membrane. Its outer part is surrounded by elastic cartilage continuous with that of the pinna. Its inner portion penetrates the outer layers of the temporal bone. It is lined with skin which contains sebaceous and ceruminous (wax-forming) glands. Stiff hairs are present at the junction of the cartilaginous and bony parts.

Middle ear

The middle ear is a cavity in the substance of the temporal bone completely separated from the external ear by the tympanic membrane. It is in communication with the pharynx by way of the eustachian tube and separated from the inner ear by a plate of bone containing two apertures, the oval and round windows, respectively. The former is closed by the end of one of the ossicles, the latter by a membrane, so that there is no communication between middle and inner ear. The cavity of the middle ear is crossed by a chain of three small bones, the ossicles.

The tympanic membrane is a fibrous membrane held in a groove of the temporal bone by a ring of fibrocartilage. It is covered on the outside by skin like that lining the meatus and on the inside by a layer of flattened epithelium.

The ossicles are called, respectively, the malleus (hammer), the incus (anvil), and the stapes (stirrup), the names being descriptive of their forms. The handle of the hammer is firmly attached to the inner surface of the tympanic membrane, while its head rests on the anvil. The anvil is articulated also with the upper end of the stirrup, while the foot of the latter is inserted into the oval window. It is by means of this chain of bones that the vibrations of the tympanic membrane are transmitted across the cavity of the middle ear to the vestibule of the inner ear.

The cavity of the middle ear is lined with flattened epithelium which rests on the periosteum of the surrounding bone. Epithelium also covers the periosteum of the ossicles.

Inner ear

Osseous labyrinth. The cavity of the inner ear forms a series of irregular spaces in the temporal bone, the whole system being known as the osseous labyrinth. The labyrinth is bordered by a layer of compact bone which may be separated by careful dissection from the spongy bone with which it blends. The bone is covered by periosteum, and the cavity is lined throughout by flattened epithelial tissue. It contains, besides the membranous labyrinth, a fluid called the perilymph. The labyrinth consists of a vestibular portion, semicircular canals, and a cone-shaped cochlear part. It has, in addition, a narrow outlet to the subarachnoid space, the vestibular aqueduct.

Vestibule and semicircular canals. The osseous vestibule is an irregularly rounded cavity from which the semicircular canals, the cavity of the cochlea, and the vestibular aqueduct diverge.

The semicircular canals are three in number. Two of these (the superior and posterior) are set vertically and at right angles to each other. The third canal (lateral) lies in a horizontal plane. Each is a horseshoe-shaped channel in the temporal bone, connecting at both ends with the cavity of the vestibule. One limb of each is enlarged near its connection with the vestibule to form the ampulla. The opposite ends of the superior and posterior canals join and re-enter the vestibule through a common opening; the lateral canal returns to it separately, so that there are five openings from the vestibule to the system of semicircular canals.

Cochlea. The canal of the cochlea pursues a spiral course from the vestibule to the apex of a flattened cone. It surrounds a central mass of spongy bone, the modiolus, which contains the spiral ganglion. A shelf of bone projects into the canal from the modiolus, following the course of the former to its apex. This is called the osseous spiral lamina.

Membranous labyrinth. The membranous labyrinth, which lies within the osseous labyrinth, is separated from it by the perilymph and is divided functionally into two parts: the portion lying in the vestibule and the semicircular canals mediates the sense of equilibrium, while that in the cochlea is the organ of hearing. Fundamentally the structure of the membranous labyrinth is that of a closed system consisting of a sheath of connective tissue lined with flattened epithelium and containing a fluid, the endolymph. The epithelium is modified in various parts of the system in order to form receptors for the stimuli involved.

Utricle and saccule. The utricle and saccule are rounded sacs which lie in the perilymph of the vestibule and are held in place by trabeculae of connective tissue extending from the periosteum of the surrounding bone. They are united by a narrow duct which has the form of an inverted V. From the apex of this duct the endolymphatic duct leads away through the vestibular aqueduct to terminate in the endolymphatic sac. Another fine duct joins the saccule with the cochlear duct.

Semicircular canals. The semicircular ducts arise from the utricle. They lie within the osseous semicircular canals, and each is attached along part of its periphery to the periosteum of the bone and is further anchored by connective tissue trabeculae.

The epithelial lining of the vestibular portion of the labyrinth contains patches of neuro-epithelium. There is one of these in the utricle, another in the saccule, and one in each ampulla of the semicircular ducts. The neuro-epithelium contains hair cells and tall sustentacular cells.

Cochlear duct. One border of the membranous part of the cochlea is attached to the bony shelf of the modiolus, the lamina spiralis. The opposite border forms a wider attachment to the outer edge of the canal, thus dividing the latter into two parts which are in communication at the apex of the spiral but not elsewhere. The upper part of the osseous canal leads from the vestibule and is known as the scala vestibuli. The lower ends at the membrane closing the round window (secondary tympanic membrane) and is called the scala tympani. The intervening space, enclosed by the cochlear duct, is the scala media (Fig. 181). The scala vestibuli and the scala tympani are lined, as are other parts of the osseous labyrinth, by flattened epithelium resting on the periosteum of the surrounding bone.

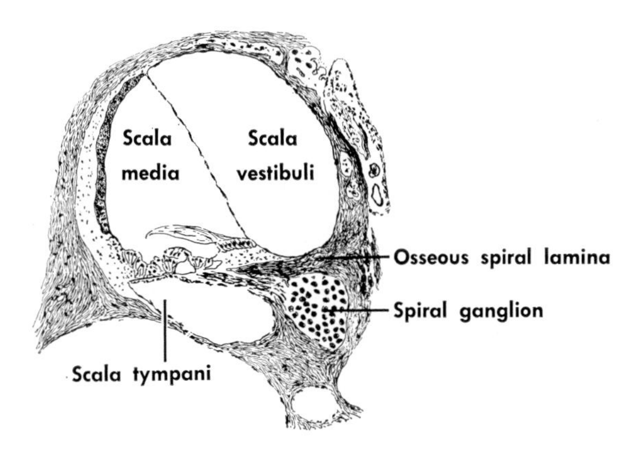

Fig. 181. Radial section through basal turn of cochlea.

The epithelium extends, also, over the outer surfaces of the cochlear duct, where the latter is not in contact with the modiolus on the one hand or the outer wall of the osseous labyrinth on the other.

The scala media is bounded by the following structures: It is separated from the scala vestibuli by a thin membrane, the vestibular membrane, which extends from the modiolus to the outer wall of the cochlear canal. Along this part of the wall the periosteum is thickened, forming a ligament, the lower edge of which projects toward the bony spiral lamina of the modiolus. The gap between the ligament (spiral ligament) and the lamina is closed by a membrane, the basal membrane. The scala media is, therefore, separated from the scala tympani by three structures: the spiral ligament, the basal membrane, and the osseous spiral lamina. Between the latter and the vestibular membrane there is a thickening of connective tissue called the limbus spiralis which projects outward from the modiolus into the space of the scala media. The vestibular membrane is attached to the upper surface of the limbus. Its lower surface is concave, forming, with the spiral lamina, a groove known as the spiral sulcus. The space enclosed by the structures just enumerated has, in section, the form of a right-angled triangle of which the vestibular membrane forms the hypotenuse.

Histologically the different portions of the cochlear duct presents striking variations from the structure of the remainder of the membranous labyrinth (Fig. 182). The vestibular membrane consists of a very thin

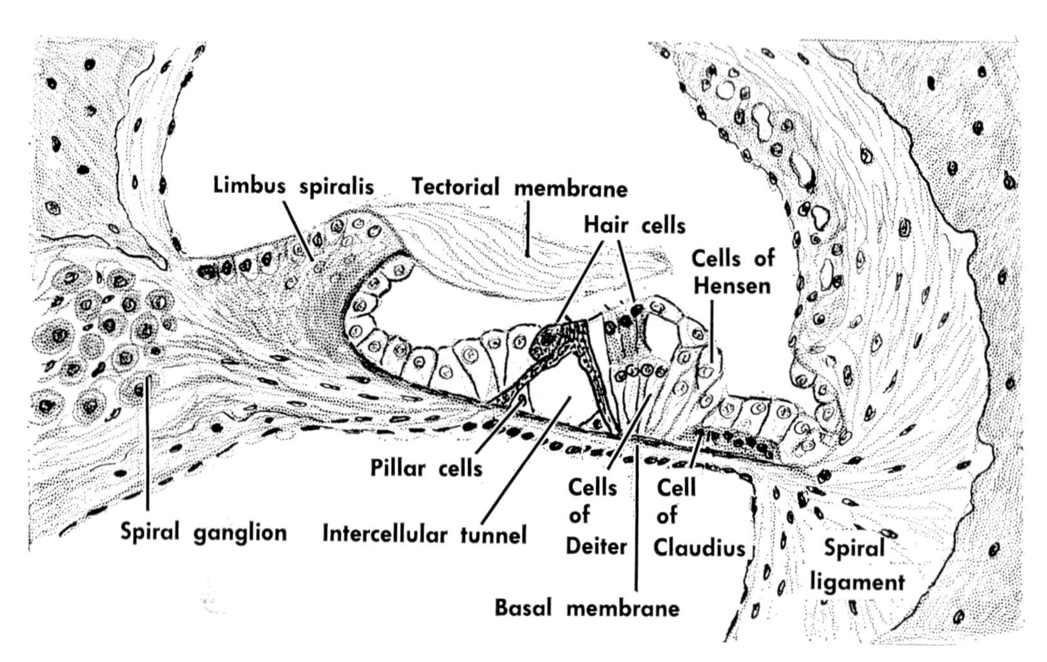

Fig. 182. Organ of Corti of guinea pig.

layer of connective tissue. It is covered on the outside by an extension of the mesothelium lining the remainder of the vestibule; its inner surface is also lined with flattened epithelium of ectodermal origin.

The epithelial lining of the scala media continues unchanged as we trace it around the outer edge of the triangle where the duct is in contact with the border of the osseous canal. The connective tissue of this portion is much thickened, forming a relatively wide band between the epithelium and the bone. A part of this layer is very vascular, and its lower portion is extended toward the modiolus as the spiral ligament. At the angle between the base and the outer side of the scala media the lining epithelium changes from flattened to cuboidal or low columnar cells.

The basal membrane running from the tip of the spiral ligament to that of the osseous lamina is a connective tissue membrane, considerably thicker than that forming the vestibular membrane. Like the latter, it has an outer covering of mesothelium which is, in this case, part of the lining of the scala tympani. The epithelium on the side toward the scala media, which is the ectodermal lining of the cochlear duct, is modified for the reception of sound waves and forms the organ of Corti. Starting at the outer edge and tracing the organ toward the modiolus we may distinguish the following parts:

1. The cells of Claudius, which are small cuboidal cells with dark, granular cytoplasm lying along the membrana basilaris between the latter and the cells of Hensen in that region.

2. The cells of Hensen lie next to those of Claudius, are columnar, and increase in height as they go toward the modiolus.

3. Outer hair cells and sustentacular cells (of Deiter), as their name implies, are provided with hairlike projections from their surfaces and are the actual receptors of the organ. They form a band, three or four cells wide, at the surface of the epithelium, but do not reach to the basement membrane. Deiter's cells rest on the basement membrane and have narrow distal ends extending to the surface between the hair cells. They have stiff cuticular borders which give a firm support to the hair cells.

4. Two rows of pillar cells run through the length of the organ of Corti. They are tall columnar cells in which the cuticular substance forms a stiff rod. One row of these rods is inclined toward the modiolus, the other away from it, so that while their distal ends meet, there is a considerable space between their bases. They thus enclose two sides of a tunnel, which is triangular in cross section, the base of the triangle being formed by the membrana basilaris of the scala media. The enclosed space is called the inner tunnel. It is crossed by naked dendrites of the cells of the spiral ganglion.

5. One row of inner hair cells lies next to the inner pillar cells. These cells are usually of the low columnar type and do not reach the base-

ment membrane. They are supported by tall columnar cells much like the cells of Hensen in appearance.

6. The spiral sulcus is lined with cuboidal epithelium. There is, however, no sharp line of demarcation between the border cells and those lining the spiral sulcus.

At the inner angle of the scala media are the osseous spiral lamina and the spiral limbus which partially enclose the internal spiral sulcus. The periosteum of the osseous lamina extends outward from the bony shelf to meet the basal membrane. The spiral limbus is composed of connective tissue and projects into the space enclosed by the scala media. Its apical convex surface is covered by columnar cells which have a thick cuticular border. Its lower surface is covered by cuboidal cells. From the border between these two surfaces projects the tectorial membrane which extends into the scala media and rests upon the portion of the organ of Corti which contains the hair cells. The tectorial membrane is a noncellular structure composed of fine fibers in an adhesive matrix. It is supposed to be attached, in life, to the organ of Corti, although the two are almost always separated in fixed preparations.

The spiral ganglion, situated in the osseous lamina, is composed of bipolar nerve cells. The dendrites of these cells pass toward the organ of Corti forming a conspicuous band of myelinated fibers in the lamina. As they leave the latter they lose their myelin sheaths. Some of them cross the inner tunnel, others pass below it, and both groups end in arborizations among the hair cells. The axons of the cells of the spiral ganglion carry impulses to the appropriate region of the brain.

The exact mechanism of the transmission of sound waves to the organ of Corti is a subject of controversy. It is clear, however, that sound waves cause vibrations of the tympanic membrane and that such vibrations are transmitted to the perilymph of the vestibule by the movement of the ossicles of the middle ear. The movement of the perilymph causes movement of the basal membrane of the organ of Corti, and the consequent alteration of position of the hair cells in relation to the tectorial membrane is the stimulus which is transmitted to the brain as sound.

OLFACTORY ORGAN

The receptors for olfactory stimuli, or sensations of smell, are located in the nose. This organ functions also as a part of the respiratory system, since air passes through it into the trachea by way of the nasopharynx. The nose consists of two passageways separated by the nasal septum. Each passage may be divided into a vestibule lined with skin and a nasal cavity which opens into the nasopharynx through an aperture known as the choana. The outline of the nasal cavity is irregular, its lateral margin having three longitudinal elevations of the surrounding tissue. These are the conchae or the turbinate bones. The lining of the cavity is, for the most part, columnar or pseudostratified epithelium but may contain some patches of stratified squamous epithelium.

The olfactory part of the nose is an area of neuroepithelium extending from the superior concha across the roof of the nasal cavity and part way down the septum. The epithelium in this region has the appearance of stratified columnar and contains the following elements: sustentacular cells, olfactory cells, and basal cells (Fig. 183).

Sustentacular cells. Sustentacular cells are tall columnar cells which form the superficial layer. Their basal portions are extended in irregular branching processes among the olfactory and basal cells. Their apical ends contain pigment granules, are ciliated, and have a distinct cuticular border. The nuclei of the sustentacular cells are oval and lie for the most part in a zone between the surface of the epithelium and the nuclei of the olfactory cells. Some oval nuclei may be found scattered among the deeper layers.

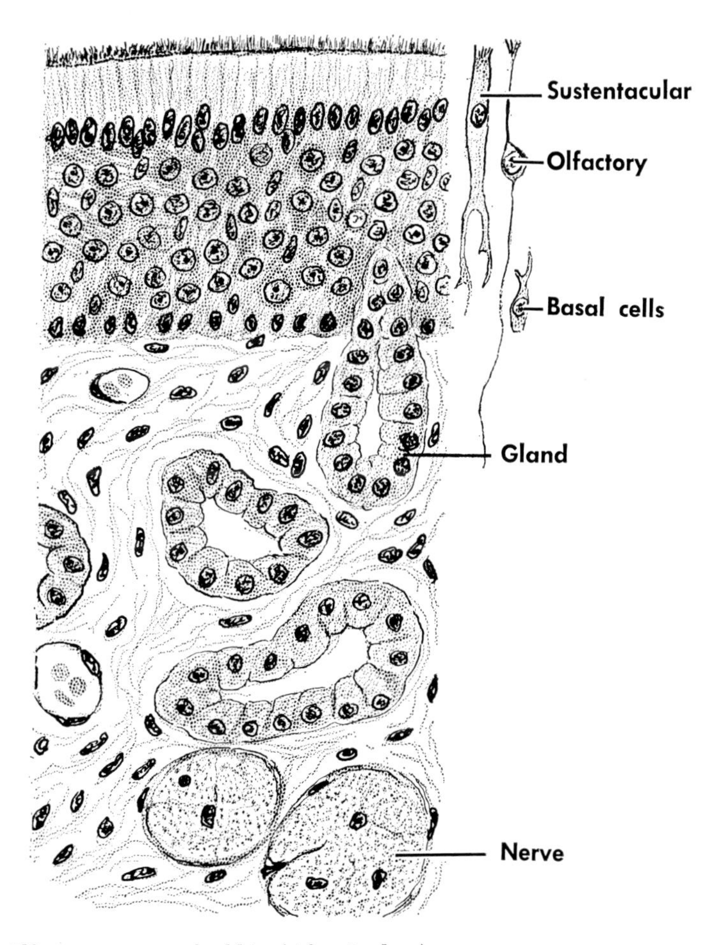

Fig. 183. Olfactory mucosa of rabbit. (After Jordan.)

Olfactory cells. The olfactory cells are true nerve cells, bipolar in form. Their dendrites extend to the surface of the epithelium, passing through minute openings in the cuticle and ending in a tuft of cilia. The perikarya are small rounded elements with spherical nuclei. They form a broad band below the zone of oval nuclei called the zone of round nuclei. The axons of the olfactory cells pass inward through the lamina propria where they may be seen as large groups of nonmyelinated fibers. They terminate in the olfactory bulb.

Basal cells. The basal cells are thought to be reserve sustentacular cells. They are short, irregularly shaped cells which form a layer next to the tunica propria. Like the sustentacular cells, they have oval nuclei. Their distal ends form short processes which extend among the branched ends of the sustentacular cells.

The tunica propria of the olfactory mucosa contains glands which open into the surface through wide ducts. The epithelium lining the glands (of Bowman) has the appearance of serous secreting tissue but sometimes contains mucus.

The olfactory mucosa has a rich blood supply, the veins of which drain into the superior longitudinal sinus.

Index

A

Absorption, intestinal, 176
Acromegaly, 74, 250
Addison's disease, 252
Adipose tissue, 48
cells of, 48, 49
fixation of, 48, 49
staining of, 48, 49
Adrenal (suprarenal) gland, 250
capsule, 251
chromaffin cells, 253
cortex, 251
epinephrine, 253
function of, 253
lipoid, 252
medulla, 253
origin, 251
sympathetic ganglia cells, 251
Aggregate lymph nodule (Peyer's patches), 175
Air sacs, lung, 203
Alveolus of teeth, 159
Ameloblasts, 152
Amphicytes, 97
Ampulla of ductus deferens, 226
of semicircular canals, 270
Anisotropic substance in muscle, 80
Annuli fibrosi, 114
Anus, 180
Aorta, 107
Apatite, 60
Appendix, vermiform, 179
Aqueous humor, 268
Arachnoid membrane, 260
villi, 260
Arciform arteries, 207
Arcuate veins, 207
Areolar tissue, 41
Argentiffine cells, 174
Arteries, 107
aorta, 107
arterioles, 110
elastic tissue of, 108
type, 108
external elastic membrane, 110
fenestrated membrane, 110
inner elastic membrane, 107
nutrient vessels, 108
sheathed, of spleen, 124
small, 110
Articular cartilage, 76
cleft, 76
Astroglia, 104
fibrous, 104
protoplasmic, 104
Atresia, 233
Atria, 203
Atrioventricular bundle (of His), 115
Auerbach's plexus, 78
Autonomic system, 99
Axon, 86

B

Basement membrane, 24
Basophils, 34, 45
Betz cells, 256
Bile, 190
Binucleate cells of liver, 189
Blood, 33
corpuscles, 33, 34
plasma, 33
platelets, 36
smear, 34
vessels, 106
aorta, 107
arteries, 107
arterioles, 110
capillaries, 106
medium-sized, 108
of bone, 73, 74
of eye, 268
of gallbladder, 193
of intestines, 181
of kidney, 207
of liver, 190
of lungs, 204
of lymph glands, 119
of mammary gland, 242
of muscle, 85
of pancreas, 187
of penis, 227
of salivary glands, 163
of spleen, 122
of stomach, 181
of urinary system, 208, 209
sinusoids, 106
small, 110
veins, 111, 112
venules, 112
Blood-forming organs, 50
bone marrow, 50
germinal centers, 52
reticuloendothelial system, 49
spleen, 120
Bone, 58
adult, 71
architecture of, 71
blood supply, 73, 74
calcium storage, 73
compact, 59

Bone—cont'd
  decalcified, 72
  development of, 58
  environmental changes, 73
  erosion, 59, 66, 71
  ground sections, 73
  histogenesis of, 59
  lacuna, 62
  lamellae, 71
  marrow, 51, 52, 75
  matrix, 58
  nerves, 74
  ossification, 58, 65
    cartilage replacement, 58, 62
    intramembranous, 58
  perichondrial, 63
  rebuilding, 59
  remodeling, 71
  repair, 74
  spongy, 58
  storage of minerals, 66
  traumatic changes, 73
  withdrawal of minerals, 74
Bowman's capsule (of kidney), 212
  glands (olfactory), 275
Brain, 254
  cerebellum, 257
  cerebrum, 254
  meninges, 254
Bronchi, 199
  glands of, 199
Bronchioles, 201
  respiratory, 201
Brunner's glands (duodenal glands), 175
Brush border in kidney epithelium, 216
Bulbourethal glands (Cowper's), 220
Bundle of His, 115

C

Calyces of kidney, 206
Canaliculi of bone, 62, 72
Capillaries, 106
  endothelium, 106
  lymphatic, 106
  Rouget's cells, 106
Capsule of adrenal gland, 251
  Bowman, 212
  joints, 76
  kidney, 206
  liver (Glisson), 187
  lymph node, 120
  spleen, 121, 122
  testis, 221
  thymus, 127
Cartilage, 53
  cells, 53
  development, 53
  elastic, 59, 269
  erosion, 59
  fibro-, 54
  function of, 57
  growth, 53
    appositional, 54
    interstitial, 53
  hyaline, 55
  lacunae, 53
  matrix, 53
  of epiglottis, 57
  of external ear, 57
  staining properties, 53
Cells, activities, 17, 22
  basket, 257
  basophilic, 34
  Betz, 256
  binucleate, 189
  blood, 33, 34
  capsule, 97
  chief, 170
  chromaffin, 253
  chromophil, 249
  chromophobe, 249
  dust, 194
  eosinophilic, 34
  fixed, of connective tissue, 43
  granule, 259
  hemopoietic, 50
  mast, 44
  myoepithelioid, 143
  nail, 144
  neck, 170
  of Claudius, 273
  of Deiter (hair cells), 273
  of gastric glands, 169
  of Hensen, 273
  of sebaceous gland, 114
  olfactory, 276
  parietal, 170
  phagocytic, 49
  pillar (of ear), 273
  plasma, 44
  prickle, 32
  Purkinje, 258
  pyramidal, 254
  reticular, 39, 49
  retrogressive changes, 22
  Rouget's, 106
  serous, 135
  Sertoli's, 224
  solitary, of cerebellum, 259
  stellate, of cerebellum, 259
  supporting, 162
  sustentacular, 275
    of eye, 267
    of olfactory organ, 275
  taste, 162
  wandering, of connective tissue, 43
Cementoblasts, 157
Cementum, 156
  lacunae, 157
  primary, 157
  secondary, 157
Centers of ossification, 58, 65
Central body, 19
  marrow cavity, 71
Centrioles, 19
Centrosphere, 19
Cerebellum, 257
Cerebrospinal fluid, 261
Cerebrum, 254
Ceruminous (wax) glands in ear, 269
Cheeks, mucosa of, 147
Chondrin, 53
Chondrogenetic layer, 55
Choroid, eye, 263
Chromatin granules, 18
Chromophil substance, 20
Chromosomes, man, 223
  relation to heredity, 223

Circulatory system, 106
blood vessels, 106
heart, 114
Circumvallate papillae, 161
Clasmatocytes, 43
Cochlea, 270
Cochlear duct, 271
Colloid, 245
Colon, 177
Common hepatic duct, 191
Connective tissue, 37
cells of, 42
fibers, 37
fibrils, 45
matrix, 37
Contractility of muscle, 77
Corium, 142
Cornea, 262
Corpora cavernosa penis, 227
Corpus albicans, 233
callosum, 254
cavernosum urethrae, 227
luteum, 233
spongiosum, 227
Corpuscles, Hassall's, 128
Krause's, 94
lamellar, 94
pacinian, 94
red blood, 33
tactile, 94
thymic, 128
white blood, 34
Cortex, adrenal, 251
brain, 254
hair, 143
kidney, 206
lymph gland, 120
Corti, organ of, 272
Cowper's glands, 220
Craniosacral outflow, 96, 100
Cribriform plate, 159
Cumulus oophorus, 231
Cuticula, enamel, 153
hair, 143
Cystic duct, 192
Cytoplasm, 19
Cytoplasmic inclusions, 19, 20

D

Dendrite, 86
Dentin, 154
dentinal fibrils, 155
tubules, 155
development of, 154
mature, 156
apatite, 156
Neumann's sheath, 156
tubiculi, 156
odontoblasts, 155
predentin, 155
Tomes' fibrils, 155
variations of, 156
abrasion, 156
caries, 156
imbrication lines, 156
interglobular, 156
secondary, 156
Dentition, 154
Diaphysis of bone, 65, 66
Diarthroses, 76
Digestive enzyme, 174
tract, 165
adventitia, 166
arrangement of muscularis, 166
coats, of, 166
lymph nodules, 165
mesothelium, 166
mucosa, 165
muscularis, 165
sphincters of, 165
submucosa, 165
Duct, bile, 192
cochlear, 271
cystic, 192
ejaculatory, 226
lung (alveolar), 202
mammary, 241
of glands, 133
pancreas, 185
parotid, 182
striated, 183
sublingual, 183
sweat gland, 143
Ductus deferens, 226
epididymis, 225
Dura mater, cerebralis, 259
spinalis, 259

E

Ear, 269
development, 69
external, 269
inner, 270
middle, 289
sound transmission, 274
Ebner's glands, 162
Ectopic pregnancy, 234
Ejaculatory ducts, 226
Elastic cartilage, 59, 269
fibers, 48
tissue, 47
Enamel, 152
development (of enamel organ), 152
inner enamel epithelium, 152
outer enamel epithelium, 152
stellate reticulum, 152
stratum intermedium, 152
formation, 152
ameloblasts, 152
cuticle, 153
rods or prisms, 152, 153
Tomes' process, 152
mature, 153
direction of rods, 153
gnarled, 154
imbrication lines, 154
interprismatic substance, 154
keratin, 153
tufts, 154
Endocardium, 114
Endocrine glands, 243
organs, 243
Endolymph, 271
Endometrium, 235
cyclic changes of, 236, 237
Endomysium, 82
Endoneurium, 92
Endothelial lining, 26
Enzymes, digestive, 171
pancreatic, 187

Eosinophils, 34
Ependyma, 105
Epicardium, 115
Epidermis, 139
Epididymis, 224
Epidural space, 260
Epimysium, 82
Epinephrine, 253
Epineurium, 91
Epiphyses, 66
Epithelia, 24
  basement membrane, 29
  cilia, 18
  ciliated columnar, 225
  columnar, 28
  cuboidal, 27
  cuticula, 25
  endothelium, 27
  germinal, 221, 223, 229
  intercellular bridges, 24
    substance, 24
  mesenchymal, 76
  mesothelium, 27
  neuro- (of nose), 275
  nonsecreting, 25
  of nipple, 242
  pseudostratified, 29
    ciliated, 203
  respiratory, 203
  secretion, 28
  simple, 25
  squamous, 25
  stratified, 30
    columnar, 275
    squamous, 31
  terminal bars, 24
  transitional, 30
Epithelial attachment (of gingivae), 157
  rests, 159
Eponychium, 144
Erectile tissue, 227
Erythroblasts, 51
Erythrocytes, 33
  cytoplasm of, 34
  hemoglobin, 34
  rouleaux, 34
Erythroplastids, 34
Esophagus, 167
  arrangement of, 167
  glands of, 167
Eustachian tube, 269
Eye, 261
  aqueous humor, 268
  blood vessels of, 268
  choroid, 263
  ciliary body, 263
  cornea, 262
  innervation of, 268
  iris, 263
  lens, 268
  optic stalk (nerve), 268
  pars ciliaris retina, 267
    irridica retina, 267
    optic retina, 264
  retina, 264
  sclera, 262
  vitreous humor, 268

F

Fallopian tube, 234
    ciliated mucosa, 234
    fimbriae, 234
Femur, bone development of, 63
Fibers, climbing, 257
  collagenous, 37
  elastic, 37, 38
  intercellular, 78
  mossy, 257
  muscle, 78, 81, 83
  myelinated, 89
  nerve, 89, 91
  osteogenic, 60
  postganglionic, 96
  preganglionic, 96
  Purkinje, 115
  reticular, 37
  Sharpey's, 74
Fibrils, collagenous, 20, 37
  Tomes' dentinal, 155
Fibroblasts, 42
Fibrocartilage, 54
Fibroglia, 39
Fibrous tissue, 41
Filiform papillae, 159
Foliate papillae, 160
Follicles, 229
  atretic, 233
  graafian, 230, 231
  hair, 142
  mammary, 240
  maturation of, 229
  primary, 231
Fossae, tonsillar, 125
Fundic glands, 169
  region, 169
Fungiform papillae, 159

G

Gallbladder, 193
  blood supply, 193
  follicles, 193
  nerve supply, 193
Ganglia, autonomic cells of, 86
  dorsal root, 88
  retinal, 265
  spinal, 88
  spiral, 270
  sympathetic, 96
Gastric glands, 169
    chief cells, 170
    mucous neck cells, 170
    parietal cells, 170
  pits, 169
Germinal centers of lymph nodes, 52
    of tonsils, 126
Giant cells of bone marrow, 51
Gigantism, 250
Gingivae, 147
  cornification of, 157
  epithelial attachment, 157
  gingival margin, 157
    crevice, 157
Glands, 130
  adrenal, 250
  associated with digestive tract, 182
  bulbourethal (Cowper's), 220

Glands—cont'd
cellular differences, 137
ceruminous, 269
circumanal, 181
ducts of, 133
duodenal (Brunner), 175
Ebner's, 162
endocrine, 131
exocrine, 133
fundic (gastric), 169
Littre's, 220
liver, 187
mammary, 240
morphology of, 134
mucous, 134
multicellular, 136
of Bowman, 276
of esophagus, 167
of hard palate, 150
of skin, 143
of stomach, 169, 170
pancreas, 185
parathyroid, 246
parotid, 182
pineal, 249
pituitary, 248
properties of, 135-138
pyloric, 171
sebaceous, 144
serous, cells and secretions of, 135
shapes and arrangement of, 136
simple, 135
sublingual, 185
submaxilliary, 184
sweat, 143
thymus, 126
thyroid, 243, 244
uterine, 235
Glisson's capsule, 187
Glomerulus of kidney, 211
Gnarled enamel, 154
Golgi apparatus, 19
Graafian follicles, 230, 231
Granulocytes, 35
Groove, nail, 144

H

Hair, 143
components of, 143
cortex, 143
cuticula, 143
epithelial sheath, 143
follicle, 142
bulb, 142
muscle of, 142
papilla, 142
sebaceous gland, 143
shaft of, 143
Henle's layer, 143
Huxley's layer, 143
medulla, 143
membrana vitrea, 143
Hassall's corpuscle, 128
Haversian canals, 70, 73
system, 70, 73
Heart, 114
annuli fibrosi, 114
bundle of His, 115
sinoauricular node, 115
Heidenhain, demilunes of, 185
Heller's plexus, 180
Hemocytoblasts, 50
Hemoglobin, 34
Henle, sheath of, 92
Hilum of lymph node, 117
spleen, 122
Histiocytes, 43
Histology, 17
Hormone of adrenal, 253
endocrine glands, 243
ovary, 233
parathyroid, 246
pituitary, 250
testis, 224
thyroid, 246
Howship's lacunae, 67
Humor, aqueous, 269
vitreous, 268
Huxley's layer of hair sheath, 143
Hyaline cartilage, 55
of trachea, 55, 56
organization of, 55
staining capacity of, 55
Hypertrophy, 233, 240
Hyponychium, 144
Hypophysis, 248
function, 250
lobes of, 248, 249
origin of, 248

I

Incus, 269
Inflammatory conditions, 44
Insulin, 187
Integument, 139
Intercalary discs, 84
Intercalated ducts, 183
neurons, 98
Intercellular bridges, 24
substance, 24
Interglobular dentin, 156
Interstitial cells of ovary, 229
of testis, 224
fibers, 158
lamellae, 73
tissue of spinal cord, 103
Intervertebral discs, 54
Intramembranous bone, 59
Isotropic substance in muscle, 80

J

Jejunum, 173
Joints, 76
Juxtaglomerular apparatus, 214

K

Keratin, 32, 153
Kidney, 206
arciform arteries, 207
arcuate veins, 207
Bowman's capsule, 212
brush border, 216
calyx, 206
capsule, 206
circulation of, 210
collecting tubules, 217
cortex, 206
cortical labyrinth, 207
distal convoluted tubule, 214

Kidney—cont'd
divisions of, 214
glomerulus, 211
gross structure, 206
Henle's loop, 214
juxtaglomerular apparatus, 217
macula densa, 216
medulla, 210
medullary rays, 210
nephron, 213, 214
pelvis, 210
proximal convoluted tubule, 214
urinary pole, 212
vascular pole, 212
renal columns, 210
sinus, 210
Krause's membrane in skeletal muscle, 81
Kupffer stellate cells, 190

L

Labyrinth, membranous, 270
osseous, 270
vestibule of, 270
Lacteals, 173
Lacunae, Howship's, 67
of bone, 62
of cartilage, 53
of cementum, 157
Lamellae, bone, 71
circumferential, 71
concentric, 73
endosteal, 73
interstitial, 73
periosteal, 73
Lamellar bodies of prostate, 227
Lamina fusca, 262
labiodental, 150
labiogingival, 150
spiralis (cochlear), 271
Langerhans, islands of, 186
cells of, 186
function of, 187
Large intestine, 176
absorption, 176
anus, 180
blood supply, 181
circumanal glands, 181
colon, 177
lymphoid tissue, 179
nerve supply, 181
rectal columns, 180
rectum, 180
semilunar folds, 176
taeniae coli, 178
vermiform appendix, 179
Lens, eye, 268
Leukocytes, 34
basophil, 35
eosinophil, 35
granulocytes, 35
lymphocytes (small and large), 35
monocytes, 35
neutrophil, 35
polymorphonuclear, 35
Lieberkühn, crypts of, 174
Lingual glands of tongue, 161
Lining of oral cavity, 146
Lips, 146
mucosa of, 146
Lips—cont'd
muscles of, 146
papillae, 146
seromucous glands, 146
skin, 146
Littre's glands, 220
Liver, 187
bile duct system, 192
capillaries of, 190
capsule of Glisson, 187
cells of, 189
circulation of, 190
development of, 187
function of, 192
bile formation, 190
storage of glycogen, 192
interlobular veins, 192
lobules, 187
nerve supply, 193
of human being, 188
of pig, 187
parenchyma, 187
portal canal, 190
sinusoids, 188
stellate cells of Kupffer, 190
reaction to vital dyes, 190
umbilical veins, 187
vitelline veins, 187
Lungs, 194
air sac, 203
alveolar ducts, 202
alveoli, 203
atria, 203
blood supply, 204
nerve supply, 205
respiratory bronchioles, 201
epithelium, 203
Lunula, nail, 145
Lymph, 36
capillaries, 118
node (gland), 118
blood vessels of, 119
capsule, 120
cortex, 120
function of, 120
germinal centers, 118
hilum of, 117
lymphocyte production, 118
lymphocytes of, 118
medulla, 120
nodules of, 120
peripheral sinus, 119
trabeculae of, 120
nodules, 119
aggregate (Peyer's patches), 176
of digestive tract, 167
of esophagus, 167
primary, 118
secondary, 118
solitary, 177
Lymphatic vessels, 116
valves of, 116
Lymphocytes, 118
Lymphoid organs, 117
comparison of, 129
lymph node, 117
spleen, 120
thymus, 126
tonsils, 126
tissue, 117

M

Macrophages, 43
Malleus, 269
Mammary gland, 240
active, 240
alveoli of, 240
blood vessels of, 242
ducts of, 241
fat droplets, 242
follicles, 240
hypertrophy of, 240
involution, 242
milk, 242
nerves, 242
nipple, 242
resting, 240
structure of, 240
Marrow, bone, 51
Matrix of bone, 58
cartilage, 53
connective tissue, 37
Mediastinum of testis, 221
Medulla of adrenal, 253
hair, 143
kidney, 210
lymph gland, 120
Medullary rays of kidney, 210
sinuses of lymph glands, 118
trabeculae of lymph glands, 120
Megakaryocytes, 51
Meissner's plexus, 180
Melanin of skin, 141
Melanoblasts, 141
Membrana vitrea, 143
Membrane, arachnoid, 260
external elastic, 107
fenestrated, 48, 110
inner elastic, 110
Krause's 81
peridental, 158
tectorial, 274
tympanic, 269
vestibular, 272
Membranous labyrinth of ear, 270
Meninges, 259
Menopause, 232
Menstruation, 236
Mesenchyme, 33
Mesothelium, 27
Metamyelocytes, 51
Microglia, 105
Mitochondria, 19
Modiolus, 270
Monocytes, 35
Mucin, stains for, 136
Mucoid, 39
Mucous connective tissue, 39
glands, 136
Mucus, 136
Muscle, 79
cardiac, 83
cytoplasm, 84
intercallary discs, 84
size, 84
syncytium, 83
circulation of, 85
diagnostic features of, 84
fascicles, 82
innervation of, 85
of esophagus, 168
Muscle—cont'd
skeletal, 79
attachment of, 82
Cohnheim's areas, 81
column of Kölliker, 81
Hensen's line, 81
Krause's line, 81
myofibrils, 81, 83
sarcolemma, 79
sarcostyles, 80
transverse bands, 81
smooth, 77
cytoplasm, 78
histogenesis of, 77
intercellular fibers, 78
myofibrils, 78
occurrence of, 79
sarcolemma, 78
voluntary, 82
Muscularis mucosae of digestive tract, 168, 169
Myelin, 89
Myelocytes, 51
Myocardium, 115
Myometrium, 235

N

Nail, 144
bed, 144
cells, 144
dermal papillae, 144
eponychium, 144
groove, 144
growth of, 144
hyponychium, 144
lunula, 144
Nephron, 213, 214
Nerve cells, 86
autonomic ganglia, 87
axon hillock, 87
bipolar, 89
chromophil substance, 86
dendrites, 86
multipolar, 89
neurofibrils, 88
Nissl bodies, 86
nucleolus, 86
of dorsal root ganglia, 88
tigroid bodies, 86
unipolar, 89
endings, motor, 93
sensory, 94
encapsulated, 94
free endings, 94
muscle spindles, 94
fibers, 89, 91
axis cylinder, 89
collaterals, 86
myelin sheath, 89
neurilemma, 89
nodes of Ranvier, 89
sheath of Schwann, 90
trunks, 91
Nerves of bone, 74
eye, 268
gallbladder, 193
intestines, 181
liver, 193
lungs, 205
mammary gland, 242

Nerves—cont'd
muscle, 85
pancreas, 187
penis, 228
salivary gland, 187
stomach, 181
teeth, 157
tongue, 162
urinary system, 221
Nervi vasorum, 108
Nervous system, 86
autonomic, 99
central, 86
parasympathetic, 100
peripheral, 86
tissue, 86
nerve cells, 86
neuroglia, 103
synapse, 86
Neumann's sheath, 156
Neurilemma, 90
Neuroepithelium of nose, 275
Neurofibrils, 88
Neuroglia, 103
cells of, 104
interstitial tissue, 103
origin of, 103
Neurokeratin, 89
Neuron, 86
association or intercalated, 98
motor, 98
sensory, 95
somatic motor, 96
visceral afferent, 100
motor, 101
Neuroplasm, 88
Neutrophil, 35
Nissl bodies, 86
Nodules, lymph, 118, 119, 120
spleen, 121
Normoblasts, 51
Nucleolus, 18
Nucleus, 17
"cartwheel," 44
internal, 254
Nutrient canal, 74

O

Olfactory organ, 274
Oligodendria, 104
Oogonia, 228
Optic nerve (stalk), 268
Oral cavity, glands of, 163
lining of, 146
Organ of Corti, 237
Organoids, 19
Osmic acid, 49
effect on myelin, 89
Osseous labyrinth, 270
Ossicles of ear, 269
Ossification, center of, 65
Osteoblasts, 62
Osteoclasts, 67
Osteocytes, 62
Ovary, 228
atretic follicles, 233
components of, 233
corpus albicans, 233
luteum, 233
development of, 229
Ovary—cont'd
egg nests of Pflüger, 229
follicles, 229
follicular cavity, 229
cells, 229
germinal epithelium, 229
graafian follicles, 230, 231
growth of follicles, 229
insemination, 229
interstitial cells of, 229
liquor folliculi, 232
primary follicles, 231
theca folliculi, 231
tunica albuginea, 229
Ovulation, 232
Ovum, 230
fertilization of, 233
implantation of, 233
maturation of, 231
Owen, lines of, 156

P

Palate, hard, 150
elastic fibers of, 150
glands of, 150
modification of mucosa, 150
Pancreas, 185
blood supply, 187
carbohydrate metabolism, 186
centroalveolar cells, 185
diabetic symptoms, 186
function of, 185
intercallary ducts, 185
islands of Langerhans, 186
nerve supply, 187
zymogen granules, 185
Paneth's cells, 175
Papillae of hair, 142
of nail, 144
of skin, 142
of tongue, 159, 160, 161
Parathyroid, 246
activity, 246
chief cells, 246
eosinophilic cells, 246
function, 246
Parotid, 182
alveoli, 184
cytoplasm of, 183
ducts of, 182
epithelium, 183
striated ducts, 183
Pars buccalis, 248
distalis, 248
chromophil cells, 249
chromophobe cells, 249
functional differences, 249
intermedia, 249
nervosa, 249
ependymal cells, 249
functional relations of, 249, 250
tuberalis, 248
Parturition, 237
Pelvis of kidney, 210
Penicilli, 122
Penis, 227
corpora cavernosa penis, 227
corpus cavernosum urethrae, 227
spongiosum, 227
erectile tissue, 227

Penis—cont'd
nerves of, 228
tunica albuginea, 227
vessels of, 227
Peptic digestion, 37
Pericardium, 115
Perichondrium, 55
Peridental membrane, 158
epithelial rests, 159
interstitial fibers, 158
principal fibers, 158
Perikaryon, 86
Perilymph, 270
Perimetrium, 235
Perimysium, 82
Perineurium, 91
Periosteal bud, 63
Periosteum, 74
Peyer's patches, 175
Pflüger's cords, 229
Phagocytosis, 49
Pharynx, 164
constrictor of, 164
epithelium of, 164
nasopharynx, 164
oropharynx, 164
Pia mater, 259
Pineal gland, 249
Pinna of ear, 269
Pits, gastric, 169
tonsillar, 125
Pituitary gland, 248
Placenta, 238
Platelets, blood, 36
Plexus, Auerbach's, 78
choroid, 261
Heller's, 180
Meissner's, 180
peritubular, 210
Plicae circulares (of small intestine), 171
Polymorphonuclear leukocytes, 35
Posterior lobe of hypophysis, 249
Prickle cells, 32
Primordial germ cells, 221
Prisms, enamel, 152, 153
Proerythroblasts, 51
Promyelocytes, 51
Prostate, 227
lamellar bodies, 227
prostatic concretions, 227
Protoplasm, 17
Puberty, 232
Pulp of teeth, 157
splenic, 123, 124
Purkinje cells (of cerebellum), 258
fibers, 115
Pyloric glands, 171
region, 171
Pyramids of kidney, 206

R

Radioautograph of bone, 69
Receptors, hearing, 270
nerve endings, 93
olfactory, 274
Rectum, 180
Reflex, somatic, 96
sympathetic, 96
Renal artery, 210, 211
columns, 210
Renal—cont'd
cortex, 206
medulla, 210
pelvis, 210
pyramids, 206
sinus, 210
unit, 211
Reproductive system, female, 228
fallopian tube (oviduct), 234
mammary gland, 240
ovary, 228
uterus, 235
vagina, 238
male, 221
ductus deferens, 226
epididymis, 224
penis, 227
prostate gland, 227
seminal vesicle, 226
testis, 221
Resorcin, 38
Respiratory larynx, 197
nasal passages, 196
nasopharynx, 197
respiratory bronchioles, 201
epithelium, 203
trachea, 198
tract, 194
alveolar ducts, 202
alveoli, 203
atria, 203
bronchi, 199
bronchioles, 201
function of, 194
Reticular tissue, 39
cells of, 39
membrane, 154
Reticulin, 37
Reticuloendothelial system, 49
phagocytosis, 49
reaction to vital dyes, 49
Retina, 264
cones, 265
fovea centralis, 267
macula lutea, 267
origin of, 264
pars ciliaris, 267
iridica, 267
optica, 264
pigmented epithelium of, 265
rods, 265
Retzius, striae of, 154
Rods, enamel, 152, 153
Root of nail, 144
tooth, 150
Rouget cells, 106
Rouleaux, 34
Rugae of stomach, 168

S

Saccule, 271
Saliva, 163
Salivary glands, 183
blood supply, 187
nerve supply, 187
parotid, 182
sublingual, 185
submaxillary, 184
Sarcolemma, 78, 79
Sarcomeres, 79

Sarcostyles, 80
Scala media, 271
  tympani, 271
  vestibuli, 271
Scalp, 142
Schwann, sheath of, 90
Sclera, 262
Sebaceous glands, 144
  cells of, 144
  secretion of, 144
Secondary dentin, 156
  papillae of tongue, 159, 160, 161
Seepage in cartilage, 53
Semicircular canals, 270
Seminal vesicle, 226
Seminiferous tubules, 221
Serosa of digestive tract, 165
Serous cells, 184
  glands, 135
Sertoli cells, 224
Sharpey's fibers, 74
Sheathed arteries, 124
Simple epithelium, 25
  glands, 135
Sinoauricular node, 115
Sinuses, cortical, 120
  medullary, 118
  peripheral, 119
  renal, 210
  splenic, 123, 124
Sinusoids of blood vessels, 106
  liver, 188
Skin, 139
  corium, 141
  cornification of, 139
  dermis, 141
  desquamation of, 139
  epidermis, 139
  hairless, 139
  hairy, 142
  of lips, 146
  sebaceous glands, 144
  sweat glands, 143
Small intestine, 171
  absorption of food, 171
  argentaffine cells, 174
  blood supply, 181
  crypts of Lieberkühn, 174
  duodental glands, 175
  lacteals, 173
  lymphatics, 173
  lymphoid tissue, 173
  nerve supply, 181
  Paneth's cells, 175
  plicae circulares, 171
  villi, 172
Space, epidural, 259
Special sense organs, 254
  brain, 254
  ear, 269
  eye, 261
  olfactory, 274
Spermatids, 222
Spermatocytes, primary, 222
  secondary, 222
Spermatogonia, 221
Spermatozoa, 222
Sphincters of digestive tract, 165
  urethra, 220
Spinal cord, 87, 96
  dorsal horn, 87
  gray matter of, 87
  lateral horn, 87
  nerve cells, 87, 96
  ventral horn, 87
Spiral ganglion, 270-274
  ligament of ear, 272
  organ (of Corti), 273
  sulcus, 272
Spleen, 120
  arteries of, 122
  blood cells, 123
  capsule, 121, 123
  circulation of, 123
  embryonic condition of, 124
  function of, 124
  nodules, 121
  penicilli, 122
  red pulp, 123
  sinuses, 123, 124
  splenic cells, 124
  theories of blood course, 122
  trabeculae, 121, 123
  veins of, 122
  white pulp, 124
Staining characteristics of cells, 21
Stapes, 269
Stomach, 168
  blood supply, 181
  cardiac region, 169
  chief cells, 170
  fundus, 169
  gastric (fundic) glands, 169
    cells of, 169
  hydrochloric acid, 171
  junction with esophagus, 168
  mucous neck cells, 170
  nerve supply, 181
  parietal cells, 170
  pits, 168
  pyloric region, 171
  rugae, 168
  zymogen granules, 171
Stratum corneum, 139
  germinativum, 32, 140
  granulosum, 139
    cells of, 140
  lucidum, 139
Sublingual, 185
  alveoli, 185
  duct system, 185
Submaxillary, 184
  alveoli, 184
  cytoplasm of, 185
  demilunes of Heidenhain, 185
Sulcus terminalis, 162
Superficial glands of esophagus, 167
Supporting cells of taste buds, 162
  testis, 224
Suprarenal gland, 250
Sustentacular cells of taste buds, 162
  testis, 224
Sweat glands, 143
  cytoplasm of, 143
  ducts of, 143
Synarthrosis, 76
Synovial fluid, 76
  layer, 76

T

Taeniae coli, 178
Taste buds, 161
  cells, 162
Tectorial membrane, 274
Teeth, 150
  alveolus, 159
  cementum, 156
  crown, 150
  deciduous, 150
  dentin, 156
  development of, 150
  enamel, 153
  gingiva, 157
  gums, 150
  neck, 150
  nerves of, 157
  peridental membrane, 158
  permanent. 150
  pulp, 157
  root, 150
  vascular supply of, 157
Tela choroidea, 261
Tendon, 47
Terminal bar, 24
Testis, 221
  capsule of, 221
  chromosomes, 222
  development of spermatozoa, 222
  germinal epithelium, 221, 223
  hormone, 224
  interstitial cells, 224
  mediastinum, 221
  parenchyma of, 221
  reduction of chromatin, 223
  scrotum, 221
  secondary sexual characteristics, 224
  supporting cells, 224
Thrombocytes, 36
Thymic corpuscle, 128
Thymus, 126
  capsule of, 127
  development of, 126
  epithelioid cells, 127
  Hassall's corpuscle, 128
  infantilism, 129
  thymic corpuscle, 128
  thymocytes, 127
  trabeculae, 127
Thyroid, 243, 244
  colloid, 245
  epithelium of, 245
  function of, 246
  functional condition of, 246
  hormone, 246
  hyperactive, 246
  hypoactive, 246
  iodine, 246
Tigroid bodies, 86
Tissue, adipose, 48
  basophils, 45
  connective, 37
  elastic, 47
  eosinophils, 45
  erectile, 227
  lymphoid, 117
  mesenchymal, 27, 76
  mesothelium, 27
  muscle, 79
  nervous, 86
Tissue—cont'd
  vascular, 106
Tomes' fibrils, 155
  process, 152
Tongue, 159
  dorsal surface, 159
  glands of, 161
  mucosa of, 159
  muscles, 159
  nerve fibers, 162
  papillae, 159, 160, 161
  taste buds, 161, 162
  ventral surface, 163
Tonsils, 125
  germinal centers, 126
  involution, 126
  palatine, 125
  pharyngeal, 126
  pits (or fossae), 125
Trabeculae, medullary, of lymph node, 120
  of bone, 58
  of spleen, 121, 123
  of thymus, 127
Trachea, 198
  cartilage of, 199
  epithelium of, 198
Tubules, spiral, of testis, 221
  straight, of testis, 224
Tubuli efferentes, 224
  recti, 224
Tufts, enamel, 154
Tunica albuginea of ovary, 229
    penis, 227
    testis, 221
  propria (digestive tract), 165
  vaginalis (of testis), 221
Tympanic membrane, 269

U

Umbilical cord, 39
  veins, 187
Ureter, 218
Urethra, female, 220
    glands of Littre, 220
    sphincter of, 220
  male, 220
    bulbourethral glands (of Cowper), 220
    cavernous portion, 221
    membranous portion, 220
    prostatic portion, 220
    urogenital diaphragm, 220
Urinary bladder, 219
    epithelium, 219
Urogenital diaphragm, 220
  system, 206
Uterus, 235
  endometrium, 235
  glands of, 235
  menstruation, 236
  myometrium, 235
  perimetrium, 235
  uterine cycle, 236, 237
Utricle, 271

V

Vagina, 238
  changes in epithelium, 238
  vaginal smears, 239

Vallate papillae, 161
Valves of heart, 114
  lymph vessels, 119
Vasa vasorum, 108
Vascular pole, 212
Veins, 111, 112
  coats of, 112
  large, 113
  of spleen, 122
  post-mortem changes, 111
  small, 112
  valves of, 113
  venules, 112
  vitelline, 187
Vermiform appendix, 179
Vestibule of labyrinth, 270
Villi, arachnoid, 260
  intestinal, 172
Vitelline veins, 187
Vitreous humor, 268
Volkmann, canal of, 73

W

Weil, cell-poor zone of, 157
White matter of cerebellum, 258
    cerebrum, 254
    spinal cord, 87
Wright's stain for blood, 34

Z

Zona fasciculata, 251
  glomerulosa, 251
  pellucida, 231
  radiata, 232
  reticularis, 252
Zymogen granules in pancreas, 185
    in stomach, 171